BIRDS OF THE
EDWARD MARSHALL BOEHM
AVIARIES

Major portion devoted to Softbills

EDWARD
MARSHALL
BOEHM
1913 · 1969

BIRDS

OF THE

EDWARD MARSHALL BOEHM AVIARIES

Major portion devoted to Softbills

BY CHARLES EVERITT

About the Author:

Mr. Everitt was born December 11, 1906 in Leyton, Essex, England. After graduation from Saint Bonaventures, West Ham, England he served in the Royal Air Force from 1927 to 1954. He served four years in Pakistan and India, two and a half years in Singapore, and three years in the Air Ministry in London. After retirement as a Squadron Leader he established the Merlin Aviaries in South Norwood, England where he concentrated on keeping, breeding and exhibiting foreign birds. He was ably assisted by Mrs. Everitt who kept, bred and exhibited Budgerigars and British softbills. Mr. Everitt came to America December 9, 1959 as Curator of the Edward Marshall Boehm Aviaries which post he held until May 1965. Since then until now he has been the Administrative Manager of the Wood Veterinary Hospital in Trenton, New Jersey. As an accredited English and foreign bird judge he has contributed articles to: English Journals; Avicultural Society, Foreign Bird League, "Cage and Aviary Birds."—American Journals: Avicultural Society "American Cage Birds", "All Pets." He is further known for these articles: The Netherlands "Onze Vogels"; Germany "Vogel Kosmos", and India "The Peacock."

Design:

Mrs. Edward Marshall Boehm; Frank J. Cosentino; and J. Doran Williams,
Visual Motivations Foundation, Morrisville, Pa.

Sketches:

Sketches appearing through the book are from originals by Edward Marshall Boehm.

Photography:

Photographs by Edward Marshall Boehm and others. All photographs of the live birds taken in the Boehm aviaries.

PRINTED IN THE UNITED STATES OF AMERICA
THE LAKESIDE PRESS
R. R. DONNELLEY & SONS COMPANY
CHICAGO

PUBLISHED BY EDWARD MARSHALL BOEHM, INC.
25 FAIRFACTS STREET, TRENTON, NEW JERSEY 08638, U.S.A.

CONTENTS

Foreword BY SIR EDWARD HALSTROM

I have written, or tried to write, a few small paragraphs. Every time I looked at it I altered it, and on each occasion it came back to the one thing. Ed was such a wonderful fellow it is so hard for a layman not used to writing to put his pen to paper and write just a few words that can tell a great story of a great man. I regard him just as that.

I have seen quite a lot of his work and I have imagined being left alone in a room with some of his fascinating thoughts portrayed in the materials used by him; I find it hard to say the things I would like to say.

Ed Boehm the man, scientist, ornithologist, aviculturist, ceramist, almost defies description.

Sydney, Australia
2nd February 1969

*Photo shows Sir Edward
with a kangaroo friend*

Foreword BY JEAN DELACOUR

Edward Marshall Boehm has had a very exceptional career as an aviculturist. It started late and, unfortunately, it ended early because of his sudden and untimely death.

During a comparative short period of time, however, he accomplished much and met with tremendous success. He built near Trenton, N.J., truly magnificent aviaries of great size, beautifully landscaped. There were adequate shelters, but their special advantage resided in a very happy innovation; the wire netting of the huge flights were covered in the autumn with transparent plastic material which transformed them into greenhouses, heated by hot water pipes. When spring returned, the plastic cover was removed, and the birds were outdoors again enjoying all the advantages of the open air.

Ed Boehm, being keen, clever and active beyond belief, managed to obtain within a few years the many species he wanted from all parts of the world. He promptly gathered a marvellous series where Passerine birds were the most numerous. Rare species, seldom if ever seen alive before, figured in his collection and many reared young at Trenton for the first time in captivity. This proved once again that the quasi-tropical summers of Eastern North America are highly beneficial to birds from the warmer parts of the world, as long as they are well sheltered from the severe cold of the winter.

Ed Boehm's achievements in aviculture must not only be recorded as a tribute to his excellent work, it also has to be available to coming generations of biologists. Aviculture, today, is not simply an interesting hobby and a challenging sport. It has become an indispensable scientific technique for suitable studies and experimentation.

Bird keeping was not Ed Boehm's main occupation, and everyone knows what an outstanding sculptor and ceramist he was. Before I ever met him, I unexpectedly received two beautiful figures of Canada Geese which he had sent me as a recognition of whatever ornithological and avicultural work he considered I had accomplished during an already long life. They stand before me as I write this and they remind me of a friend who was an highly gifted artist as well as a prominent aviculturist.

I trust that readers interested in birds and their life will find a great deal of information in the following pages and derive much pleasure as well from the account of the Birds in the Boehm Aviaries.

Cleres, France
20 July 1969

Foreword BY KENTON C. LINT

Although each person makes some contribution to those around him during his life, it is given to comparatively few to make life richer for countless numbers of his fellow men throughout the world, Edward Marshall Boehm was one of those men.

As he created the exquisite porcelain figures which brought him fame he worked increasingly to make them perfect in every detail.

After he "discovered" the world of birds, he pursued this avocation with the same dedication to perfection. His deep devotion to both native and exotic birds led to many innovations in caring for the extensive collection which he gathered together.

When it was my pleasure to visit his gardens at Washington Crossing, I was impressed with the thoughtfulness which had created the Boehm Aviaries, and the real concern Ed Boehm had for the care and comfort of his charges. We spent enjoyable times observing the birds and discussing them—their habits and their importance in our world.

I am sure that this volume, which will tell of the fine collection of birds Edward Marshall Boehm had collected, describe their care and relate the breeding accomplishments, will be most interesting and helpful to aviculturists all over the world.

San Diego, California
1970, U.S.A.

Charles Everitt

Introduction

MY FIRST CONTACT with one of the most forceful, knowing exactly where he was going, men, was by a 45-minute trans-Atlantic telephone call. It was this conversation that ultimately led to my wife and I coming to the United States. During the five years I acted as curator of his marvellous range of aviaries we bred some 60 different species, 32 of them being "firsts" for North America, and 12 were recognised as first breedings in captivity in the world.

Basically, Mr. Boehm was a lover of nature in all its forms, be it animal, vegetable or mineral. The words "can not be done" were anathema to him. The purpose of the aviaries was not just to satisfy his craving to be near to nature, but to provide living models for his porcelain creations, and to prove to himself that correct feeding and correct environment could not but result in the propagation of the species. I had the pleasure of being able to work closely with him and, from my various notes made over the years, these memoirs have been evolved.

Although this book deals mainly with softbills, Mr. Boehm also had an extensive collection of parrot-like, seed-eaters, waterfowl and gallinaceous birds, over 800 species all told. Some of them may be mentioned in the following chapters, but it was with softbills that he was mainly interested, so that phase of his activities has been concentrated on in the chapters following.

The arrangement of Orders and Families throughout this book is based upon that used in "A New Dictionary of Birds", edited by Sir A. Landsborough Thomson, being that of the "Check-list of Birds of the World" by the later J. L. Peters and others. In view of the general trend to convert to the decimal system, I have recorded metric measurements and centigrade temperatures in parentheses.

I would like to express my appreciation for the help that Charles Rogers, Curator of Ornithology in the Princeton University Department of Biology, gave us in the early days in identifying rare species; to John J. Yealland, one-time Curator of Birds, Regent's Park Zoo, London, England, for his help and suggestions; to the Avicultural Society for their permission for me to make use of the material in articles written on the Boehm aviaries exclusively for the Society; for the information on the distribution of the various species gleaned from the writings shown in the bibliography; and lastly, but by no means least, to Mrs. Boehm for arranging the publication of these memoirs which I hope will give readers as much pleasure as it did me in compiling them.

CHARLES EVERITT

Mrs. Charles Everitt and Mrs. Boehm
with "Ebb" and "Flo" Costa Rican Toucans

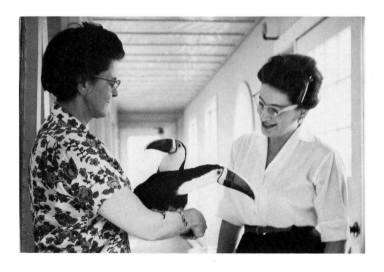

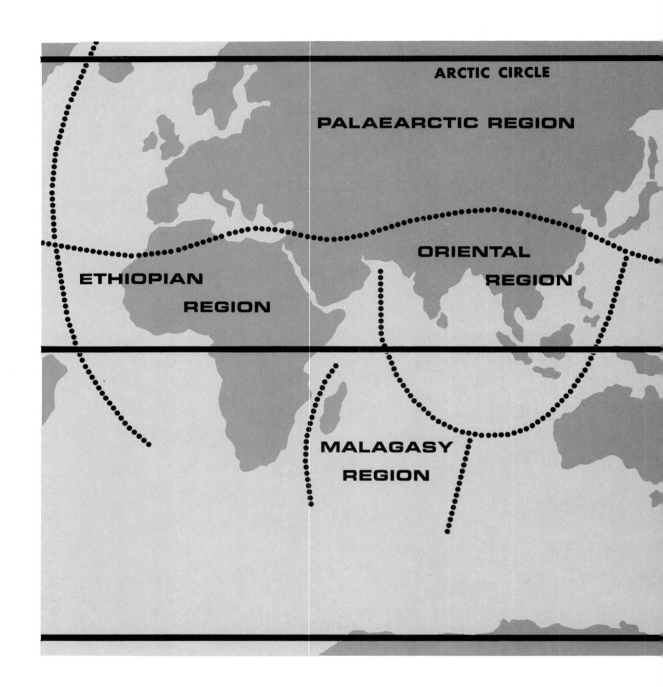

ARCTIC CIRCLE

PALAEARCTIC REGION

ORIENTAL REGION

ETHIOPIAN REGION

MALAGASY REGION

Shown above are the major regions authorities attribute to the habitat of certain species of birds and animals in order to act as a basis of international understanding when discussing in documentry or other research those areas designated. This regional classification is an absolute necessity in the study of bird habitats.

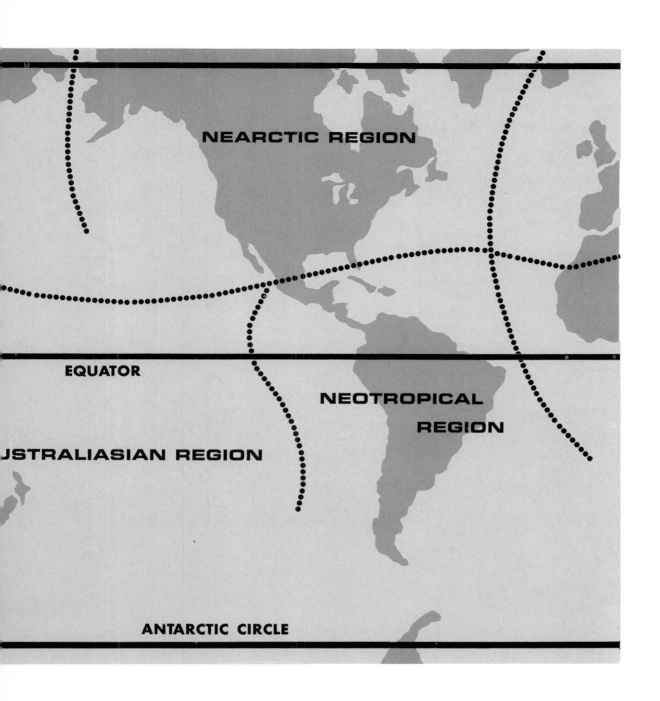

ZOOGEOGRAPHICAL
REGIONS

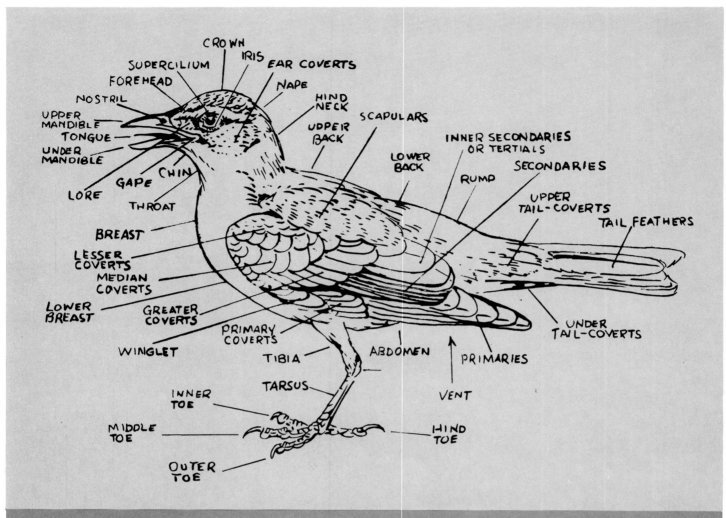

EXTERNAL PARTS OF A BIRD

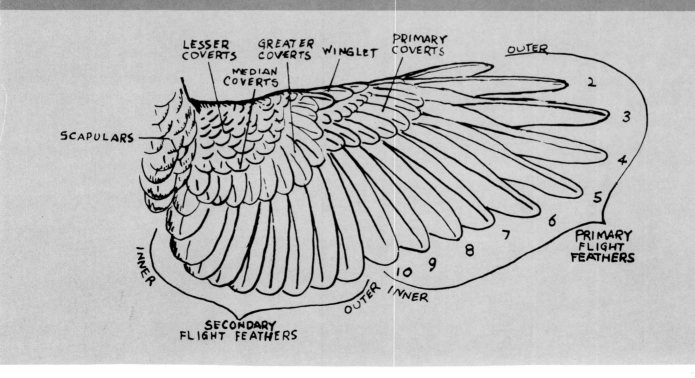

From a diagram drawing by Mr. Boehm

Mr. Boehm throwing meal worms into the air in one of the aviaries

The Aviaries . . .

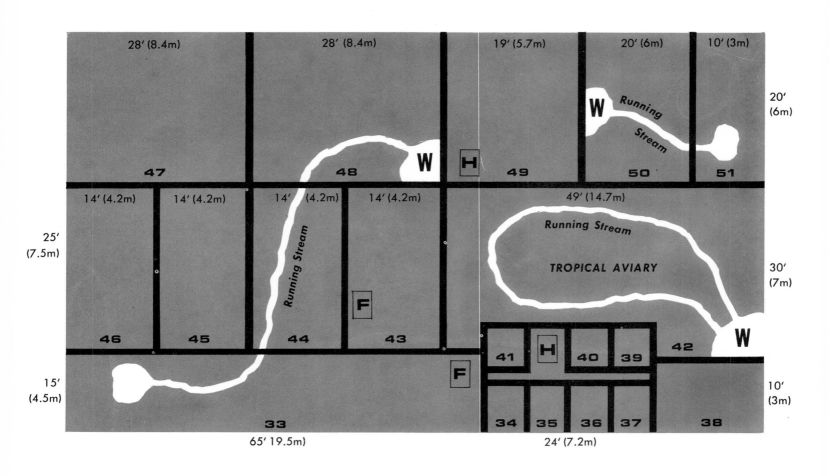

Hillside Bird-house and Aviaries

Waterfall **W**

Oil Burning Hot Water Heaters **H**

Hot Air Fans **F**

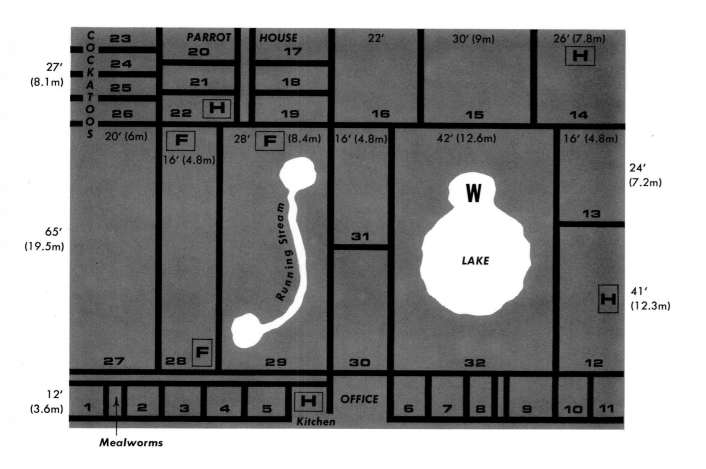

Lower Bird-house and Aviaries

H Oil Burning Hot Water Heaters

F Hot Air Fans

ONE OF THE MOST IMPORTANT factors to successful propagation of a species is an environment that instils a sense of security, and correct feeding. Bearing this in mind, Mr. Boehm designed a main bird-house and a range of aviaries and flights that extended over some four acres. Some of the aviaries had arched roofs, some flat and many had Dutch-style ridge roofs. Each one was individually designed and landscaped to portray, as near as possible, the natural surroundings of the various birds it was planned to accommodate. They were all constructed of wood, many of them having running streams and waterfalls. Hot-water heating plants, six of them in all, were installed and there were literally miles of copper tubing running round each aviary for the heating-pipes were set at two levels, one round the base-boards, the other about six feet (2 metres) up maintaining the temperature at 60 degrees F (15.5 degrees C). In addition, hot-air blowers were installed in those aviaries planted with the more delicate and tropical plants to keep them at 85 degrees F (29.5 degrees C).

Rock waterfalls were constructed, all the water used being piped up from a canal about three hundred yards (273 metres) distant, and it was engineered on a circular flow system so that all water drawn from the canal was fed back into it. Tropical plants were brought up from the southern states, it only being the strict agricultural regulations of the Federal Government that prevented Mr. Boehm bringing in plants from Africa, South America and New Guinea. Fully grown trees were installed for Mr. Boehm was an impetuous man when it came to getting a job done, and he felt there was no time to stand by waiting for saplings to grow. Every aviary and the landscaping of them was designed personally by him and the work was executed under the supervision of his maintenance manager, Dominic Angelini, a specially-selected master craftsman.

Each year any plant, shrub or tree that showed signs of

withering was removed and immediately replaced so that nothing could mar the beauty of the aviaries. During the winter months the aviaries were covered with plastic and it was rare for there not to be some flowering tree, shrub or plant at any time of the year. The only flights left exposed to the elements were those of the cockatoos and those leading out of the parrot-house.

To do real justice to the careful thought that Mr. Boehm had put into laying out the aviaries it would be necessary to describe each in detail, with illustrations, but space does not permit of that here. However, it is hoped that the plans on pages 18 and 19 will convey some idea of their expanse, if not of their magnificence.

It will be noted that every bird-room, flight and aviary was individually numbered, this being essential for the maintenance of accurate records for feeding purposes, explained in the chapter on "Feeding", and the breeding records. For example, we bred Black-headed Sugarbirds in four different aviaries one year and it was only by having the record of the colour of the various leg-bands we had fitted, and the location of that particular breeding, that we were able to control subsequent breedings and avoid any brother-to-sister or such like relationships. A complete check of all birds was made daily and this, together with details of any plants requiring replacement, was entered in the "Aviary Diary".

Although the use of numbers instead of names does tend to make one feel that individuality has been lost, with an operation the size Mr. Boehm maintained, it was the most practical course to pursue. It was nothing to find instructions from Mr. Boehm as to what he wanted done in some particular aviary chalked up on the board in the office, for he had a habit of walking through the aviaries late in the evenings and early in the mornings studying the birds, and nothing missed his eagle eyes.

Feeding...

JUST AS IMPORTANT as accommodation is the feeding of birds. This can be no haphazard affair for attention has to be paid to the individual requirement of each species. Mr. Boehm made extensive studies of their food in the wild; of the protein content of manufactured or prepared foodstuffs; the nutritional value of various fruits; and then drew up formulas of diet to satisfy the requirement as closely as possible. It was on rare occasions that he could not just come up with the right thing, this being primarily due to lack of some particular fruit, berry or form of live-food.

The basic soft-food mixture was comprised of turkey-starter mash, soya bean flour, brewer's yeast and proprietary Clovite, to which was added ground hard-boiled egg and grated fresh carrot to make the mixture crumbly moist for serving. Flamen oil was added to those portions fed to the cocks-o-the-rock and such like colorful birds. In the majority of cases ground raw beef, finely sprinkled with steamed bone-meal, was mixed in with the soft-food, but in some instances the two feeds were served separately. Fruit cocktail, raisins, diced apple, plantain and sweet potatoes were supplied as the fruit-mix, with chopped grapes and cherries on alternate days, and blueberries served separately each day.

The nectar mixture was made of hive honey, dark karo syrup, Gevral Protein, beef extract, ABDEC and raw egg yolks, the whole being mixed with hot water. This was found acceptable by all the sunbirds, hummingbirds, lories, and lorikeets, in fact, by all the birds, and it could be found in every aviary either in nectar tubes or open dishes. Two or more drops of ADBEC were added to all drinking water containers each day, this additional vitamin supplement we were certain contributing in no small manner to the fact that we never had any bird "stuck in the moult".

Sixteen pounds of mealworms weekly.

For live-food we had mealworms, sixteen pounds arriving weekly; crickets, two boxes every fortnight; and the flying insects caught in the black-light night-traps positioned throughout the gardens. When serving the mealworms they were first treated with a very fine film of cod liver oil and then sprinkled with steamed bone-meal. This method was not adopted until we ran into a spate of rickets with nestlings but, once it was started, we had no further such trouble. For the benefit of the kingfishers, twice-weekly trips were made to neighbouring streams to net minnows which were then released into the various pools in the aviaries. We never put them in the running streams for they would only have found their way back to the canal. For the birds-of-paradise, jays and magpies we maintained a white-mice breeding room and anything up to 30 or so mice would be served in one day.

In some instances with new birds it did take several days to come up with an acceptable supplementary food in addition to live-food, but in most cases they readily took to what they were given. We did run into problems with Paradise Flycatchers and their habit of taking food on the wing but, after almost a week of feeding them by tossing mealworms and insects in the air to them, they finally came down to the feeding pans to help themselves and then started on the soft-food and the ground raw beef. Similarly with hoopoes, for which we had to bore the centre out of a sweet potatoe, stuff it full of mealworms and then arrange it on the floor of their room. No birds were released into an aviary until such time as we knew they were feeding.

Every aviary, bird-room or flight had its own diet sheet and the pans used in each enclosure were marked with the relevant number so that, irrespective as to who did the feeding, it was assured that they each got the correct food. With the exception of the parrot-like birds who were fed but once a day, all others were fed once in the early morning, this being replenished again at noon and in the evening, as required. In the very hot weather it was often necessary to carry out a complete new feeding late in the afternoon for the food would either have dried up or, in the case of fruit, might even have begun to rot. No chances of mould ever forming on the food was taken and the fact that we never had a case of aspergillosis in the aviaries throughout the years was no doubt due to this precaution.

Individual diet sheets and numbered pans.

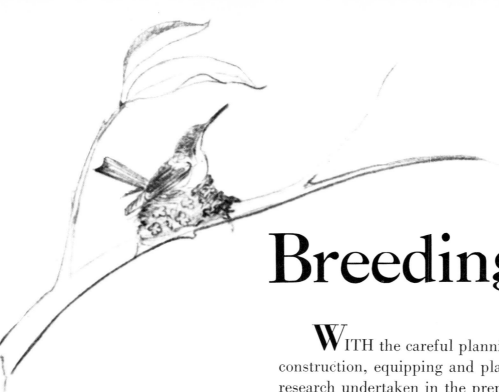

Breedings 1960·1969

WITH the careful planning that had been put into the construction, equipping and planting of the aviaries, and the research undertaken in the preparation of food, Mr. Boehm's efforts to breed some of the rarer species were rewarded. Over the ten years these memoirs cover, some sixty different species breedings, as listed hereunder, were achieved, many of which are described in detail. Those marked with an asterisk were, so far as we could ascertain, the first breeding of the species in North America, and those with the double asterisk, the first recorded breeding in captivity in the world.

*Bird of Paradise, Magnificent
*Bird of Paradise, Princess Stephanie's
*Bird of Paradise, Ribbon-tail
  Blackbird, European
*Blackbird, Grey-winged
**Bulbul, Red-eyed
  Bulbul, Red-vented
  Bulbul, White-eared
  Cardinal, Green
**Cotinga, Black-throated
  Crake, Black
 *Crake, Red & white, or White-breasted
  Dove, Mourning
**Fairy Bluebird
  Flycatcher, Derby, or Kiskadee
**Greenbul, Joyful
 *Honeycreeper, Green, or Black-headed Sugarbird
**Hoopoe, Eastern, or Long-billed
  Killdeer
**Kingfisher, Natal
  Lovebird, Peach-faced

```
 *Magpie, Azure-winged
  Magpie, Red-billed, or Occipital Blue Pie
  Mesia, Silver-eared
**Mynah, Gold-crested
  Mynah, Pagoda
 *Niltava, Rufous-bellied
**Oriole, Black-headed
  Parrakeet, Mealy Rosella
  Parrakeet, Red-rumped
  Partridge, Chukar
  Partridge, Green Wood, or Roulroul
  Pheasant, Palawan Peacock
  Pigeon, Pied Imperial
 *Pitta, Bengal, or Indian
  Quail, Bob White
  Quail, Chinese Painted
**Reedling, Eastern Bearded
 *Robin, Natal
**Robin, Pale-vented
  Rosy Pastor/Pagoda Mynah Hybrid
  Sibia, Black-headed
  Siva, Blue-winged
**Starling, Red-winged
  Starling, Royal/Spreo Hybrid
  Starling, Spreo
 *Sunbird, Bronzy
 *Sunbird, Scarlet-breasted
  Tanager, Black
  Tanager, Blue-headed
 *Tanager, Magpie
  Tanager, Silver-blue
  Tanager, Silver-eared
 *Tanager, Variable
  Thrush, Dhyal, or Magpie Robin
 *Thrush, Kurrichane
  Towhee, Eastern
 *Turaco, Knysna
 *Turaco, Schalow's
  Turaco, White-cheeked
 *Wood-swallow, Masked
 *Wood-swallow, White-browed
 *Wood-swallow, White-browed/Masked Cross
 *Wren, Fairy Blue
**Yuhina, Black-chinned
```

The ORDERS . . .

*While it is not the intention in this book to feature the porcelain
sculptures of Edward Marshall Boehm it is appropriate to
show, at the beginning of each Order, at least one creation
by Mr. Boehm of that order. The birds and their breedings
furnished immeasurable knowledge upon which he drew to establish
the fidelity and the beauty of much of his work. Shown
here are his "Kestrels" (Falco sparverius) fitted for Falconry.
This is a single instance of the integral importance of the
aviaries to Mr. Boehm's famous works featuring birds.*

FALCONIFORMES

This Order is comprised of birds of prey such as eagles, hawks, falcons and the Secretary Bird, and scavengers such as vultures and kites. The very nature of the type of birds Mr. Boehm kept precluded having any of the larger birds of this Order for their mere presence would have struck fear into the majority of birds we were trying to breed.

. . . their mere presence would have struck fear . . .

However, we did have a pair of RED-THIGHED FAL-CONETS, *Microhierax caerulescens,* that came to us from India. About 6 inches in length (15.18 cm), the female was slightly larger than the male but they were very similar in colour. Black above; forehead, chin and throat white; face white with a large patch of black through and behind the eye; remainder of under parts rufous buff. Thighs rich rufous; bill, legs and feet black.

In the wild they are largely insect eaters, hawking them flycatcher-like but, whilst with us they were confined to a large cage and had little opportunity for this activity. The diet we kept them on was ground raw beef, mealworms, crickets, strips of raw meat and each day they had a small white mouse each. These were fed to them dead for, typical of the falcons, they do not immediately kill their catch but hold it with their foot and tear it apart with their finely hooked and very sharp bill. They used to skin the mouse completely, turning the skin inside out and then discarding it. They became very tame and would settle on my hand but, one touch of that sharp bill was like a needle prick and always broke the skin. We never heard them make a sound the entire time we had them.

The Indian Falconets

Oriental Pheasant porcelain sculpture by Edward Marshall Boehm

This is an Order of mainly ground-feeding birds, often partly arboreal, and, mainly, they are of medium size. Often referred to as "gallinaceous birds", several species have been domesticated, the barnyard chicken being a typical example. The Order is comprised of the megapodes, curassows, grouse, pheasants, quail, partridges, francolins, junglefowl, peafowl, guineafowl, turkeys and, lastly, the hoatzin, although this species sometimes is treated as a separate Order.

In view of their ground-feeding habits it is not possible to keep the larger of them in grassed aviaries since they just scratch it all to pieces, so special arrangements for their accommodation had to be made by Mr. Boehm. We had some fifteen different species over the years, four of them being retained purely as living models for porcelain creations, and then returned to the wild.

. . . living models . . .

Undoubtedly the rarest species we ever had was the WHITE-BREASTED GUINEAFOWL, *Agelastes meleagrides,* classified in the Numididae family of the Order. It is confined to Liberia and Ghana forest areas of West Africa and is seldom seen in captivity. About 18 inches (48 cm) in total length, it can be recognized by the rose-red naked skin of the head which fades to milky-white on the neck; the feathers of the lower neck, upper mantle and complete breast being white. Remainder of plumage black, finely vermiculated with white; primaries dark brown margined outwardly with grey; secondaries sepia with fine white vermiculations on the outer webs; bill greenish-brown; legs and feet greyish-olive.

Unfortunately they were not with us very long since, due to a breakdown of the heating system one very cold night, they developed pneumonia and died. Their skins were presented to various natural history museums to all of whom they were the first of their kind. During their short stay they readily took the ground raw beef, soft-food mixture, finch seed mixture, a little fruit and as much live-food as we were prepared to feed to them. They were very tame, coming right up to anyone entering the aviary.

It was of the family Phasianidae, partridges, pheasants and quail that we had most species.

The CHUKAR PARTRIDGE, *Alectoris graeca,* has a wide distribution in Europe, western and central Asia and has been imported into the United States as a game bird. About 15 inches (38 cm) in length, the upperparts are brownish-olive to ashy, tinged across the shoulders with vinous red; crown grey, bordered by a buff line over the eye; ear-coverts dull chestnut; a black band across the forehead, through each eye continuing behind and round the throat as a gorget, the enclosed area buffy-white with a small black spot on the chin, and one on each side of the gape. Outer scapulars pure ashy with broad rufous edges; primaries brown partly edged with buff; tail drab ashy, terminal halves of outer feathers pale chestnut. Breast ashy tinged with brown and washed on the sides with vinous; remainder of lower plumage buff, darkening towards the tail, the flanks heavily barred black and chestnut.

Mr. Boehm undertook to house a pair for a sportsman friend until such time as he could get his pheasant and quail breeding pens renovated. This was in early April and the pair went to nest with us within two weeks. The female scraped a hollow under a low growing hemlock, lining it sparsely with dried leaves and grasses. Eleven eggs were laid over the period April 17 to May 7, but were then deserted. The eggs were pale yellowish, splotched and freckled with pale reddish-brown, and averaged 50 by 32 mm. Her next nest was not discovered until there were ten eggs in it, the final clutch being 17 of which 14 hatched on June 23. The chicks were little buff-coloured balls of fluff, lightly barred black. The owner was advised of the event and he came and picked up the entire family.

The owner advised . . .

Whilst with us they fed on a mixed grain feed as used by the local pheasant farms plus plenty of ground raw beef and soft-food mixture, but their continual foraging and scratching in the planted aviary did a lot of damage to the plants and grass and we were not sorry to see them go.

The BAMBOO PARTRIDGE, *Bambusicola fytchei,* is an Asiatic species to be found in Assam and Burma. About 11 inches (28 cm) in total length, they are largely olive-brown, variegated with chestnut, black and white, the chestnut breast being spotted with white. They have a most distinctive call, a loud ringing cackle of but two notes, repeated rapidly. They did not make good aviary birds for they were too nervous, rising and flying into the sides and roof of the aviary whenever anyone entered. It was after one of them had stunned itself by flying into the upper rafters that it was decided to dispose of them.

The SCALED QUAIL, *Callipepla squamata,* is a North American bird being found from central Arizona to western Texas and south to the valley of Mexico. About 9½ inches (24 cm) in length, the general colour is bluish-ash, more bluish on throat and neck; white on the abdomen which is centrally tinged brown. The head and full, broad crest is soft brown tipped white; neck all round, upper breast and upper back feathers sharply edged with crescentic black lines; remainder of underparts pale brown with elongated arrow-shaped darker spots. Exposed surface of wing tinged light ochre; inner secondaries strongly edged buff forming a lengthwise stripe. They were originally acquired to serve as living models but, on the decision to use other species, the Scaled Quail were shipped out to Texas to be released to the wild.

. . . released to the wild.

The FERRUGINOUS WOOD PARTRIDGE, *Caloperdix oculea,* is an Asiatic species more or less confined to the Malaysian area. About 10½ inches (27 cm) in length, the sexes are alike except that the male has larger spurs on each leg. The head, neck and underparts, reddish chestnut, darker on the crown, paler on the throat and face and almost white on the centre of the abdomen; short, dark streak behind each eye; mantle and sides black, barred white; flanks and vent spotted black; back and tail black, spotted and barred chestnut. Wings olive-brown marked with black. Unfortunately we had two females that each year used to scrape, lay four to six eggs and share the futile task of sitting on them. They were good aviary birds, seldom taking to flight, and subsisted well on ground raw beef, soft-food mixture, and a small seed mixture. Like most of their kind, they were always ready for their mealworm ration.

The BOB WHITE QUAIL, *Colinus virginianus,* is another North American species, their range being from southern Ontario, south-western Maine, across to South Dakota and southwards to eastern and northern Texas, the Gulf Coast and northern Florida. About 10 inches (25 cm) in length, the sexes differ. The forehead, lores, line over eye extending to back of head, the chin and throat of the adult male are white; line from gape, below eye, and side of head deep dusky; crown, back of head, neck all round and upper breast, reddish-brown; underparts a mixture of chestnut, black, ashy and tawny; upper breast deep dusky brown outlining the white throat; remainder of underparts white, tinged brown. The female differs in having the throat buff instead of white; less black on the breast, and the reddish tints in the male replaced by a dull pinkish hue. They have a characterisic call, a series of two syllables best interpreted as "more-wet, more-wet", in a ringing, high pitched tone.

Once they have served their roles as models they were retained in the aviaries with the intention of releasing them to the wild in the spring. However, they decided to go to nest making a scrape under a wild honeysuckle bush. Twelve eggs, pure white, were laid and, after about 24 days of incubation, they all hatched. Although during the day only one bird sat on the eggs, the male and female sharing this duty, in the evening both birds would be on the nest side by side but facing opposite directions. I was fortunate enough to witness the complete hatching of the twelve eggs, this taking about 45 minutes from start to finish. Both birds were on the nest during the event, facing different ways as in the evenings, and it was interesting to see the chicks emerge from the nest, seven coming out in front from under the female, and five in the rear from under the male. The parent birds ejected the empty egg-shells as each bird emerged.

The chicks were little balls of brown, barred blackish-brown, and they developed rapidly, being sexable at about six weeks of age. The entire family was disposed of to the gentleman who owned the Chukar Partridges mentioned earlier.

The PAINTED QUAIL, *Coturnix chinensis,* also referred to as the Blue-breasted Button Quail, is widespread through Asia to Australia, there being several races. A small bird, about 5 inches (13 cm) in total length, the sexes differ in colour and the female is usually slightly larger than the male. The pair we had were from Malaysia and the male was brown, mottled with black and thinly streaked with pale buff above, this colouring embracing the wings also. The short tail, normally hidden, is chestnut; chin and throat black; white patch, edged black, below the eye; a white crescent edged with black on the lower throat; breast and flanks slaty-blue, gradually shading to a deep chestnut at the vent. The female is of much more sombre colouring being generally brown mottled black, and streaked buff throughout. They are very peaceful birds, except with other quail, and are mainly ground birds but do tend to fly straight up when startled and it is best to have about seven feet (2 metres) headroom in their flight as their ceiling is about six feet (1.8 metres).

They are very peaceful birds . . .

When the female decides to go to nest she often lays single eggs in various locations but, after about five have been laid, she gathers them together and begins to build a nest at the final selected spot, usually in a clump of grass or under a covered shelter. We always used to put such a shelter in a corner of the aviary and it was about 18 inches (48 cm) square, 8 inches (20 cm) high and the front open. The nest is just a scrape and the normal clutch varies from nine to fourteen eggs and, once the incubation commences, all by the female in our experience, the male brings her pieces of grass and she then builds a cover over herself. It was fascinating to watch her throw the lengths of grass in an apparent haphazard fashion over her back. However, there was nothing haphazard about it for, in a very short time, she had a complete woven grass shelter over her.

The incubation period is 14 days and it is then that special precautions have to be taken. The chicks when hatched resemble bumble bees, both in colouring and size, and are running about within 30 minutes of leaving the shell. They are so small that ½ inch (1.26 cm) mesh is no enclosure for them. To prevent any straying we used to erect a six inch (15 cm) barrier all round the bottom of the aviary and ensure there were no deep holes in the ground. It is only necessary to keep the barrier in position for about ten days for, by that time, they have grown sufficiently for the normal wiring to contain them. It is always just as well to watch the male's behaviour at hatching time for all males do not respond in the same manner. We had one male that mothered the chicks everytime, but two other males seemed to think the chicks were playthings, picking them up by one leg and tossing them in the air, in the majority of cases maiming them so badly that they had to be put down. To be on the safe side it is better to remove the male just before the eggs are due to hatch.

. . . and tossing them in the air!

Whereas the adult birds can be kept on a normal finch seed mixture, when the chicks arrive it is essential to provide special rearing food. Live ants' eggs and small mealworms are best for the live-food portion but, in addition, finely chopped hard-boiled egg with a little blue maw seed sprinkled over it should be given. Further, a very shallow pan of water should be provided for the young birds are very thirsty little individuals.

. . . very thirsty little individuals.

They are sexable at about four weeks of age and it is as well then to separate males from the females as the former are inclined to quarrel amongst themselves. If ever they are kept in cages, or packed in boxes for transportation, it is essential that the cage or crate is fitted with a soft, false roof or else they may easily crack their skulls as they leap upwards when disturbed. We always fitted a cloth roof about 2 inches (5 cm) below the actual solid roof or lid and experienced no difficulties.

. . . sexable at about four weeks . . .

Another North American species Mr. Boehm retained for a

short period as live models was the MEARN'S QUAIL, *Cyrtonyx montezumae mearnsi*. This species is almost extinct now but used to be found in the arid regions from central Arizona and New Mexico eastwards to central Texas and south to the mountains of north Mexico. Their very nature contributed to depletion for they are very confiding birds, making no attempt to protect themselves by flying away, and, since they make very good eating, they were killed easily by just walking up to them and striking them on the head with a stick. It was locally known as the "Fool Hen."

About 9 inches (23 cm) in length, the sexes differ. The upperparts of the adult male are streaked with black, reddish and yellowish brown; forehead black with small streaks of white changing to brown through the crest; throat patch black; black streak on cheeks and a black streak over the eye continuous with another from the gape along lower side of head, meeting the black of the throat and enclosing a broad, oval white space; remainder of head and broad space below throat patch, white; below this white area there is a narrow streak of black extending from the nape across front of chest; wings marked with round black spots, the primaries browner and spotted with white or buff; sides of neck, sides and flanks ashy with large round white spots; middle line of breast and abdomen rich dark chestnut; under tail-coverts velvet black. The head of the female is mostly greyish-cinnamon and is devoid of stripes; upperparts variegated and finely barred black, tawny and dull lavender, the feathers with broad white shaft streaks; chin whitish; neck bluish-ash, freckled and bordered with black; remainder of underparts pale lavender-brown, the breast and sides with blackish shaft streaks.

The CRESTED FIRE-BACKED PHEASANT, *Lophura ignita,* is an Asiatic species with races in Malaysia, Sumatra and Borneo. The male is about 27 inches (68 cm) in length with a general colour, including crest, of metallic blue-black, glossed with violet; greenish gloss on wings; rump orange, merging into metallic violet; tail arched, centre feathers white; facial skin patch blue; some white streaks on sides of breast; bill whitish; legs and feet red. The female is smaller, about 23 inches (58 cm) and is chestnut, finely pencilled with black above; lower parts dirty white, mottled on breast with black and brown.

A pair of these birds were in the Boehm aviaries for some ten years but it was only when the female was separated from the male that the latter's crest developed. As soon as they were

American Mearns Quail porcelain sculpture by Edward Marshall Boehm

reunited she proceeded to pluck it, a habit he appeared to enjoy for he used to lower his head the better to enable her to get at it. He was a proper showman, opening his wings and agitating them with a whirring sound almost on demand, a great favourite with the visitors. In the early days, prior to his aviary being heated, he used to develope corns on his feet from walking on the frozen ground. I used to cut these periodically and it was a very tricky business for he had two powerful spurs on each leg, and one slash from these could have inflicted a very nasty wound. Only once did he give me a slight cut and that was the very first time I operated on his feet, but thereafter he was most co-operative.

He was a proper showman . . .

The SILVER PHEASANT, *Lophura n. nycthemerus,* a Chinese species also to be found in the eastern hills of Burma, is fairly common in captivity, the adult male being about 26 inches (66 cm) in length, excluding the long tail of some 20 to 24 inches (50 to 60 cm). The upperparts are almost white; crimson facial skin; black crown, crest and underparts. The female is olive-brown with a darker brown crest and lacks the long tail of the male.

The GREY PEACOCK PHEASANT, *Polyplectron bicalcaratum,* is to be found in the eastern Himalayan foothills with races through to Burma and down as far south as Malaysia. About 28 inches (71 cm) in length, including a tail of some 12 to 16 inches (30 to 40 cm), the adult male is greyish-brown with pale tawny spots; the wing-coverts bear blue-purple ocelli, bordered black and white; the tail has larger "eyes" with blue and green reflections. Facial skin pale yellow; a pointed crest; chin white. The female is smaller and darker in plumage, the ocelli being dark, barely visible and bearing no reflections.

The PALAWAN PEACOCK PHEASANT, *Polyplectron emphanum,* is slightly smaller than the preceding species, the adult male having a black head, neck, crest and breast and a metallic green mantle. The ocelli on the wing-coverts and tail are bluish-green with purple reflections. The female is smaller, dark brown and, as with the Grey Peacock Pheasant female, the ocelli bear no reflections.

The pair we had for several years finally decided to go to nest laying two eggs in a scrape the female made in the ground ivy. Incubation lasted some 20 days and was by the female only, one chick hatching out. Since this breeding took place in one of the larger aviaries that had a running stream connecting two deep pools in it, both mother and chick were transferred to a smaller enclosure that had but a shallow pool. The chick was a lighter brown than the adult female and was barred lightly with black. At nine days of age, wing feathers of a darker brown were showing. There was one period of consternation on my part when, late one afternoon I could not find the chick but the female was roosting in a hemlock at about 4 feet (1 metre) above ground level. Finally I spotted a little head peaking out from under its mother's breast. The following day I purposely kept watch as the afternoon came to a close and witnessed the little bird work its way up from ground level by clinging to various branches until it finally reached the parent bird. The whole operation took about 35 minutes. At three months of age the blue in the tail of the young bird indicated that it was a male.

He just looks like a huge gyrating fan.

The display pattern of peacock pheasants is most fascinating, the male raising and spreading his tail and then opening the wings, one upwards and the other towards the ground, and then going round in circles with head lowered. He looks just like a huge gyrating fan.

The CRESTED GREEN WOOD PARTRIDGE, *Rollulus roulroul,* also known as the Roulroul Partridge, is to be found throughout Malaysia, parts of Thailand and Burma, and even as far afield as some islands of the Mergui Archipelago and Borneo. It is a bird of the forest and bamboo groves, spending most of its time scratching around for beetles, ants and any grubs that form a basic part of its diet. In addition it eats fruit and seeds and, in captivity, does well on diced mixed fruits, a good insectile mixture, ground raw beef and live-food in practically any form. They are not adverse even to catching the occasional moth, leaping up in the air to snatch them. Although they spend most of their time on the ground, they do roost in trees at night.

About 10 inches (25 cm) in length, the sexes differ. The adult male is dark, glossy blue-green above, becoming greener on the lower back and rump; wings dark brown, paler at the tips and washed with blue on the shoulders; short tail, black. The head is the most striking feature with its long, cockade-like crest of bristling red feathers with a white patch in between that and the long, black, hair-like bristles on the forehead. Patch of red skin around the eye; remainder of head and neck black, glossed blue, the same colour as the underparts. The small curved bill is red at the base, remainder black; legs and feet crimson; claws horn coloured. The female has the frontal bristles on the forehead but lacks the crest and the white patch, the head being grey. Mantle, back and underparts green; wings rich cinnamon-brown; tail black; legs and feet as with the male; bill black throughout.

The males do tend to be quarrelsome amongst themselves and it is best not to keep two males in the same enclosure. One male can be kept with several females but, invariably, he will select but one as his mate and will keep with her throughout their life span. They have been bred often in captivity but usually by removing the eggs and either giving them to a bantam hen to sit, or putting them in an incubator. Neither of these methods was favoured by Mr. Boehm who always strived to adhere as closely as possible to nature. One pair we had made a scrape under a polydendron bush and laid five eggs. They were yellowish-white and averaged 39 by 32 mm in size.

Incubation, by the female only, lasted 21 days and four hatched. The newly born chicks were covered with dark brown down, had dull red legs and feet, dark bills and were running around within an hour of vacating their shells. Both parents tended the chicks leading them to feeding places and, like so many of this family of birds, picking up pieces of food and dropping them down in front of the chicks for them to help themselves. At seven days feathering in the wings was visible, and, at the end of a further week, the wing feathers had light tips and the underparts were lightly marked with pale, pinhead spots. The next change in colouring occurred in the upper plumage which took on the green of the adult birds, lighter in the females. It was from this that they were sexable at four weeks old. Now is the time to remove the young males or else they are liable to be killed by their father. The females may be left for, as stated earlier, the males are not polygamous. They were in full colour at seven months of age.

The CRIMSON TRAGOPAN, *Tragopan satyra*, is from the central and western Himalayas. The adult male is about 28 inches (71 cm) in length and is of very stocky build. Head black; facial skin blue; eyebrows, neck and upper mantle fiery red, the latter dotted with white spots rimmed with black; bib blue in the centre, green with red spots on the edges; tail black; underparts brown with tiny white spots. The female is smaller and is brown with black and tawny spots, and long tawny spots on her breast.

When the male displays he raises his tail like a fan, lifts his head high, and inflates the bib showing the green and red outside edges to their full advantage.

Both parents tended the chicks . . .

Mr. Boehm with one of his rare birds, a male Satyr Tragopan from the Tibetan Himalayas.

Family Tetraonidae

Another North American species Mr. Boehm had purely for modelling purposes was the LESSER PRAIRIE CHICKEN, *Tympanuchus pallidicinctus,* which is to be found from Kansas south to west central Texas. About 16 inches (41 cm) in length, the colour above is yellowish-brown, spotted with black; underparts white, barred pale dusky brown; tail short and rounded; tarsus feathered to base of toes which are webbed at the base. A tuft of narrow, stiff feathers about 3 inches (8 cm) long on each side of neck overlying a patch of bare skin; head with a slight soft crest.

During the mating season the feather tufts on the neck are erected like horns, tail raised, wings drooped, and the male dashes forward a few steps; lifts his head, at the same time inflating the pale-yellow air-sacs on the lower throat with a jerky movement and producing a booming sound that can be heard for a considerable distance.

As stated earlier these birds were obtained purely to act as models and were returned to the wild on completion of the project. This was just as well for their enormous appetite for live-food could have been a severe strain on our resources during the breeding season of the many insectivorous species in the aviaries.

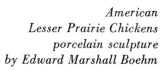

*American
Lesser Prairie Chickens
porcelain sculpture
by Edward Marshall Boehm*

*The famous "Bird of Peace" (Mute Swans) Boehm porcelain
sculpture presented by President Nixon to Mao Tse-Tung in 1972*

GRUIFORMES . . .

GRUIFORMES . . .

This Order consists essentially of ground-living, ground-feeding and mainly ground-nesting birds, many of which seldom fly, and some never. Of the eight suborders within the order we were concerned with the following only:-

Suborder Grues
    Superfamily Gruoidea
        Family Gruidae   ——Cranes
        Family Psophiidae ——Trumpeters
    Superfamily Ralloidea
        Family Rallidae   ——Rails
Suborder Eurypygae
        Family Eurypygidae——Sunbittern

Family Gruidae

Cranes are large birds, up to five feet (1.5 metres) in height, long-necked and have powerful flying abilities. Their main diet is vegetable matter and small animals such as earthworms, insects, beetles, small rodents and small birds. Mainly terrestrial in habit, some are ground-nesters, others building in trees. They are to be found in all continents but are absent from South America, Malagasy, Malaysia, New Zealand and the Polynesian Islands. All the northern species are migratory and, although gregarious at these times, normally they go about in pairs and it is thought that they may mate for life.

The DEMOISELLE CRANE, *Anthropoides virgo*, has a general distribution from southern Europe to northern China and North Africa, migrating to Egypt, the Sudan, Arabia and India during the non-breeding season. They are fairly large, standing about 3 feet (91 cm), and are generally grey; flights, face and underside of neck black; long white plumes on the ear-coverts, and the sexes are alike. We had two of them housed in an unheated aviary throughout the year and their hardiness was most apparent during the winter. With snow on the ground and the temperature several degrees below freezing level, all we had to do was to ensure that paths were cut through the snow so that they could get to the feeding place. Their main food was ground raw beef and fruit-mix, both items having to be fed in small quantities and very frequently during the winter months since they would freeze up before the birds had satisfied themselves. We also gave them an occasional white mouse of which they quickly disposed.

We also gave them an occasional white mouse . . .

The SOUTH AFRICAN CROWNED CRANE, *Balearica regulorum,* is slightly larger than the Demoiselle Crane and more colourful. The nominate race is to be found from South Africa up to southern Angola. The subspecies we had, *B. r. gibbericeps,* was from Kenya. The general colour is black; neck grey; top of head black with a crown of upright yellow feathers; white face patch, upper margin red; upper wing-coverts white; innermost straw coloured; secondaries chocolate; under wing-coverts white. The sexes are alike.

During a very severe snow storm with winds up to forty miles an hour, the aviary the Demoiselle Cranes occupied collapsed. The cranes were rescued unharmed but, since we had no other suitable accommodation for them, they were presented to a zoo. The following spring, Mr. Boehm obtained the Crowned Cranes and, with their wings clipped, they were released into the same area which, although bounded on all sides by other aviaries, was now roofless. All went well, the birds becoming very tame and following one everywhere, all the time their flights gradually growing in. One day one blissfully took flight and sailed over the adjoining aviaries the sides of which were 12 feet (3.5 metres) in height. The other followed it. They stayed around the neighbourhood and many attempts were made to catch them, all to no avail. One zealous outside helper did bring in a Blue Heron, a local wild bird, he had caught and was a little upset when told that the reward offered was not payable on it. Eventually, after about fourteen days had elapsed, both birds were found dead in a corn-field about half a mile apart from each other. It was thought that they could have been poisoned by the insecticide spray used on the local crops for, being summer time, there was no lack of natural food in the way of insects, vegetable matter etc., in the area.

One day one blissfully took flight . . .

Family Psophiidae

This is the family of trumpeters of which there are but three species, all from the humid, tropical, forested regions of South America. They are virtually ground birds, flying poorly, but they roost in trees getting up to a considerable height.

We had a pair of COMMON, or GREY-WINGED, TRUMPETERS, *Psophia crepitans,* from Ecuador. They are about 20 inches (50.6 cm) in height with a pheasant-like body on long legs, and they have a long neck. The sexes are alike, the general colour black; feathers of the upper breast edged metallic blue. The grey feathers from the centre of the back are elongated, the webs much decomposed and turning ochre colour towards the ends. The head feathers are short and soft, feeling velvety to the touch; the bill olive-yellow; legs and feet bluish-grey.

. . . following us around like dogs . . .

They became very tame in captivity, following us around like dogs, and were most accommodating in giving their booming, trumpet-like calls whenever we had visitors. They were most easy to cater for, taking the ground raw beef and the fruit-mix readily. Although they have not got webbed feet they are excellent swimmers, an ability one demonstrated for us when it fell into the large pond in the aviary, swam right across it, and then walked round the edge to join us once more.

Family Rallidae

The family of rails, crakes, gallinules and coots consists of some 130 species and they occur throughout the nonpolar regions of the world. They vary from small, drab, flightless birds to bright greenish-purple birds of some considerable size. They are mainly gregarious, keeping together in flocks during the non-breeding season and in families at other times of the year. Their food consists mainly of insects, grubs, small molluses and vegetable matter and they are relatively easy to cater for in planted aviaries. The common name of rail and crake is synonymous.

The SPECKLED CRAKE, *Coturnicops nutata,* may be found from southern Canada down to Chile, Argentina, the West Indies, Trinidad and Bahamas. About 5 inches (12.65 cm) in length, the sexes are alike. Blackish, tinged olive-brown above; head and neck finely dotted with white; back with narrow broken white bars. Throat white; feathers of breast edged white and flanks barred white; bill, legs and feet black.

The WHITE-BREASTED, or RED and WHITE, CRAKE,

Laterallus leucopyrrhus, is a South American species found from Argentina northward through Eucador and Brazil. About 6 inches (15.18 cm) in length, the sexes are alike. Head and neck rich chestnut-brown; back, wings and tail chocolate coloured; flanks adorned with black and white barrings; throat, breast and lower abdomen white. The lower mandible yellow; upper black, changing to yellow at the base; legs and feet red; eye deep brown with a red iris.

We had three of these charming little birds and it was noticed that they spent a considerble part of their time climbing about in the branches of the hemlock in which they roosted at night. There were some open wicker nest baskets in several of the trees that had been placed there in the hope that some of the birds might make use of them. It was the crakes that took one over, making a nest by just filling it loosely with dried leaves. It was obvious that but two of the crakes were concerned with the nesting when two plain white eggs were laid incubation beginning with the laying of the first. These two birds shared the incubation, the third crake just going about its business but joining up with either of the other two when one was off the nest. As they were colour banded it was easy to tell which was the nesting pair, but still no difference could be detected in the birds. During the day only one sat the eggs but, as evening approached, that one would be joined by the other and the two of them would nestle down together. The period of incubation was 24 days, one hatching one day and the other the next. Being of the nidifugous class of birds, the chicks vacated the nest within an hour of leaving their shells. They were covered with black down, their wings practically nonexistent, but their legs were strong and these they used to their full advantage. Tiny little things, extremely difficult to keep in sight as they ran about after their parents through the ground ivy for, immediately a movement was made by any of us, the chicks froze where they were and seemed to just disappear into the ground. Their diminutive size, coupled with the fact that the aviary wire-netting was ¾ inch (1.8 cm) mesh, through which they could have passed without any problem, called for prompt action. Accordingly, a portable 4 by 3 feet (1.21 m x 91 cm) compound of ¼ inch (6 mm) mesh was constructed and placed in the aviary. As it had been observed that the first chick had returned to the nest in the evening, that same nest was taken out of the tree and fitted in a low bush around which the compound had been located. The catching of the young birds was facilitated by there being a bird-

. . . and the two of them would nestle down together.

43

house at the far end of the aviary and, using mealworms as bait, the parents were enticed into there, the young ones following them. This gave us an opportunity to examine the chicks and it was disclosed that, with the exception of the white egg-tooth situated on the upper mandible, they were completely black, even down to their legs and feet. The normal food supplied to the adults was our soft-food mix, ground raw beef and mealworms. For the benefit of the young birds an extra amount of ground hard-boiled egg was added to the soft-food, and small mealworms were given. Their feeding habits are similar to domestic fowl, the parents searching for the food and then calling to their chicks to come and get it.

African Black Rail

They grew rapidly, returning with their parents to the nest each evening and at 10 days old they were considered big enough to be given full run of the aviary. They were nearly four weeks old before feathers began to show; yet at six weeks they were fully feathered. The upper plumage was dark brown and the lower parts grey. This grey gradually lightened to the white of the adult birds and, at three months of age, they had assumed full adult colouring, including the feet and legs. All five birds went around together and there was never any trouble with them.

The BLACK RAIL, *Limnocorax flavirostra,* is from Africa where it may be found from south of the Sahara right down to Cape Town, South Africa. They are common, abundant birds, inhabiting any marshy piece of ground in any type of country.

About 8 to 9 inches (20 to 23 cms) in length, their general colour is wholly blackish-slate, relieved by brilliant orange-red legs and feet and a bill of bright yellow-green, and a bright red eye. The sexes are alike. We had two of them, received in a consignment from Kenya, that were released into a large planted aviary that had a stream running through it, and was well equipped with clumps of umbrella grass, cultivated honeysuckle and other cover plants. Although shy at first, scampering under cover whenever anyone entered the aviary, the tossing of a few mealworms in the grass soon drew them out. It was late in February one year that they built a nest of dried grasses and reeds in one of the stands of umbrella grass. Three eggs were laid, buffish pink, speckled reddish-brown and blotched with lilac under-markings and they averaged 23 by 31 mm in size.

Although one of them was on the nest constantly, it was now revealed that they did not confine their activities to ground level and it was nothing to see one of them in the upper branches of the hemlocks and pines one moment, and on the ground the next. As with most of the Rallidae family of birds, they do not use their wings a great deal for flying, mostly running over the ground, the wings merely being opened when they needed lift to surmount an obstacle or to get either into or out of a tree.

All three eggs hatched after a period of 18 to 19 days incubation, the chicks being little black balls of fluff with bright yellow bills and black legs and feet. They left the nest about three hours after hatching and the parent birds promptly began to lead them around to feed, picking up mealworms and dropping them at the feet of the young birds. The bills darkened at five days and, by the time they were four weeks old, they were feathered up, olive-brown above, throat whitish, but the bill, legs and feet still dark. The legs did not begin to change colour until they were some two months old, by which time the bills had begun to lighten from the base outwards. Full adult colouring was attained at about five months of age. However, prior to this stage of development, the parents had nested again, this time in a clump of honeysuckle, and four eggs were laid. In fact, by the time the first round had reached

African Black Rail Fledgling

the full adult colour, the parents had had three more rounds of four, three and three chicks, thus giving a total of 13 young crakes. It almost seemed as if the young birds were encouraging their parents to keep up the good work for all the newly hatched chicks were taken over by the round immediately preceding them. For example, the first round tended to the second; the second to the third; the third to the fourth and so on right down the line. There were six rounds that season resulting in 19 young birds.

The same site was selected the following February but there had been some changes made in the occupants of the aviary. As soon as a crake chick hatched and left the nest it was picked up by a female Princess Stephanie's Bird of Paradise and devoured. This was despite the fuss and noise created by all of the crakes and their ganging up on the bird of paradise. However, once the honeysuckle had regained all its summer foliage, they were well concealed and eventually produced another fifteen or so chicks of which but one or two were lost to the predating birds of paradise. From their prolific breeding it is apparent that they must suffer great predation in the wild or else they would over-run the entire African continent in a "population explosion" of their own.

. . . picked up . . . and devoured.

We never learned for sure at what age they do breed for it was the same pair that flooded us out each year and they were all disposed of in the autumn of the second year. They make excellent aviary birds being peaceful, easy to cater for as they take any standard soft-food, ground raw beef, any live-food and constantly forage for themselves through the trees, bushes and on the ground.

The LESSER GALLINULE, *Porphyrula alleni,* is an African species to be found from Senegal across to the Sudan and southward to South Africa. About 10 inches (25 cm) in length, the sexes are alike, green above; purple below with a blackish head and rump. Frontal shield green; bill, legs and feet red. A handsome bird but they tend to be very shy and swiftly take to flight upsetting many of the birds in a confined aviary.

The PURPLE GALLINULE, *Porphyrula martinica,* is a New World species found from the southern United States to Argentina and also in the West Indies. There is another species bearing the same common name but that is from Africa, and bears the generic name *P. alba.*

Mr. Boehm brought back a pair of the *P. martinica* from

Ecuador and they settled down well in the same aviary as a pair of Pheasant-tailed Jacanas and the Demoiselle Cranes. About 13 inches (33 cm) in length, the head and hind-neck dark blue; forehead, breast and upper belly violet-blue; upper mantle, sides of breast and wing-coverts verditer blue; remainder of back olive. The belly and flanks black; under tail-coverts white; bill red with a yellow tip; frontal shield blue; legs and feet yellow.

Gallinules generally are very peaceful birds, feeding mostly on vegetable matter, but they do take insects and were very partial to the ground raw beef.

. . . very peaceful birds . . .

The LESSER SPOTTED CRAKE, *Porzana pusilla,* of which there are at least two races, one being found in central and southern Europe, north Africa and Iran, migrating as far south as Angola and Somali during the non-breeding season; another is resident to Ethiopia, Kenya and Angola through to South Africa and also in Malagasy. It was one of this latter race, *P. p. obscura,* of which we had a pair. They are a small bird, about six inches (15.18 cm) in length, with a short bill, the adult male being dark brown and black with white flecks on the mantle, lower back, scapulars and inner secondaries; sides of head slate; underparts dark grey; lower flanks and under tail-coverts black, barred white. The female is very similar except that the throat and centre of the chest to belly are whitish.

As stated earlier, the entire Rallidae family make good aviary birds, are comparatively easy to cater for and, provided they are given the right conditions, there is no reason why they should not breed in captivity.

Family Eurypygidae

The SUNBITTERN, *Eurypyga helias,* is the sole member of this family and is to be found in the forested regions of America from southern Mexico to Bolivia and Brazil, through which area at least three races are recognised. The single specimen we had, *E. h. major,* came from Colombia. About 18 inches (45.5 cm) in length, the top and sides of head black; stripes above and below the eye white; throat white; back and sides of neck finely barred black and fulvous. Stripe down front of neck fulvous; breast mottled and barred black and buff; abdomen whitish. Mantle barred black and buff; lower back and upper tail-coverts barred black and white. Remaining plumage is mainly grey and olive, with prominent black bars and white spots. The long tail is crossed by two broad bands of black and chestnut.

It is only when the sunbittern spreads its wings that it reveals its brightest colouring, a large shield of deep orange-chestnut in a surround of pale orange-buff in the middle of each wing. When one sees this it can be understood how the adjectival noun "sun" became part of their common name. They have a long neck and longish, sharp, pointed bill, upper mandible blackish, lower orange. The eyes are deep red and the long, naked legs and the feet are yellow. Mainly insect eaters, their method of approach is similar to that of the jacanas, the neck going back and forth with each step.

The one we had became very tame and would display, that is spread its wings, almost to order. It had a thin plaintive cry, like a long drawn out whistle, but it was only when feeding time might have been delayed that we ever heard it. In addition to live-food in the form of mealworms and crickets, it also took a fair amount of ground raw beef and was continuously walking up and down the running stream searching for food there.

American Common Tern sculpture by Edward Marshall Boehm

Drawing of the African Jacana by Mr. Boehm

This is an Order comprised of wading birds, shore birds, plovers, gulls, etc, and is made up of four suborders and fifteen families of which, over the years, we had specimens from eight of these families.

SUBORDER CHARADRII

This suborder embraces the "waders" of British and the "shorebirds" of American usage. Birds of small to moderate size, they are ground-living and mostly ground-nesting, to be found in the vicinity of water, either inland or by the sea. They are strong flyers and, for short distances, can run swifty on the ground.

Family Jacanidae

This is the family of the jacanas, often referred to as "lily-trotters", particularly the African species, and they are to be found in tropical and subtropical areas in South America,

Africa, Madagascar, Asia and Australia. They are long-legged waterfowl ranging from 10 to 13 inches (25 to 33 cm) in length, the length of the leg being accentuated by the bareness of much of the tibia. Their feet are a characteristic feature, excessively long toes and straight claws, the claw of the hind toe much longer than the toe and tapering to a fine point. This form of foot enables them to move easily over floating vegetation. Their main food is insects and larva, both land and water, and the seeds of water plants.

The AFRICAN JACANA, *Actophilornis africanus*, has a general distribution from Gambia across to the Sudan and Ethiopia and southwards to South Africa. They average 10 to 12 inches (25 to 31 cm) in length and the sexes are very much alike, although the female generally is slightly larger than the male, and the crown of the head is often white, that of the male being slate-grey. Sides of face, throat and neck all round to upper breast, white; back and wing-coverts grey; two white feathered wattles depending from the chin; forehead, lores and chin covered with red wart-like protrusions. From the breast to abdomen black; bill red; legs and feet slate-grey. They have a peculiar bell-like croak which they utter as they walk over aquatic plants, their necks going back and forth at each step, a characteristic with jacanas, shore-birds and waders. This neck movement is necessary so that their eyes can focus for they have monocular vision, that is, each eye has its own range outwards, the focussing of both eyes on one object being limited to about 6 degrees directly forward of the direction in which the head is pointed.

The PHEASANT-TAILED JACANA, *Hydrophasianus chirurgus*, has a wide distribution throughout the Indian Peninsula, Ceylon, Burma, Malaysia and as far eastward as south China, the Philippines and Java. The sexes are alike in colouring both in their summer and winter plumage. They are about 18 inches (45.5 cm) in length in winter dress, but the long tail plumes of their summer attire adds a further 8 to 10 inches (20 to 25 cm) and the females usually are some 3 inches (7 cm) longer than the males. In breeding, or summer dress, they are dark brown above with bronzy reflections; underparts chocolate-black; tail elongated and chocolate-black; back of neck pale yellow edged by a black line that connects with the black crown. Remainder of head and neck and a large patch on the wing, white; bill bluish; legs and feet greenish. In winter dress the upperparts are pale glossy bronzy-brown with barring at the base of the tail which is shorter and white, except for the central brown feathers. The forehead black barred white; head brown with a white streak above the eye merging into a yellow line down the sides of the neck. There is a black line below the eye that follows the yellow line and merges into a dark brown patch on the breast. Forehead buffish; chin, throat and remainder of the underparts white; wings as in summer dress but with brown pencilling on the shoulders. They have a peculiar mewing, nasal call.

The exotic water lillies seen in the illustration on page 53 were brought in from the south by Mr. Boehm to provide the birds with near to nature surroundings. Since the aviary was unheated both the lillies and the jacanas had to be transferred to pools in the heated avaries for the winter months.

The BRONZE-WINGED JACANA, *Metopidius indicus*, has a wide range from India through Burma, Thailand, Java and the Celebes and is a rare migrant to Malaysia. About $11\frac{1}{2}$ inches (29 cm) in length, the sexes are alike. Head black washed with metallic green, with a white streak above the eye and a small white spot below it; mantle dark bronzy green; wings similar but blackish at the edges; back, rump and upper tail-coverts metallic purplish-chestnut; back of neck and sides of breast black, washed with metallic purple; frontal lappet blue, pink near the gape; bill bluish-green. Under tail-coverts and tail chestnut; rest of underparts black washed metallic green; legs and feet bluish-slate.

Feeding the birds did not present any great difficulties for, in addition to their regular issues of mealworms and crickets, they also took a considerable amount of ground raw beef and, since they were housed in aviaries with running streams and lily ponds, they were able to forage much for themselves.

Family Rostratulidae

This tropical and subtropical family of birds is to be found in Africa, Asia, Australia and South America and they have the peculiarity that the females are not only larger, but they are more colourful than the males. Further, the domestic duties are in reverse to the normal with the Old World species of the genus *Rostratula*, the males doing the incubating and rearing of the young.

The PAINTED SNIPE, *Rostratula benghalensis*, of which there are two races, the nominate one being found in Asia and

The Indian and Oriental Pheasant-tailed Jacana

Africa, the *R. b. australis,* being confined to Australia. The specimen we had was from Kenya. As stated above the sexes differ in size and colouring, the male being about 10 inches (25 cm) in length and the females 11 inches (28 cm.) The adult male is olive brown with a bottle-green gloss above; centre longitudinal streak from the bill, over the crown, yellow buff; buffish white patch around the eye; back olive-brown widely barred with blackish and with two longitudinal buffish steaks; rump pale grey, barred black and white with round white and pale buffish spots; winged-coverts golden-brown with sparse blackish bars and paler golden-brown round spots. Flight feathers and tail silver grey with round golden-yellow spots and some broad black bars on the outer webs of the outer primaries; throat white; neck and chest mottled olive-brown; broken black band on breast; remainder of underparts white. The female differs from the male in having the sides of the head and neck rich chestnut; wing-coverts green with a fine barring, and a broad black band on the chest. Their main diet is worms and insects and, as is quite common with polyandrous species, the female displays to the male. They are weak flyers in comparison with the ability of the true snipe. They also took a considerable amount of ground raw beef.

Family Charadriidae

This is the family of plovers and lapwings and they are to be found throughout both the New and the Old Worlds. They are mainly insect, worm and small mollusc eaters, with the shore species also taking aquatic insects and larvae.

The BLACK-WINGED PLOVER, *Charadrius melanopterus,* is an African species to be found in eastern Sudan and Ethiopia southwards to eastern South Africa. The species we had, *C. m. minor,* was from Kenya. About 10½ inches (26.5 cm) in length, the sexes differ slightly in colouring. The forehead of the adult male is white; head and neck grey, crown darker; brown above washed bronzy; a white band across the wings; outermost secondaries with black tips, the innermost purely white. A broad black band between the grey neck and the whiter abdomen; tail white with a broad subterminal black band; under tail-coverts and under wing-coverts white. The female is similar except that the head and neck are ashy. They have a harsh, scolding type call note.

The KILLDEER, *Charadrius vociferus,* is a North American bird with a breeding range extending from Canada to Mexico, wintering in the Pacific States and in an area from Illinois to Long Island Sound. It has been given various local names such as Killdeer Plover, Noisy Plover, Chattering Plover and just plain Killdeer. Groups of killdeer also winter as far south as Peru, where there is a non-migratory, resident species. It is considered that some of the visitors mingle with the residents and stay there and, in a similar manner, some of the residents group up with the winter visitors and leave with them. Until such time as members of both groups are banded and reported upon wherever they are recaught or found, the intermingling of the two groups of birds can only be surmised. The Killdeer is a true plover, having the short legs, rounded head and prominent eyes, characteristics of that family. One of its most distinguish-

American Killdeer porcelain sculptures by Edward Marshall Boehm

ing features is two breast bands as compared to the single band borne by the other "ringed" plovers. As one of the synonymous names implies, they are noisy birds with an oft repeated call, best illustrated phonetically as "kil-de", but, when harassed, they give vent to a plaintive cry of "dee-dee", uttered with a rising inflection. Typically plover-like in guarding their breeding territory, they simulate the actions of an injured bird, trailing one wing on the ground and running away from the vicinity of their young or nest. It is whilst making this decoy move that they give their mournful cry. In the event of there being young, these immediately "freeze" where they are and remain motionless until reassured by either of the parent birds.

About 10 inches (25 cm) in total length, their colouring above is olive-brown with pure white on the underparts. A head-on view of them shows four black bands, two on the head and two on the breast. The sexes are alike, the crown of the head, cheeks and back, including the wings, brown; forehead, chin, throat and underparts white, but the two breast bands are black with a white stripe between. They also have a small whitish-buff stripe from above the back of the eye towards the back of the head. The white of the throat extends round the nape as a collar, gradually diminishing in width as it passes round the back of the head. The rump rich rufous, most conspicuous when the bird is in flight, the same applying to the white tipping of the tail feathers. The under tail feathers are rufous but not of such a rich shade as that on the lower back.

They are ground nesters, just making a scrape, and a clutch varies from two to four eggs which are dull olive-green, speckled dark brown, and they blend in with the surroundings making them extremely difficult to find. The incubation period is twenty-eight days and, with the pair we had, was carried out by the female only, commencing with the laying of the second egg. There were four eggs, of which one was clear, the others all hatching out. As members of the nidifugous class of birds, the chicks were running around within an hour of vacating their shells. They were covered with grey and brown striped down, with lighter underparts, and were about two inches (5 cm) in total length. As with quail and such ground birds, the parents sought out the feeding spots, calling as new delicacies were disclosed. Their normal feed in the wild consists of insects and grubs, plus a certain amount of vegetable matter that they find on their natural feeding grounds such as pastureland, ploughed fields, shore-dunes, etc. Within the confines of the aviary they

. . . calling as new delicacies were disclosed . . .

had access to our soft-food mixture, ground raw beef and regular supplies of mealworms, gentles and crickets. As soon as they hatched, a six by four feet wire (2x1.2 metres) enclosure was erected around the mother and her family so as to obviate any danger of their straying, falling into the stream, or becoming victims of any of the larger birds in the aviary. The enclosed family was supplied with the feed mentioned above plus some chopped hard-boiled egg. At three weeks they were considered grown enough not to come to any harm and were released from their confinement. Although the male had been separated from the family during this entire period, as soon as they were freed he joined them and was as attentive to them as if they had never been parted. Although often seen in flocks in the wild, they become very territorially minded at the breeding season and the males get very quarrelsome amongst themselves. However, we left the entire family together throughout the winter (the aviary was heated) and experienced no trouble at all. Just prior to the spring they were all disposed of to zoos to make room for new inmates.

. . . like the ring of iron hitting stone.

The BLACKSMITH PLOVER, *Vanellus armatus,* is about 12 inches (30 cm) in length and is to be found from Angola across to Kenya and southward to South Africa. The sexes are alike, forehead, crown, back of neck, upper tail-coverts, abdomen, under wing-coverts and rump, white; pale grey upper wing-coverts and scapulars; tail white with a broad black terminal band, narrowing on the outermost feathers; remainder of plumage black. The wings are equipped with sharp spurs. Normally a silent, unobtrusive bird, they do have a loud, ringing, clinking cry, just like the ring of iron hitting stone. We had three of them and they all became very tame, taking mealworms from our fingers, but they never evinced any interest in going to nest so they may well have been all the same sex. Their main diet was live-food, the ground raw beef and the soft-food mixture.

. . . being flighty and disturbing . . .

The SPUR-WINGED PLOVER, *Vanellus novae-hollandiae,* is from Australia where it can be found in south-eastern Australia and Tasmania. In these parts it is also called the Wattled Plover and the Alarm-bird. The sexes are alike and they are about 14 inches (35 cm) in length. The crown, black; face, hind-neck, rump and underparts white; tail white, tipped black; wattles on face yellow. They never settled down to aviary life being flighty and disturbing the nesting birds, so they were disposed of to a zoo.

Family Scolopacidae

This is the family of sandpipers, curlews, woodcock and snipe, and we had but one specimen over the years. A solitary LEAST SANDPIPER, *Calidris minutilla,* that was brought to us with an injured wing having been found in the salt-marshes on the New Jersey shore. We had the bird some three years, its broken wing never being of use in flight and, although it would come readily at live-food feeding times, it was always shy and scuttled away with it's quick little steps under cover as soon as anyone approached it. About 6 inches (15 cm) in length, it had a change of plumage in summer and winter. In winter the entire upperparts are pale greyish-brown, each feather darker centrally; secondaries and primaries white-tipped; breast shaded very pale brownish-grey. In summer dress the entire upperparts are dusky brown, striped on head and shoulders with chestnut, each feather on back and shoulders edged chestnut, remainder grey edged white; breast washed pale rusty and spotted with brown; throat and abdomen white. This bird apparently was migrating through the eastern shore States for it is only at these migratory periods that we have them in New Jersey, although they are to be found in both North and South America, breeding from north-western Alaska through to Nova Scotia and migrating as far south as Chile, and westward to eastern Siberia.

. . . an injured wing . . .

Family Recurvirostridae

This is the family of avocets and stilts, members of which may be found in both the New and the Old Worlds. Like others in the order Charadriiformes, they also are worm, insect, larva and small mollusc eaters. They are long-billed, long-legged wading birds of from 11 to 19 inches (28 to 48 cm) in length, including the bill.

The BLACK-WINGED STILT, *Himantopus himantopus,* has a general distribution in southern Europe, western Asia, Arabia, parts of Africa and Malagasy. They are about 15 inches (38 cm) in length and the sexes differ in colouring. The adult male's mantle, scapulars, wings above and below are blue-black, glossed with green; tail greyish; rest of plumage white. The bill is longish, straight, thin and black, and the long legs and feet vermillion red. The feet are characteristic in that the outer and middle toes are slightly webbed and there is no hind toe. The female differs in that the hind crown, nape, mantle and scapulars are mousy-brown. They did not settle down to aviary life, being extremely nervous, flying up and down constantly, making a plaintive piping sound whenever anyone approached.

The AVOCET, *Recurvirostra avosetta,* has a wide range through southern Europe, Asia, and throughout western Africa during the non-breeding season. Some, however, do breed in England and Africa and their migration is more limited. About 17 inches (43 cm) in length, the sexes are alike. Crown of head, back of neck, scapulars, wing shoulders and a bar along the wing and primaries, black; remainder of plumage white. A long, thin, upcurved bill, long legs pale grey and webbed feet. These birds settled down well, seldom took to flight, being just content to walk if disturbed. Live-food is an essential part of their diet and the access to a running stream is an advantage. There also are species of avocets in North America and Australia, and they are an occasional migrant to New Zealand.

Family Burhinidae

This is the family of thickknees, stone-curlews and stone-plovers and it is widely distributed in the Old World. They are not strong flyers, preferring to walk or run, but, whenever they do fly they run first so as to get lift to take off, and they make a glide approach to land. The only member of this family we ever had was a solitary STONE-CURLEW, *Burhinus magnirostris,* from Australia where it has a general distribution throughout the open country, sandy plains and sparse woodlands. Just over 20 inches (51 cm) in length, the sexes are alike and we were never sure as to what ours was. The crown dark grey, marked black; round the eye white; throat buff, chest and abdomen whitish streaked blackish; white patch on the wing. The bill is short, greenish and black tipped; legs long and greenish in colour. The head is large, broad, and the eyes are owl-like in their comparatively large size and roundness. Its main food is insects and larva but it did very well with us on a diet of ground raw beef, mealworms, crickets and whatever other insects it could forage for itself in the aviary.

They are not strong flyers . . .

Family Glareolidae

This is the family of pratincoles and coursers, widely distributed throughout the Old World.

The BLACK-WINGED PRATINCOLE, *Glareola nord-*

manni, breeds in south-eastern Europe and Asia Minor but migrates to Africa during the non-breeding season. The pair we had were trapped in Uganda and the sexes were alike. About 8 inches (20 cm) in length, above they are earth-brown, lighter on the nape and sides of neck; upper tail-coverts white; throat and breast pale tawny, with a black ring from below the eye to base of neck. Chest tinged earth-brown; abdomen and under tail-coverts white; under wing-coverts and axillaries black; base of forked tail white. They are very quiet little birds, scurrying over the ground in their constant search for insects and grubs. Live-food is a necessity to keep them in good shape in captivity.

The EGYPTIAN PLOVER or CROCODILE BIRD, *Pluvianus aegyptius,* although commonly called a plover, is one of the coursers. The common name of Crocodile Bird is founded on a story first reported by Herodotus that they enter the mouths of crocodiles to pick their teeth. Although this has never been substantiated by any modern observers, the name still is used. They have a range from Senegal to Upper Egypt and are also in Angola and northern Uganda. The sexes are alike, grey above and creamy white below; crown of head, streak through the eye, upper back and band across the chest, black washed bottle-green. Flight feathers black and white and the elongated feathers on the back are black, washed bottle-green. They become very tame in capitivity and make excellent aviary birds but, as with the entire order, live-food is an essential.

. . . they enter the mouths of crocodiles to pick their teeth.

Family Laridae

This is the family of gulls and terns and is world wide in distribution. We had but one, an INCA TERN, *Larosterna inca,* from the west coast of South America where it can be found from Peru to Chile. It is a slender built bird with slate-coloured plumage; crimson bill, legs and webbed feet; yellow gape wattles, and an ornamental whisker-like white plume running from below the eye and curving downwards towards the shoulders. They are about 16 inches (41 cm) in length. The one we had thoroughly enjoyed giving an aerial display as he dived and swooped to water level to catch mealworms as they were tossed to him. An excellent aviary bird, interfering with no other inmates and being troubled by none. Even when it had its leg in a splint after breaking it, no birds bothered it as it hopped around to the feeding pans of ground raw beef, and the leg was completely mended in about three weeks.

All the Charadriiformes require a constant supply of live-food when in an aviary for they are not able to forage enough for themselves in a restricted area when in competition with other insectivorous species. Occasionally some would take some of the ground raw beef, but this was an exception and not the general rule.

American Mourning Doves porcelain sculpture by Edward Marshall Boehm

This is the Order embracing all the pigeons, doves and sandgrouse and it is almost cosmopolitan in its distribution, only the Arctic, sub-Arctic, Antarctic, some sub-Antarctic regions and a few oceanic islands being devoid of birds of this Order.

The names pigeon and dove are almost interchangeable, common usage normally associating the name "dove" to the smaller forms, and "pigeon" to the larger. Most of the species are gregarious, strong flyers and partly arboreal, but a few are ground or cliff-dwellers. Seeds, fruit, berries and other vegetable matter are their main diet but some do take small snails and other invertebrate animals.

They do tend to have rather profuse droppings and the artistic lay-out of the Boehm aviaries was often marred by this habit, particularly so far as the fruit pigeons were concerned, so special aviaries were allocated to the few species we did have over the years. The majority were with us for a short time only, so extensive studies were not made of most of them.

The Order is divided into two suborders, Pterocletes (sandgrouse) and Columbae (pigeons and doves). It also includes the extinct Dodo in the family Raphidae in the suborder Columbae, the pigeons and doves being in the family Columbidae, which is itself divided into two subfamilies, Columbinae (the typical pigeons and doves) and Teroninae (fruit-eaters).

Subfamily Columbinae

The CRESTED BRONZE-WING PIGEON, *Ocyphaps lophotes*, is about 13 inches (33 cm) in length and is to be found in most parts of Australia with the exception of the North-western Territories. The sexes are alike, the upper-parts fawn; crown and underparts grey; crest black; black bars on the bronze wings, and the tail is white tipped.

The TAMBOURINE DOVE, *Tympanistria tympanistria*, has a general distribution through equatorial Africa from Sierra Leone in the west to Ethiopia in the east and down through the Congo and across to Mozambique. About 9 inches (23 cm) in length the adult male is olive-brown above, crown of head more olive; forehead, streak over eye, cheeks, and from chin to belly, white; blue-black spots on the inner secondaries; underside of wings, axillaries and flanks chestnut; under tail-coverts dark olive-brown. The female is very similar except that the sides of the neck and chest are washed with grey.

The common name of Mourning Dove has been given to

several species throughout the world but the one we had was the EASTERN MOURNING DOVE, *Zenaidura macoura,* a native of the eastern states of America. About 12 inches (30 cm) in length, it is readily distinguishable in the field by the long, pointed tail which bears large white spots, but these are only visible when the bird is in flight. Of a vinous hue, the adult male and female are identifiable as the male has a metallic violet-green area around the base of the neck, this feature being absent in the female. Both sexes have a black spot behind each eye and, in general build, the males usually are larger than the females. The pair we had came to us one at a time, in each instance it being an injured bird that was brought to the aviaries, about six months apart, but it turned out that they were a true pair, and they went to nest.

They took readily to an open type platform nest-box, just adding some twigs and coarse grass as padding. They are most prolific, this pair having seven rounds in one season, but we removed the last two rounds of eggs since a total of ten young was all we could cope with. As may be assumed from above, there were two eggs in each round and they had no special features being plain white and, on the average, measured 27 by 19 mm. The incubation period of 13 days was shared, each bird sitting for about five hours at a stretch during the daylight hours. There is nothing unusual about the chicks; they are typical dove squabs. The rearing was shared and the young had their eyes open at five days old. Feathering was fairly rapid and, at 12 days, the young birds left the nest. Their colouring was rather drab at this stage and the long tail not formed. However, by the time they were a month old they were fully independent, had their long tails, and bore black markings in the flight feathers. The first sign of the purplish-green collar of the male did not make itself apparent until they were about six months of age. It was not until a year when this marking extends right round the hind-neck that one can be certain of their sex. Of the ten we bred the sexes were evenly divided. Although a number of females appeared to live quite happily together, the same could not be said of the males during the nesting season.

They are very hardy, remaining in the eastern states throughout the winter during which time the temperatures are many times well below the freezing level for days on end. At the commencement of spring we released all of them into the gardens, after they had been banded, and at least two pairs were still around four years later.

. . . ten young was all we could cope with.

Subfamily Teroninae

The NICOBAR PIGEON, *Caloenas nicobarica,* is an Oriental species frequenting the islands from the Nicobars to Christmas Island, the Malaysia Archipelago and New Guinea. About 16 inches (40 cm) in length, the adult male is mainly dark metallic-green with bronzy reflections, head, neck and hackles darker, with blue and purple reflections, hackles elongated to form a mane; black knob at base of black bill; very short tail, white; feet and legs plum coloured. The female has shorter hackles and the knob at the base of the bill is smaller.

. . . difficult to cater for . . .

They spent most of their time on the ground and, with their short tail and upright carriage of the head, looked very unlike pigeons. Although reported to eat fallen fruits in the wild, we found them difficult to cater for as they took very little of whatever fruit we might offer, showed complete disinterest in the ground meat, the soft-food mixture or any variety of seed or vegetation, but did accept mealworms as long as we liked to offer them. They were one of the few species that defied all our efforts to find what they could be kept on, the longest period we ever had a pair being about two months, but they all appeared to be well fed when they died. It was later that we learned that they mainly exist on fruits of the nutmeg family, fruits we had never employed in our feeding.

The IMPERIAL GREEN PIGEON, *Ducula aenea,* is widely distributed through India, Pakistan, Ceylon and clear across to Malaysia, Borneo, Java and the Philippines, several races being recognised. The two we had, *D. a polia,* came to us from central Malaya. About 17 inches (43 cm) in length, the sexes are alike. Back, rump and tail metallic-bluish-green; wings darker green washed with bronze and greyish at the edges; patch under tail chestnut; remainder of plumage lavender grey, paler on the chin and forechest; bill grey, crimson at base; feet and legs crimson.

The PIED IMPERIAL, or NUTMEG PIGEON, *Ducula bicolor,* is slightly smaller and two of them were received with the Green Imperial Pigeons mentioned above. They are mainly white, the edges of the wings and lower half of the tail, black; bill, legs and feet lavender grey. They were a true pair, nesting in an open platform nest-box, and had one young that was allowed to remain with its parents even after it was independent. It turned out to be a female and the following year the male mated with both his old mate and with his daughter. The young female occupied another platform nest-box and she was left entirely alone by her parents who were busy rearing yet another young one. This did not deter the young female who herself also reared one young.

This fashion of breeding carried on right through the following year and eventually we had nine of them, all in one aviary. Being prolific fruit eaters they soiled all the shrubberies and plants which had to be washed down every day. Finally they were all disposed of.

The WOMPOO PIGEON, *Megaloprepia magnifica,* is a large bird, about 19 inches (48 cm) in length, and is to be found in New Guinea, the Moluccan Islands and in the coastal areas of eastern Australia as far south as New South Wales. We only ever had one specimen, a beautiful bird with head and neck of lavender grey; centre of throat, breast and abdomen deep purple; lower belly yellow; wings green with a yellow band; under tail-coverts brown.

Whereas all the pigeons and doves that we had used to "coo", the fruit pigeons had much more booming notes and, when all the Pied Imperial Pigeons started up, usually just prior to feeding time, it could be heard from a considerable distance.

*American
Tumbler Pigeon
porcelain sculpture
by Edward Marshall Boehm*

Macaw porcelain sculpture by Edward Marshall Boehm

This is the Order of the parrots, all grouped in one family, Psittacidae, but split up into many subfamilies. Parrots are to be found in the entire intertropical zone of the world and have spread to subtropical, and even to Patagonia, Tasmania and New Zealand, colder parts of the Southern Hemisphere, and into those of the Northern Hemisphere in the Americas and Asia. Varying from 4 to 40 inches (10 cm to 1 metre) in length, they are mostly of very similar general appearance. The bill is short, strongly hooked and the upper mandible is articulated and not firmly joined to the skull, thus permitting some independent movement. They have short necks; compact bodies; short legs; zygodactyl toes covered with tiny granular scales, these features being some of the general characteristics of the family as a whole.

Certain of the subfamilies are confined to definite areas of the world, such as the macaws and conures to Central and South America; cockatoos, lories and lorikeets to the Australian Region. The term parrakeet normally is applied to the smaller species with long pointed tails, the name parrot usually indicating a larger bird with a square or box tail. With two exceptions they are hole-nesters, the exceptions being the QUAKER PAR-RAKEET, *Myiopsitta monachus,* of South America which builds communal nests in trees, and the AUSTRALIAN GROUND PARROT, *Pezoporus wallicus,* which nests on the ground. Normally they are gregarious in their habits and their diet is mainly vegetarian, although some do take insects and grubs.

Over the years we had 36 different species in the aviaries, as listed hereunder:

Cockatoos:

Calyptorhynchus funereus	Yellow-tailed black or Funereal Cockatoo
Kakatoe g. galerita	Greater Sulphur-crested Cockatoo
Kakatoe haematuropygia	Red-vented Cockatoo
Kakatoe l. leadbeateri	Leadbeater's Cockatoo
Kakatoe roseicapilla	Galah or Roseate Cockatoo

Conures:

Aratinga guarouba	Queen of Bavaria's Conure

Fig Parrots:

Opopsitta d. diophthalma	Double-eye Fig Parrot

Lories and Lorikeets:

Charmosyna papou stellae	Stella's Lorikeet
Domicella garrula flavopalliata	Yellow-backed Lory

Domicella l. lory	Black-capped Lory
Glossopsitta pusilla	Little Lorikeet
Trichoglossus haematod moluccanus	Swainson's or Rainbow Lorikeet
Trichoglossus haemotod rubritorquis	Red-collared Lorikeet

Lovebirds:

Agapornis fischeri	Fischer's Lovebird
Agapornis roseicollis	Peach-faced Lovebird

Macaws:

Ara macao	Scarlet Macaw

Parrakeets:

Alisterus s. scapularis	King Parrakeet
Aprosmictus e. erythropterus	Crimson-wing Parrakeet
Bolborhynchus l. lineola	Lineolated Parrakeet
Melopsittacus undulatus	Budgerigar
Oreopsittacus a. arfaki	Blue-cheeked Alpine Parrakeet
Platycercus adscitus palliceps	Mealy Rosella
Platycercus caledonicus flaveolus	Yellow Rosella
Platycercus elegans adelaide	Adelaide Rosella
Platycercus e. elegans	Pennant's Parrakeet
Platycercus zonarius macgillivrayi	Cloncurry Parrakeet
Polytelis alexandrae	Princess of Wales' Parrakeet
Polytelis swainsonii	Barraband's Parrakeet
Psephotus haematonotus	Red-rumped Parrakeet
Psittacula eupatria nipalensis	Alexandrine Ring-neck Parrakeet
Purpureicephalus spurius	Red-capped Parrakeet

Parrots:

Deroptyus a. accipitrinus	Hawk-headed Parrot
Lorius roratus pectoralis	Red-sided Eclectus Parrot
Lorius r. roratus	Grand Eclectus Parrot
Pezoporus w. wallicus	Ground Parrot
Psittacus e. erithacus	African Grey Parrot

At the Boehm home, spring of 1960, Governor and Mrs. J. Lindsay Almond, Jr. with Mr. Boehm and one of his Macaws

It is not my intention to go into descriptive details regarding the entire 36 species mentioned above, but just to relate some of the more interesting experiences with some of them. Firstly, the design of the aviaries and the exotic plantings did not make them suitable for the majority of the parrot family with its reputation for chewing and defoliating. The only species we ever had in the aviaries were the Princess of Wales' Parrakeets and the Stella's Lorikeets.

The Mealy Rosellas, Red-rumped Parrakeets and Peach-faced Lovebirds were bred in the parrot-house, and the Double-eyed Fig Parrots in a birdroom. This last breeding was the first of the species in captivity in North America and, therefore, merits some detail.

. . . the first of the species in captivity . . .

The subspecies we had was from the eastern parts of New Guinea and are about 6 inches (15 cm) in length, the sexes differing. The adult male is bright green on most of the upperparts; forehead, crown, cheeks and ear-coverts, scarlet, with a yellowish border round the back of the head; blue spot in front of each eye; blue band behind each ear bordering the red cheeks; sides of body yellow; outer webs of the primaries and wing-coverts bright blue; outermost primaries black, as are the inner webs of the remainder. Under flight-coverts pale yellow on the inner webs, remainder pale green with a concealed red spot on the inner web of the innermost flight-covert; tail green above, dull bluish below; remainder of underparts a paler green than the back. The female resembles the male except that the cheek patches are dusky buff with a red line running along the upper edge from the lores to the ear-coverts.

Two pairs of these birds were received from New Guinea, a gift from the late Sir Edward Hallstrom, and our first question was how to feed them. Literature advising that in the wild they normally fed on berries and wild fruits, they were given diced apple, cherries, grapes, peaches and blueberries and, in sympathy with their common name, dried figs. In addition, a small pot of sunflower seed was placed in their room. They took to the fruit immediately but, with the figs, they only ate the seeds, casting all the fleshy part away. With the sunflower seed they took a few seeds each day. For drinking they were given both water and a dish of nectar which they consumed completely each day.

The four birds lived congenially together for about a year and then it became apparent that they had paired up. Strangely enough, one of each sex required to have its upper mandible trimmed at regular intervals and, when it came to them selecting their own mates, these two birds split up, each taking a non-overgrowing-bill-bird as a partner. It was decided to separate

the two pairs so one was transferred to a cage, the other being left in the bird-room. Their indoor pen was about 10 x 6 x 8 feet (3 x 1.8 x 2.5 metres) and a tree trunk with an old woodpecker's nest in the upper portion was placed in there. For ease of transporting, the trunk had been sawn into three 2 feet (61 cm) lengths and before it was reassembled in the room a tin tray was fitted at the base of the upper portion to contain water so as to ensure there would be ample dampness and humidity for the nest-hole. Further, a hinged lid was fitted to the top of this section of the tree trunk so that any activity in the nest could be observed.

Whilst this entire operation was taking place the birds were completely undisturbed and watched our movements with interest. No sooner had I closed the door of their room than the female was exploring round the tree and, after about five minutes of this, she entered the nest-hole. Four days later, on early morning rounds, there was no sign of the female but the male was perching just below the entrance hole. They were both very tame by now and he never moved when I lifted the lid to the nest and saw the female at the bottom. As if she knew what I was after, or very proud of herself, only she knew the answer to that one, she moved to one side so that I could see her first egg. It was clear white, rather like a good sized budgerigar's egg, and later when I was able to get the measurements of some of them, they averaged 23 by 20 mm.

*. . . she
moved to
one side . . .*

A further egg was laid two days later, but, incubation, by the female only, had commenced with the laying of the first. The period of incubation was 19 days and the newly hatched chicks were covered with pale lemon fuzz. Although the diet we had the adult birds on appeared to be adequate, such apparently was not the case, the chicks dying at ten days of age. By that time their eyes were open and quill feathers were beginning to show in their wings and down the centre of their backs.

A full month elapsed before they went to nest again and this time they did rear one chick which, on leaving the nest, closely resembled the adult female. As their quarters were required for a consignment of birds of paradise, a further gift from Sir Edward Hallstrom, the fig parrots and their young were presented to a zoo.

All the cockatoos were accommodated in unheated, open-air flights the entire year through, the temperatures during the winter months often being several degrees below freezing level for days on end. The only protection they had was a roof over half of the flight and heated perches. These latter were 1½ inch (3.75 cm) piping through which flowed warmed glycol maintaining the perch at 40 degrees F., (4.5 degrees C) thus obviating frost bitten feet. They were always in splendid feather, not even becoming tatty during their moult. In the parrot-house itself, although the flights were completely open to the elements and unheated, they all had a house at the end which could be closed in during the winter, just leaving a bob-hole for them to come in and go out. This portion was kept at a temperature of 50 degrees F. (10 degrees C.) We only had one catastrophe there for, despite their warmed quarters, many of them used to spend the night in the nest boxes out in the flights. The Queen of Bavaria's Conures had a big barrel as their nest box and, after a heavy snow-fall and freeze, one of them was found to have got frozen into the ice that had formed at the bottom of the barrel. It had obviously died of loss of blood rather than of cold for it had chewed one foot off completely trying to free itself and was half way through the other leg.

. . . chewed one foot off completely . . .

The remaining bird was brought into the main bird-house and within a month went into such a terrific moult that it lost every feather on its body, in its wings and in its tail. It was a completely naked bird. Although all the birds were fed ABDEC in small quantities in their water every day, this bird was put on a concentrated course, five drops being administered direct into its mouth every morning and evening. It may be just a fad of mine but I have always had great faith in ABDEC, particulary in respect of any birds of the parrot family and, no matter what it was, the conure was in full feather again after a lapse of some nine months. By this time it had become so tame that I could walk around with it on my shoulder with no fears of it flying away.

One of our best known members of the parrot family, so far as visitors were concerned, was "Cocky," a Greater Sulphur-crested Cockatoo that had been given to Mr. Boehm by the late Thomas Gilliard whose son had collected it as a nestling during one of his father's ornithological trips to New Guinea and Australia. "Cocky" was not kept in the flights but had his own special cage in the bird-house where he used to attract visitors to him with his cheery "Hello, Cocky. Scratch Cocky." As soon as they had concentrated around him he would swing over from his perch to the top of his cage and back and greet them with "Hello stupid." Fortunately no-one ever took offence. Although we could do anything with him we never permitted strangers to attempt to touch him for, like so many of the parrot family, he could be most unpredictable.

. . . "Hello stupid."

He escaped twice from his cage during the years he was with us being away 40 hours the first time and for four complete days on the second occasion. Each time he eventually came back to his cage which had been placed on the outside steps of the bird-house. His favourite perch during these hours of freedom was in a huge tulip tree that overhung the aviaries. Whenever we attempted to get him he would take off over the neighbouring gardens. Until he was ready to come down he just stayed there repeating over and over his "Hello Cocky" refrain.

The Australian Greater Sulphur-crested Cockatoo, "Cocky"

We did have one killer parrot, a female Red-sided Eclectus. Her first victim was her own mate. She tore his upper mandible completely off and then bit him through the neck. We had heard a commotion in the parrot-house and by the time we got there she was just finishing him off. We transferred her to the quarantine quarters and two days later she had chewed through a $5/8$ inch (2 cm) marine plywood dividing partition into the next cage containing a pair of Crimson-wing Parrakeets. They were both torn to pieces and she was sitting on their perch with her face covered with blood. The following day she went off to a zoo, but not before they had been given a complete dossier on her temperament.

*Photograph of a South African
Boehm Aviary Turaco*

This is an Order comprised of two suborders, Cucli and Musophagi.

SUBORDER CUCULI

Family Cuculidae

This family, with the substantive common name of cuckoo, has a worldwide distribution with some 120 species grouped in 38 genera, constituting 6 subfamilies. They range in size from 5 to 27 inches (13 to 68 cm) in length, the body tending to be elongated. They are mainly arboreal but some, like the ROAD-RUNNER, *Geococcyx califorianus,* are terrestrial. Largely insectivorous, small vertebrates, molluscs and fruit also are eaten. Most of their calls are a monotonous repetition of loud notes and it was from the call of the European species, *Cuculus canorus,* that they got the name of cuckoo.

We only ever had 4 species, all of the subfamily Cuculinae, which is comprised of some 47 species, all parasitic, that is, selecting the nest of other birds in which to deposit their eggs. Normally the female lays but one egg in any particular nest and then goes off to find the next available depository. They have been known to lay two or more eggs in the same nest, but this is a rare occurrence. The remaining 5 subfamilies are non-parasitic and both parents share in the incubation of the eggs and the rearing of the young.

The DIDRIC CUCKOO, *Chrysococcyx caprius,* is an African species to be found over the entire continent from about 15 degrees latitude north and southward to the furthermost parts of South Africa. The adult male is iridescent bottle-green, violet, bronze and golden-green above with white spots on the wing-coverts and secondaries. There is a white streak behind the eye and some white in the centre of the head. Underparts white, flanks bronzy-green; underside of wings barred black and white; outer tail feathers iridescent greenish-black with white spots. The female is duller above; the throat and chest are buffish and the flank barring extends on to the chest and sides of neck. They are 7 to 8 inches (18 to 20 cm) in length and have a peculiar call *"di-di-didric"* that sounds like "di-di-didric," and it was from this that the common name evolved.

The EMERALD CUCKOO, *Chrysococcyx cupreus,* is about the same size as the preceding species but there are two races in Africa. The nominate race has a limited range from Gambia to Ethiopia and southern Sudan, whereas the subspecies we had, *C. c. intermedius,* is to be found from Cameroon clear across to the east coast and southward to South Africa during the summer months, migrating northward to Tanzania during the winter. They are a beautiful bird, the adult male's upperparts, head, neck and chest a shining emerald green, washed with old gold, each feather having a dark centre producing a scaly appearance; tail slightly graduated, outer tail feathers barred white. From breast to abdomen they are canary-yellow; under tail-coverts white with emerald bars; under wing-coverts white. The female is iridescent moss green above, barred with chestnut; crown of head brown with buff bars; underparts barred iridescent moss green and white. They have a clear whistling call note of some five syllables.

The KLAAS'S CUCKOO, *Chrysococcyx klaas,* is slightly smaller than the Didric Cuckoo but is to be found over the same range throughout Africa. The male is iridescent dark green and bronze above, white below. The female differs from the male in having the head, upper back, rump and tail bronzy-brown; wing-coverts and scapulars green barred dark buff, primaries brown with buff spots on the outer webs; flanks buff barred dark brown; throat buffish. They have a feeble, monotonous call of some six notes in groups of two.

The RED-CHESTED CUCKOO, *Cuculus solitarius,* is about 12 inches (30 cm) in length and the sexes differ slightly in colour. It is an African species with a general range from Gambia clear across to the Sudan and southward over the entire continent. The adult male is dark slaty-grey above; throat grey; chest chestnut; breast to belly buff, barred black; under tail-coverts clear buff. The chestnut on the chest of the female is paler and the throat is washed with pale chestnut. They have a distinct call of three notes, repeated at close intervals, but the alarm note is high pitched and of five or more notes at a time.

All these cuckoos were avid live-food eaters and became rather an embarrassment in the aviaries where we had insectivorous species breeding. Since we had none of the various species on which they normally are parasitic in their natural habitats, and the provision of sufficient live-food presented great problems during the winter months, they were disposed of to various zoos.

. . . avid live food eaters . . .

SUBORDER MUSOPHAGI

This suborder is comprised of but one family, the Musophagidae, which, in the past, has been associated with either the

Galliformes or the Cuculiformes and, for a period, was regarded as a distinct order, the Musophagiformes. It consists of birds commonly known as turacos, plantain-eaters, go-away-birds and louries, and the family of some 18 species is confined to the African continent. They are arboreal birds, inhabiting the forest regions and their strong and dexterous feet enable them to run along branches with the agility of a squirrel. Their main food is fruit and berries but, in captivity, they are very partial to ground raw beef and, when raising young, took enormous amounts of mealworms, gathering them off the ground like a fowl, and then taking them up to the nest to regurgitate to the young whose head they almost completely envelope during the feeding process.

. . . with the agility of a squirrel:

The entire family has many peculiar features, such as the semi-zygodactyl feet, the outer toe most often almost at right-angle to the main axis of the foot, but it can be moved either farther back or directly forward; the nostrils can be slit-shaped or circular, and the young are hatched with thick down and with their eyes open, and are capable of leaving the nest within hours of leaving the shell, as in the manner of precocials. This trait was demonstrated in one instance during one of our breedings, although the others were definitely semi-precocial, that is, their eyes were open, they were covered with down, but they stayed in the nest to be reared by their parents.

Many of the species are referred to as plantain-eaters, rather than turacos, and, within their own family they are split into two groups, 14 of the species having red flight feathers, the others having grey. The group with red in their flights have body colours of green and various shades of blue ranging through to purple. A feature of this group is that it is one of the few groups of birds that have true green pigment (turacovendin) in the feathering. The red in the flights also being a true pigment. This used to be attributed solely to the presence of turacin, a copper compound, but research revealed that a much more valuable product also was involved. This is uroporphyrin, averaging 3 mg. to a feather, and is among a group of complex compounds called porphyrins, of which one of the substances is part of the haemoglobin molecule in blood, resulting in the red colour. Occasionally the mechanism of the human liver becomes deranged, resulting in a very unpleasant, and at the moment incurable, disease called porphyria. Uroporphyrin is used mainly in medical research concerned with that disease and other liver ailments. Apart from blood and red turaco flight feathers, porphyrins are also found in minute quantities in oyster and egg shells, under feathers of night birds, and in certain bustard feathers. All red flight feathers moulted out in the Boehm aviaries used to be sent to Koch-Light Laboratories, Colnbrook, Buckinghamshire, England where the substance was extracted by a soluble process, the feathers still being a pale pink at the completion, no doubt due to the turacin not having been recovered. The production of uroporphyrin had to be called to a halt due to lack of sufficient red feathers, but would be restarted once supplies became available again.

The GIANT or GREAT BLUE TURACO or PLANTAIN-EATER, *Corythaeola cristata,* it being known by both names, is easily distinguished by its size, 28 to 30 inches (70 to 76 cm), of which the tail accounts for almost half, and it is the largest species of the Musophagidae. They are to be found in Africa from Senegal to the Sudan, and down into Angola, the Congo and Uganda. The sexes are alike in colouring and, although they appear greyish in the dull light of forested regions or enclosures, they actually are a verditer-blue through the entire upperparts, neck and chest. They have a large blue-black crest; heavy bill with a red tip; outer tail feathers yellow-green, remainder verditer-blue but all the tail feathers have a broad black terminal band, the central feathers having blue tips. From the chest to the belly, yellow-green; lower belly and under tail-coverts chestnut; legs and feet black. Despite their size they are very graceful in flight and it is then that the yellow outer tail feathers with the black terminal bands are most conspicuous. They have a variety of calls, the most frequently heard being a "cow-cow-cow-cow" rapidly repeated; a rolling "coo-o-o-o," and a slower "cu-lock-culock-culock."

. . . very graceful in flight . . .

The GO-AWAY-BIRD, or GREY TURACO, *Corythaixoides concolor,* is a wholly grey bird with a pronounced crest, the sexes being distinguished by the black bill of the male and the pea-green bill of the female. Their general distribution is from Tanzania and the Congo to South Africa, but not over into Namibia. They have a loud, nasal call of "g'way-g'way".

The BARE-FACED GO-AWAY-BIRD, *Corythaixoides personata,* of which there are three races, the species we had being *C. p. leopoldi,* from eastern Tanzania. The sexes are alike, the general colour above grey; face and throat bare; chest greenish; breast and abdomen vinous-brown; underside of wings and tail washed with green. They have a loud bleating call of "go-ah, go-ah".

ROSS'S TURACO, *Musophaga rossae,* has a limited range from Cameroon to the Sudan, down through western Kenya and across Tanzania into the northern parts of Rhodesia and Angola. The general colour is wholly blue-black and violet set off by the crimson in the flight feathers and crest. The bill extends right on to the forehead and is bright yellow, fading into reddish at the hind part of the shield. They have a variety of calls and usually terminate all with a loud, cackling cooing. We had three of them but, since we used to get as many as five or six eggs in a nest at the same time, it was fairly conclusive that they were all females as the normal clutch consists of but one or two eggs.

The KNYSNA TURACO, *Tauraco corythaix,* also has a limited range from the forests near Mosel Bay in South Africa, and round the coastal belt through Malawi and eastern Tanzania. They are known as louries in this area. The sexes are alike in colouring, the head, neck, back, wing, tail and breast, green with a slight iridescence and bluish reflections; a rounded green crest, edged white; bare skin around the eye red; a white line beneath the eye. The scapulars, wing-coverts and innermost secondaries are violet, blue and green, and the greater part of the flight feathers is crimson. Bill orange-red; legs and feet black.

We had three of them in a large planted aviary for some three years before they decided to go to nest. The nest structure was very fragile so, as had been done in the case of the White-cheeked Turaco the breeding of which is described later, a shallow wire-mesh basket was fitted in the Canadian hemlock they had selected as a nesting site. Two eggs were laid, pure white and about 41 by 33 mm in size. The incubation was shared, lasting 17 to 18 days. It apparently began with the laying of the first egg for they hatched on consecutive days. Although we had bred other species of turacos and were familar with the thick down on the chicks and their eyes being open, it was with the Knysnas that we experienced a day-old chick travelling some 20 feet (6 metres) to another tree and settling itself down in an old Grey-winged Blackbird's nest. It was revealed when checking the nest on the evening of the day the first one hatched. All that there was was but one egg with one of the adult birds sitting by. The other adult was over in a conifer busy feeding the chick in the adopted nest. Except for a bout of squawking as I lifted the chick out of the nest and carried it back to its original home, the parent bird made no other objection. The following day the second hatched but the first one was continually crawling out on to branches although it never made a journey like that of the first day. When they finally vacated the nest at just under four weeks old, the plumage of the young birds was dull green; there was no white edge to the crest, and the bare skin around the eye was dusky. However, the crimson in the flight feathers was visible. Full adult colouring was attained at about 9 months of age. The Knysnas did not take as much live-food to rear their young as the other species we bred did, their main rearing food being fruit and buds off the trees and shrubs.

The HARTLAUB'S TURACO, also known as the BLUE-CRESTED PLANTAIN-EATER, *Tauraco hartlaubi,* is to be found in Kenya and north-eastern Tanzania. The crest is iridescent blue-black; there is a large white spot in front of the eye and a white line below the eye. The wing-coverts, inner secondaries, rump and tail, deep violet; neck, mantle and underparts green; flight feathers partly crimson; legs, feet and under tail-coverts dusky; bill olive, with a red tip. Again the colouring of the sexes is identical. They have a noticeable call, a loud squawk, followed by short, harsh, bark-like sounds.

The WHITE-CRESTED TURACO, *Tauraco leucolophus,* is one of the smaller turacos and is to be found in Cameroon across to southern Sudan and Uganda, and in the northern parts of the Congo. The forehead, crown and around the eyes, purple; crest, nape, sides of face and chin white; upper mantle, chest and upper abdomen green; lower mantle, inner secondaries, wing-coverts and tail, violet; flight feathers partly crimson; belly grey washed with violet. They become very tame in captivity and, as they perch and open their wings, they give vent to an almost hysterical laugh-like sound, the normal call being a deep guttural "kuroo".

They become very tame in captivity . . .

The WHITE-CHEEKED TURACO, *Tauraco leucotis,* is to be found in Eritrea, through Ethiopia to south-western Sudan. The sexes are alike in colouring, the head, neck, back and breast, green; crest navy-blue; white patches on the ears and in front of the eyes. The eye is surrounded by wattle-like bare skin of orange-red the same colour as the bill. Greater part of the flight feathers crimson; wing-coverts and rump blue-grey; broad feathered tail dark blue; belly dark grey; legs and feet black.

The first year they bred at the Boehm aviaries, 1963, they had four rounds from which seven young were reared to maturity. The first nesting was in April of that year and the female selected a site about 10 feet (3 metres) up in a white pine, about

North African White-cheeked Turaco with young

3 feet (1 metre) higher than where an Indian Pitta was nesting. It was a very fragile nest of twigs, prepared by the female alone, in a crutch in the branches, so a wire-mesh basket about 12 inches (30 cm) across and 3 inches (7.5 cm) deep was placed where the twigs had been located and the materials replaced therein. The female took to it immediately, rearranging the twigs to her liking, and laid two eggs, one on each successive day. They were pure white and averaged 41 by 33 mm in size. Incubation, lasting 17 to 18 days was shared and it was on the hatching of the first chick that one of the peculiarities of the family was revealed. The chick, on emerging from the shell, resembled a precocial hatchling, for it was covered with thick, black down and its eyes were opening. However, despite these two characteristics, it became apparent that it did not possess the thermal control of newly hatched precocial birds, for both parents brooded it constantly for the first ten days or so. The chicks' bills were

pink with a black tip, of the basic shape of the adults' bills, and the gapes were pink with no signs of marginal lining or other feeding "targets". The bill gradually darkened until, at seven days old, it was the base of the lower mandible only that was light coloured. As with the incubation, the rearing was shared and it was now that the great consumption of mealworms began. Either parent, one remaining on the nest, would descend to the ground to collect as many mealworms as it appeared to require, this being about 30 at first increasing to nearly 100 as the nestlings grew. They would then drink from the stream, eat fresh buds from the shrubs and some fruit, and then fly up to the nest to feed the youngsters by regurgitation. They literally pumped the food down the throats of the nestlings, going from one to the other, and it was possible to watch the whole operation as we had rigged up a big "A"-ladder so as to get photographic shots of them. Quills were showing at five days, the tail commencing to show four days later. By the twelfth day white barrings were visible in the wings, and by 19 days, the young birds were crawling around on the branches in the immediate vicinity of the nest. Red showed in the flights at 20 days and they vacated the nest on the 25th day. At that period it could be seen that, in addition to the colour in the flights, green was showing on the neck, the remainder of the plumage being dull blackish-green.

They literally pumped the food down . . .

At the age of seven weeks the young birds were seen to be eating leaves and, from then on, could be regarded as self supporting. A white cheek patch was now beginning to show, as was the white mark in front of the eyes. However, it was not until after the eleventh week that the bill and eye circle began to change colour. The full adult appearance of the eye was attained at 108 days, but the bill did not complete its change for a further four weeks. It must be mentioned that it was necessary to remove the young birds as soon as the next round hatched as the adult male began to persecute them and drive them away from all the feeding places. In subsequent years yet more White-cheeked Turacos were reared and the first round chicks themselves went to nest in their second year.

The VIOLET-CRESTED TURACO, *Tauraco porphyreolophus*, is confined to east and south-east Africa, being found in Uganda, Kenya, northern Zambia and the Zambesi River valley. The top of the head and crest are deep iridescent violet; forehead, ear-coverts and around eye, iridescent green; upper mantle, neck and underparts grey; tail violet and blue; wing-coverts, scapulars and inner secondaries washed azure blue;

flight feathers partly crimson; bill, legs and feet blackish. They have a resonant call like "kurri-kurru-kurroo", terminating it with a loud hoot.

The SCHALOW'S TURACO, *Tauraco schalowi*, from eastern Kenya, southern Somalia and north Tanzania is the third species of turaco that we bred in the aviaries. The head, upstanding long crest, neck and breast, green, the crest tipped with white; white line under the eye; back and wings iridescent green; tail violet and purple; flight feathers partly crimson; underparts green the belly and under tail-coverts slightly dusky; bill red; legs and feet blackish. This breeding followed exactly the same pattern of the White-cheeked Turacos except that the red in the flight feathers did not become apparent in the young birds until they were about eight weeks old. Here again the young had to be removed as soon as they were independent as the male would attack them. The Schalow's Turaco was the only species of turaco we had that we were not able to house with any species of the same family. We made several attempts to keep them with Knysnas, White-cheeked and White-crested but, in every instance they would attack the other birds viciously.

All the turacos in addition to taking vast quantities of our fruit mixture were given chopped lettuce in an attempt to try to save some of the young leaves on the trees and shrubs for which they had great partiality, particularly at breeding time. They also took ground raw beef and, as mentioned earlier, a great amount of live-food when they had young in the nest. At other times it was only the White-cheeked Turacos that ever bothered about mealworms and even then they only took the odd one or two.

*Rufous Hummingbirds
porcelain sculpture by
Edward Marshall Boehm*

This Order is made up of two structurally related sub-orders, Apodi (swifts), and Trochili (hummingbirds). Since we had no swifts at any time it is only with the family Trochilidae, hummingbirds, that we are concerned here. The structural relationship consists of a large keeled breast-bone, a shortened humerus, and elongated, flattened forearm and manus. The almost free ball and socket joint of the humerus of the hummingbird, and the pectoral muscles that are, relatively, the largest in the animal kingdom, enables them to hover, and even to fly backwards, motions denied to the swifts. It is these characteristics and the fact that they have only six to seven very short secondaries that enables them to make tremendously fast wing movements. During courtship and aerobatics the wing beats can reach up to 200 per second, normal flight being from 75 to 100. This rapid movement causes the humming sound from which their common name was derived. The smallest known bird in the world is the BEE HUMMINGBIRD, *Melisusa helenae*, which has a body length of .6 inches (1.3 cm), a bill the same length, and a tail just over one inch (2.5 cm).

Hummingbirds are confined to the New World being counterparts, so far as iridescent colouring and feeding habits are concerned, to the sunbirds of the Old World. There are some 580 species and subspecies in all, 18 of them being found in North America or the Nearctic Region, although 13 do migrate to South America where some 560 species are resident. Colombia and Ecuador are the most richly endowed for over 300 species varying from 3 to 8 inches (7 to 20 cm) in length may be found in those areas.

We only had five species in all but did not find them difficult to keep although they are birds that cannot be neglected in any way. The main things are adequate warmth, not heat, correct feeding, and an ever available supply of fruit flies or other such minute flying insects. We employed the same nectar mixture for them as we used for all our other nectar feeding birds and found it perfectly satisfactory. When housed in a cage it was noted that they fed about every 35 minutes; in a flight room this was reduced to about every 25 and, in an open aviary, to about every 20 minutes. These variations in time are roughly proportional to the amount of energy expended by the birds, or the amount of flying room they have. One peculiarity of the hummingbird is that it has no ankle joint as such, and that is why they are never seen walking or hopping on a branch or on the ground. Their entire life is spent either on the wing or perching, except, of

. . . no ankle joint . . .

course, when a female is on her nest. They are absolutely fearless, flying at any other bird they might feel is menacing their territory, and appear to have no fear of humans. There was one little Wood Nymph female that used to feed out of a flower held between Mr. Boehm's lips and actually seemed to look for it every time he entered her sanctuary.

GOULD'S HEAVENLY SYLPH, *Aglaiocercus coelestis,* is one of the larger species, the male being some 8 inches (20 cm) in length, 5 (13) of which is accounted for by the tail. The female is smaller, 3½ to 4 inches (8 to 10 cm), for she lacks the elongated tail. Their range is western Ecuador and the adult male has a crown of glittering emerald green; upper back shining green; lower back strongly tinged with blue. The elongated tail is mainly shining violet with glittering green tips to all but the outer feathers. Throat patch violet-blue; remainder of underparts shining bronzy green. The female has a shining blue crown and bronzy green back. The main feature that distinguishes her from other females of the same genus is the white chest, sharply defined from the rufous of the remainder of the underparts.

The RUBY-THROATED HUMMINGBIRD, *Archilochus colubria,* one of the North American species, is about 3½ inches (9 cm) in length and the sexes differ. The adult male is metallic bronzy green above, this colour extending to the central pair of tail feathers. Wings darkish-slate, faintly glossed purplish; tail, except the central feathers, dark bronzy purplish; chin, cheeks and sides of head velvety black; throat brilliant red, changing to golden or even greenish according to the light reflections. Chest brownish white, gradually passing into brownish grey on the lower breast and abdomen; sides and flanks darker, overlaid by a tinge of metallic bronze-green. A spot behind the eye, the thigh tufts and tufts on each side of the rump are white. The female is very similar except that she lacks the throat colouring and her underparts are dull greyish white throughout. Normally the females are slightly larger than the males.

The SPARKLING VIOLET-EARED HUMMINGBIRD, *Colibri c. coruscans,* may be found from western Guyana through to Venezuela and Ecuador. About 5 inches (13 cm) in length, the upper plumage iridescent green; chin, upper throat and a patch on the centre of the breast, violet-blue; patch below eye and prolonged over the ear-coverts, violet-blue; tail brilliant dark blue with a deep subterminal band of purplish blue except for the central pair of feathers which are greenish-blue; thigh tufts white; remainder of underparts green. The female is similar but duller throughout.

The AMETHYST-THROATED SUN ANGEL, *Heliangelus amethysticollis*, is about 3¾ inches (9.5 cm) in length, and has a range from western Venezuela to Bolivia. The adult male has a crown of dark green; feathers of the forehead edged bright green; back shining green; tail blue-black except for central pair of feathers which are shining green to bronze green; chin, sides of head and throat greenish-black, the throat itself being glittering amethyst; white band across chest bordered by glittering green; under tail-coverts white; remainder of underparts mouse-coloured. The throat of the female is dull black and, except for being duller, she resembles the male in other colouring.

The ROYAL WOODNYMPH or FORK-TAILED WOODNYMPH, *Thalurania furcata*, is to be found from Mexico southward to Venezuela and south-eastern Brazil and on the Isle of Trinidad. The male is about 4 inches (10 cm) in length, the female slightly smaller. The crown of the adult male is glittering purple or green, edged bluish-purple; back bronzy green with a band of purplish across it; chin, throat and upper breast glittering emerald green; lower breast and belly violet-blue; the long tail is forked and steel blue in colour. The female is bronze green above; rump bluish; central tail feathers steel-blue tipped white; underparts grey, sometimes washed with green on the lower breast and abdomen.

The fascination of hummingbirds is undoubtedly their flying abilities, their fearlessness, and their iridescent colourings which seem to change with every movement of the bird, or as the light alters. For a collection of mixed species to be kept together safely it is essential that they have plently of flying space and numerous feeding places for they do tend to become very possessive of the latter.

Mexican and South American Royal Wood Nymph Hummingbird

TROGONIFORMES

Drawing
of a
Trogon
by
Mr. Boehm

This is the Order of the trogons and they rank amongst the most beautiful birds to be found in the Neotropical, Ethiopian and Oriental Regions. They are surprisingly uniform in colour pattern and shape, and are all classified in the family Trogonidae. In all species the adult males have breast and abdomen bright red, pink, orange or yellow, and they vary in size from 9 to 13½ inches (23 to 35 cm). Insects form their main diet although fruit and berries are greatly taken by the American species. They are hole-nesters but, although many such locations were in the aviaries housing them, we did not breed any of this family.

NARINA TROGON, *Apaloderma narina,* is an African species to be found from Sierra Leone clear across to Ethiopia and southward to South Africa, there being several races throughout their range. The birds we had were of the nominate race, *A. n. Narina,* from Kenya. About 13 inches (33 cm) in length, the upperparts, sides of face, shoulders of wings and throat to chest of the adult male are metallic green; inner secondaries and median wing-coverts are finely vermiculated black and green; upper side of tail green and steel-blue; three outermost tail feathers edged and broadly tipped white; breast to under tail-coverts pinkish to blood red. The female differs in that the sides of face and throat to chest are brown; breast grey, tinged with pink; remainder of plumage as with the male.

The QUETZAL, *Pharomachrus mocino,* is a bird of the mountain cloud forest from southern Mexico to western Panama. The male is one of the most beautiful birds, all things considered, to be seen. This is due to the intensity and arresting contrast of his colouration, the resplendent sheen of his plumage, the elegance of his ornamentation, the symmetry of his form, and the noble dignity of his carriage. The whole head and upper plumage, foreneck and chest are an intense and glittering green, lower breast, belly and under tail-coverts are of the richest crimson. The green of the chest meets the red of the breast in a line which is convex downwards. The head is ornamented by upstanding bristly feathers which form a narrow, sharply divided ridged crest extending from the forehead to the hind-neck. Bill bright yellow and rather smaller than that of other trogons. The wing quills are concealed by long, golden green feathers of the coverts which stand out against the crimson that shows between them. The dark, central tail feathers are concealed by the greatly elongated upper tail-coverts, which are golden green with blue or violet iridescence. The two central feathers, longer

. . . the noble dignity of his carriage . . .

than the entire body, form a long, gracefully curving train which hangs below the bird while he perches upright on a branch, and ripples behind him as he flies.

The female is far less colourful, her upper plumage being green like the male's, but the head is dark, smoky grey with no trace of a crest. The upper tail-coverts green and elongated but to a much lesser degree. Only her lower belly and under tail-coverts are red, and the outer tail feathers are narrowly barred black.

They are undoubtedly the most colourful of all the trogons with a body length of 14 inches (35 cm) but the male's elongated upper tail-coverts can be anything up to 24 inches (61 cm) in length. Today the Quetzal is honoured in many ways as it is the national bird of Guatemala; the "quetzal" is the unit of currency in that country, and Quezaltenango, Guatemala's second largest city, means "the place of the Quetzal."

In the wild they feed on a variety of insects, small amphibians, lizards and fruits. In captivity we had some difficulty in keeping them as they all began to suffer from swollen, gout-like feet. We could only attribute this to an excess of fruit and insufficient live-food of the type they were accustomed to for our live-food supplies were restricted to mealworms, crickets and any flying insects caught in the night-traps.

The SPLENDID TROGON, *Pharomachrus pavoninus*, also referred to as the Pavonine Quetzal, is from the northern parts of South America being found in Venezuela, Ecuador, Colombia, Peru, northern Bolivia and north-western Brazil. In body size it is slightly larger than the Quetzal which it resembles closely although it lacks the frontal crest, has a black tail, and the male does not have the elongated tail plumes. Further, the lower breast and belly of the female are pinkish crimson. With the specimens we had the diet of fruit, ground raw beef, mealworms and crickets appeared to be totally adequate for we experienced none of the foot problems such as we had with the Quetzal.

The CUBAN TROGON, *Priotelus temnurus*, is, as its name implies, a West Indian species found in Cuba and on the Isle of Pines. About 11 inches (28 cm) in length, the sexes are alike. The upperparts are mostly green; crown dark violet-blue; wings have conspicuous white bars and spots; throat white; breast pale grey; belly through to under tail-coverts geranium-red. Tail long but squared off and with white raggedy edges; upper mandible dusky, lower reddish. We had a pair in an aviary

The South American Splendid Trogan

with a mixed collection of sunbirds and other nectar feeding birds for a considerable time with no problems whatever. We then introduced some Orange-gorgetted Flycatchers and the trouble started. The trogons had been used to sole consumption of the daily issues of mealworms, coming down to the ground to collect them but, since this also was the habit of the flycatchers, the two clashed. It was not until we actually witnessed it that we knew how the flycatchers' heads had been crushed. Up to then it had been thought that they had got caught in the door of the aviary as it opened or closed for the bodies, three of them, had been found in that vicinity. However, one day after I had tossed some mealworms around on the ground Mr. Boehm and I saw a Cuban Trogon dive down on a flycatcher that had just picked up a mealworm and seize it by the head, snatching up the mealworm as it was released. The flycatcher's skull cracked like an eggshell. Needless to say the trogons were caught up and transferred to an aviary where there are birds of a more comparative size.

The BLACK-TAILED TROGON, *Trogon melanurus,* has an extensive range from Panama to the Guianas, Venezuela, Colombia, eastern and western Ecuador, Brazil, Peru and Bolivia. About 12 inches (30 cm) in length, the head and breast of the adult male are blue; back metallic green changing to blue on the upper tail-coverts; wings black; outer tail feathers black tipped white; central tail feathers bronze-green with a sharply defined terminal black band; abdomen through to under tail-coverts orange-yellow. The female is similar except that there are dusky grey vermiculations on the wing-coverts and the lower breast is pale grey.

The WHITE-TAILED TROGON, *Trogon viridis,* about 10 inches (25 cm) in length, is to be found from Costa Rica southward to Trinidad, Venezuela, the Guianas, Brazil, Paraguay, Ecuador, Peru, Bolivia and Argentina. About the same size as the preceding species, the adult male has crown, hind-neck and breast a shining violet-blue; throat, cheeks and wings black; lower breast, belly and under tail-coverts orange-yellow; back shining blue-green shading to peacock-blue on upper tail-coverts; outer tail feathers black, diagonally tipped white; central tail feathers blue-green. The female has the upperparts and breast dusky-grey; wing-coverts narrowly barred white; outer tail feathers notched and tipped white; belly and under tail-coverts orange-yellow.

As stated earlier, with the exception of the quetzals we experienced no difficulty in keeping any of the trogons we had for they all took to our fruit and soft-food mixtures, the ground raw beef and the live-food. The reason why none went to nest may well have been due to the fact that, in the wild at breeding times they are inclined to be solitary in their pairs and become very territorially minded. With our all-species aviaries it was not possible to provide such conditions for them.

Mr. Boehm studying his birds in the "Lakeside Aviaries"

American Fledgling Kingfisher porcelain sculpture by Edward Marshall Boehm

This Order is comprised of four suborders and nine families of birds such as kingfishers, hornbills, bee-eaters, hoopoes etc., and in the Boehm aviaries we had specimens of six of the families and recognised first breedings in captivity from two of them. The Order as a whole is cosmopolitan but, of the families, this is true of the Alcedinidae (kingfishers) only. Of the others, two are Neotropical; the Todidae (tody) is restricted to the West Indies; the Leptosomatidae (cockoo-roller) to Malagasy, and the remainder to other parts of the Old World. One of the main characteristics of the Order is that each family has a specialised bill, some long, slender and decurved; others thick and sturdy but, in the majority of cases, all terminating in a sharp point.

Family Alcedinidae

The kingfisher family is cosmopolitan, the majority being found in the tropical regions of the Old World. Varying from 4 to 18 inches (10 to 46 cm) in length, they have compact bodies, short necks and large heads. The bill is long and heavy, normally terminating in a point. The legs are very short and the feet syndactyl, the 3rd and 4th toes being joined through most of their length; the 2nd and 3rd basally joined. Despite their common name, the majority are not fish-eaters but prey on insects, small rodents, small birds, reptiles and crustaceans. They are hole-nesters, the fish-eaters burrowing in river banks, the others making use of holes in trees, termite nests and banks of earth. Their calls are in no manner musical, consisting of a resonant chatter, one of the largest members of the family, the AUSTRALIAN KOOKABURRA, *Dacelo novaeguineae*, being colloquially known as the Laughing Jackass from the braying-like sound it makes.

Their calls are in no manner musical . . .

The MALACHITE KINGFISHER, *Alcedo cristata*, is about 5½ inches (14 cm) in length and the sexes are alike. The head and crest is narrowly barred greenish-blue and black; sides of face rich tawny; remainder of upperparts ultramarine blue; throat white; remainder of underparts, including under wing-coverts, rich tawny; bill, legs and feet red. Their general distribution is throughout Africa south of the Sahara, with the exception of Gabon, Rio Muni and Somalia. Their preference is for wide waters or swamp lands for their habitat, and they feed on both fish and water insects.

The BROWN-HOODED KINGFISHER, *Halcyon albiventris*, is about twice the size of the preceding species being about 9½ inches (25 cm) in length and the sexes do differ in colouration. It has a much more restricted range, below the equator except for an intrusion into Somalia, ranging from southern Gabon, Angola, the Congo and Rhodesia. The head and sides of face of the adult male, brown; base of neck buff; mantle, scapulars, innermost secondaries and wing-coverts black; rump bright blue; tail greenish-blue. Flight feathers edged greenish-blue, ends black; throat white washed with buff; remainder of underparts, including wing-coverts and inner webs of flight feathers, buff, varying in intensity individually; bill, legs and feet red. The female differs in having the mantle, scapulars, innermost secondaries and wing-coverts a sooty brown. They are birds of the bush country or open woodland, preferring to be near water but, as long as the grass is short, the presence of water is not essential for they can get all the insects they require in the grass. They take grasshoppers, small reptiles, worms and crabs as items of their diet.

The STRIPED KINGFISHER, *Halcyon chelicuti,* is about 7½ inches (19 cm) in length and the sexes are alike. With a distribution similar to that of the Malachite Kingfisher, except that they are not to be found in the southern parts of South Africa. The head is ashy, streaked blackish; hind-neck white; mantle, scapulars and wings ash coloured; flight feathers edged blue, median wing-coverts and base of primaries white; rump and tail blue; underparts buffish white, streaked on the flanks; bill, legs and feet red. Their food is mainly insects of the larger variety and they did not make good aviary birds as they were too pugnacious, attacking any bird that ventured into the area they had staked out for themselves.

. . . too pugnacious . . .

There are two species bearing the common name WHITE-COLLARED KINGFISHER, one, *Halcyon abyssinica,* from Ethiopia, and the other, *Halcyon chloris,* from the Oriental Region where it is widespread throughout Burma, Indo-China and Malaysia. Length of the latter about 9 inches (23 cm), the sexes differ slightly in colouring. The pair Mr. Boehm had came from Malaysia, the sub-species *H. c. humii.* The male was mainly blue above and white below; a greenish tinge on the blue of the crown and wings; face bluish; sides of forehead and a spot below the eye, white; a black eye-streak continuing in a thin line around the nape; white collar; abdomen and flanks tinged buff; bill mainly blackish, pinkish white at base; legs and feet greyish. The female is more greenish blue. Another insect eater that also takes ants and crabs as part of its food. Ideal aviary birds but preferring high perching so that they can wa. all below and be in an advantageous position to pounce on ar. insect they see.

The PIGMY KINGFISHER, *Ispidina picta,* is one of the smallest of the family, only about 4½ inches (11 cm) in length of which more than an inch is accounted for by the bill. It is to be found over a wide area in Africa; north of the equator its habitat extending from the west coast; south of the Sahara, through Nigeria and clear across to Ethiopia and Somalia. It also spreads southward to Angola, through the Congo and up into Kenya. A subspecies, *I. p. natalensis,* known as the Natal Kingfisher, carries on down the east coast through Tanzania, Mozambique, Rhodesia and the eastern parts of South Africa.

Mr. Boehm had seen the nominate race during his collector's trip to Kenya in 1960, but had not been fortunate enough to procure any at that time. In June 1961, a consignment of three of the subspecies mentioned above were received from Mozambique, but two were dead on arrival. The third had managed to survive on the mealworms provided in transit but, judging by the voracious manner in which it went for those offered it in the cage we put it in, it would not have lasted much longer. By the time the next consignment came in, March 1962, this one bird was fully acclimatised and was feeding on strips of meat, mealworms, crickets and even taking minnows out of a shallow pan of water.

Eight new birds arrived in all and they were in perfect health and were released into the same room housing the older bird. I say older, for all the new arrivals were young birds, their bills not being completely out of the immature black phase. They promptly took to the diet being supplied to the original bird. This entailed more frequent trips to the stream from which the minnows were netted for they had as many as four or five each per day in addition to their strips of meat, mealworms and crickets.

The sexes are alike in colouration, the forehead and crown deep violet-blue with light blue barrings, the violet-blue colouring extending through the mantle, wings, rump and tail; underparts deep rufous. This rufous shade is evident also in a superciliary stripe reaching to the nape of the neck. The ear-coverts and cheeks are mauve, except for a patch below the ear, the upper portion of which is violet-blue, the lower part white. Throat patch white; bill, legs and feet bright orange. The difference in the sexes lies in the shape of the lower mandible, that

African Pigmy Kingfisher

of the female being more keel-shaped than that of the male.

Mr. Boehm gave careful thought to the breeding of these little jewels for it was realised that special provisions would have to be made for them. With this sole object in view, some small aviaries were cleared of birds, stripped down, and reconstructed into one single flight of some 60 by 16 feet (18 x 5 metres), the height being increased to 12 feet. (3.6 metres). Across 12 feet (3.6 metres) of the lower end, against the bird-house wall, an earth embankment 3 feet (91 cm) wide and 2 feet (61 cm) high was erected. It was held in position by 2 by 1 inch (5 x 2.5 cm) wire-netting, faced with concrete. In this facing, holes, 4 by 2 inches (10 x 5 cm), were made through the cement and wire so as to expose the bare earth beyond. The top of the bank was planted with azaleas and various shrubs to hold the earth together and to avoid washouts in the event of a heavy storm. Further, a shallow pool with continuous running water was installed, the entire aviary replanted and it was ready by the spring of 1963. In the meantime Mr. Boehm had presented four of the kingfishers to the Bronx Zoo, retaining three males and two females for himself.

In May it was decided that the weather was sufficiently settled to permit birds being transferred from their winter quarters in the bird-house and pairs of Lesser Niltavas, Black-chinned Wren Babblers, Crimson Chats, Red-headed Tits, Yellow-billed Chlorophonias and the five Natal Kingfishers were released into this new aviary. As was our custom, every bird was colour banded, those alloted to the male kingfishers being blue, orange and green, the females being banded red and white. The bird originally received in 1961 was the female with the white band.

As is the usual case with outdoor aviaries, we were blessed with our following of field mice so, when scrapings and small holes began to be made in the exposed patches in the face of the embankment, little attention was paid to them at first. However, at one early morning check, on June 10th to be exact, a king-fisher was missing, the one with the white band. With the aid of an electric hand-torch, the holes in the bank were checked and, at the end of a tunnel about 20 inches (50 cm) long, the head of the bird was seen. The passage-way was perfectly straight, a great asset from the viewpoint of making regular observations of the nesting. Later in the day the female was seen on a branch overhanging the pool and a quick look into the nest-hole showed that another bird was in there. Another "band" check pin-

. . . a kingfisher was missing . . .

pointed the "blue" male kingfisher as being the new occupant. The days following proved this conclusively for "blue" or "white" was always perched in close proximity to the nest hole and it was noted that a change over was made every 2 hours or so, at least during the day.

Incubation lasted 18 days and on June 28 one of the parent birds was seen to fly into the nest with a small minnow in its bill. It made this trip four times in fairly quick succession, not being in the nest more than about 15 seconds at a time. A look into the burrow showed nothing but the head and breast of an adult bird and it was not until the sixth day that two little bald heads were first seen endeavouring to get out of the beam of light from the torch. As with the incubation, the rearing of the young was shared and it became apparent that none of the food taken to the nest was for other than the nestlings, for, as soon as the change-over by the parents was effected, the bird vacating the nest promptly had a good meal itself and then a bath. They did not discriminate in the food taken to the nest for they were seen to take minnows, strips of meat, mealworms and crickets and even an occasional moth they had caught for themselves. In the early days the fish they selected for the nestlings were small but, as time progressed, they were observed taking fish of 2 to 2½ inches (5 to 6 cm) in length, and spending no more time on the feeding than they did with the smaller ones. A careful study of their feeding pattern revealed that they fed the young birds about 8 courses every hour.

. . . two little bald heads . . .

It became easy to know whether they were going to eat a fish themselves or feed it to the young for, once they had snatched it out of the pool, their method of killing it differed. If for their own consumption, they held it across the bill by the head when knocking it on a branch to stun it and then, with a deft flick of the head, transferred it lengthwise so that the fish's head was in their bill, swallowing it thus, head first. When it was caught to feed the young, they held the fish towards the tail crosswise in their bill, killing it in the same manner as described above. This time, however, the flick transferred the fish tail first into their bill, leaving the head protruding. When it came to larger fish they looked rather grotesque as they flew off with about 2 inches (5 cm) of fish sticking out in front of them. The reason for the head-first method of swallowing is because fish are streamlined from head to tail and it obviates any chance of the fish's gills or dorsal fin getting lodged in the bird's throat.

. . . tail first into their bill . . .

On the 10th day, 2 soiled eggs, pure white, almost round

and measuring 16 by 14 mm., were found on the ground below the nest hole. They were both clear. From the 12th day onwards, both parents spent most of the day out of the nest, making their hourly trips with feed, and it was normal for each bird to make 4 or 5 sortees at a session. The nestlings were now feathering up and the bright violet-blue of the head and the rufous underparts were clearly visible in the light of the torch. It was on July 16, at eighteen days old, that they vacated the nest.

Except for the general colouring being softer, the bills shorter and black in colour, the fledglings were replicas of their parents. As during the nesting time, the adults continued to share in the feeding of the young birds, one of which was seen to make an ineffective dive towards the fish pool within hours of leaving the nest. They became independent within five days when they were selecting food for themselves, although they still accepted tid-bits from either parent.

During this entire breeding period the other three adult kingfishers spent most of the time at the far end of the aviary, making secretive raids on the minnow pool or cricket box whenever the coast was clear. On July 23 fresh scrapings of earth were seen below the entrance to the old nest and a quick look showed that there was a bird in there. A check revealed that it was the same female and male involved and, from this second round, one more chick was reared to independence. It seemed that once again four eggs comprised the clutch for three, all clear, were rolled out of the nest prior to the nestling leaving.

. . . secretive raids on the minnow pool . . .

It was not until the young birds were some 18 months old that the black of the bill had disappeared and it was nearer to two years before the bill became the complete orange of the adults. It was observed that once the first round was out of the nest the parent birds did not take kindly to the other adult kingfishers in the aviary and it was necessary to remove them. During the non-breeding season they all lived quietly together but, at breeding time, it is strongly recommended that only one pair be kept in an enclosure.

These little kingfishers are not difficult to keep provided there is an ample supply of live-food available for them, in addition to the strips of meat and the fish. This breeding has been recognised as the first of the species in captivity.

Family Momotidae

This is a family confined to continental tropical America

and is best represented in northern Central America and south Mexico. There are some 8 species in all varying from 6½ to 19 inches (16 to 48 cm) in length, and they are all colourful. Their structural pecularities are the serrated edges of the bill which is broad, almost as long as their head, and decurved at the end; their feet, where the outer toe is united to the middle one for most of its length, and only one toe is directed backwards. They are mostly insect eaters, although some do take fruit and the majority are burrow nesters.

The RUFOUS MOTMOT, *Baryphthengus ruficapillus,* is one of the larger species, about 18 inches (46 cm) in length, and the sexes are alike. The crown, upper mantle, sides of neck, throat and breast, cinnamon rufous; lores, stripe below the eye and spot on the breast black; back grass green; tail blue, central pair of feathers terminating in a bare shaft and racquet with a black tip. Breast cinnamon rufous, extending to the upper belly; remainder of belly greenish. They are to be found from Nicaragua southward to western Ecuador and northern Argentina.

The TURQUOISE-BROWED MOTMOT, *Eumomota superciliosa,* from Central America is about 14 inches (37 cm) in length, of which the tail accounts for some 8 inches (20 cm). The noticeable feature is the slightly iridescent pale turquoise blue patch or "brow" above each eye. The middle of the chin and throat, black, bordered at either side by a pale blue line; lores and elongated ear-coverts black, bordered below by narrow pale blue line; most of the wings and tail rich turquoise blue, but top and under side of tail black. Belly, sides, under tail-coverts and middle of back, rufous; remainder of plumage brownish-green.

As stated earlier, they are mainly insect eaters and, whilst with us we never saw them take any of the ground raw beef or the soft-food mixture, but they did consume a fair amount of fruit. With our breeding pairs of insectivorous birds, they became quite a problem and were disposed of.

Family Meropidae

This is an Old World family, predominantly Afro-Asian and restricted to the tropical and milder temperate regions. They vary from 6 to 14 inches (15 to 35 cm) in length and are insectivorous, bees and wasps being largely taken on the wing. The majority are brightly coloured and, although they are hole-nesters, they are arboreal in their other habits. The bill is characteristic, rather long, slender, laterally compressed and decurved with a sharp point.

The BLUE-CHEEKED or BROWN-BREASTED BEE-EATER, *Merops superciliosus*, is about 12 inches (30 cm) in length, is a migrant to Africa from Malagasy and Iran and there are several races in their distribution right through to New Guinea. The sexes are alike, general colour green; forehead white; top of head brown; streaks above and below the eye white; black streak through eye; chin yellow; throat chestnut; central tail feathers elongated.

The BLUE-BEARDED BEE-EATER, *Nyctyornis athertoni*, is an Asiatic species found in India, Pakistan, Burma and Thailand. About 14 inches (35 cm) in length they are green with a blue cap and a line of pale blue running from the chin down to the breast; underparts dull yellowish buff.

Mr. Boehm maintained bee hives to obtain the pupa for feeding purposes and, once we received the above mentioned bee-eaters, it was a daily task to collect bees for them as long as they were housed in the bird-house. This necessitated fly-screening their doors and windows so as to keep the bees within the confines of their room. However, when released into the aviaries this task was unnecessary as there were always plenty of yellow-jackets (wasps) available for them. During the winter, back to the bee hives once more and this had to be done very carefully for the honey-bees became very angry when disturbed and the collectors got stung so many times that eventually the birds and the bees had to be disposed of. In addition to the bees and wasps, they also took practically any flying insects they could catch and helped themselves to the ground raw beef.

. . . the collectors got stung . . .

Family Coraciidae

This is an Old World family of some 12 species and is restricted to the tropical and milder temperate regions. They range from 9½ to 13 inches (24 to 33 cm) in length, not allowing for the tail streamers present in some species. They got their common name of rollers from their habit of rolling in the air during their aerial display, and they are very strong on the wing. Carnivorous, taking insects, beetles, small rodents and, at times, small birds, they are arboreal in their habits and hole-nesters.

The INDIAN ROLLER, *Coracias benghalensis*, is distributed through southern Asia from eastern Arabia to Cambodia, and at least three distinct races are recognised. About 13 inches (33 cm) in length, the sexes are alike. Top of head bluish-green; back and sides of neck deep vinous; upper plumage dull greenish-brown with a blue patch above base of tail. Wings mixed blues and green, the quills deep purplish blue marked conspicuously with a broad band of pale blue. Tail deep blue, with a broad terminal band of pale blue interrupted by the central pair of feathers which are dull greenish. Sides of head and throat purplish-lilac, streaked whitish; breast vinous, also faintly streaked with white; remainder of underparts pale blue; bill blackish-brown; legs and feet brownish-yellow; naked skin round the eye gamboge. In India this bird is often referred to as the Blue Jay.

The LILAC-BREASTED ROLLER, *Coracias caudata*, is about 14 inches (36 cm) in length and has a general distribution from Uganda and Kenya to Angola, Rhodesia, Botswana and eastern South Africa. The sexes are alike, head green; back and scapulars brown, strongly washed with green; entire shoulders of wing, outer webs of flight feathers and rump, violet; base of primaries and primary coverts pale greenish-blue; outer tail feathers elongated. From chin to breast rich lilac, the chin streaked white; remainder of underparts greenish-blue.

The RUFOUS-CROWNED ROLLER, *Coracias naevia*, has a distribution from central Namibia through Botswana and northward to Senegal, across to Ethiopia. About 15 inches (38 cm) in length, the sexes are alike. Crown vinous brown; distinct white superciliary stripe; white patch on nape; back olive brown; rump and upper tail-coverts violet; square tail violet, except for central pair of feathers which are olivegreen. Wings violet, lilac and bronzy brown; underparts brownish lilac to pure lilac on belly, streaked with white; under wing-coverts pinkish-white; under tail-coverts violet and blue.

The BROAD-BILLED ROLLER, *Eurystomus glaucurus*, is a smaller bird, about 10 inches (25 cm) in length and again the sexes are alike. It breeds in Malagasy, migrating in the non-breeding season to Mocambique, Rhodesia, Tanzania and even as far north as the Congo and Ethiopia. Chocolate brown above, the nape is glossed with deep lilac; flight feathers and outer wing-coverts violet; upper tail-coverts greenish-blue; tail greenish-blue with violet tips. The underparts are deep lilac washed with purple; under tail-coverts green.

The main diet of the above species of rollers with us was mealworms, crickets and ground raw beef, together with a white mouse each daily. We never had any trouble with them so far as other birds were concerned, but, in all instances we were

. . . a white mouse each daily.

104

careful to house them only with birds of a comparative size. With the exception of the Broad-billed Rollers they all became very tame and would take mealworms from our fingers.

Family Upupidae

There is but one species in this family and it bears the common name of hoopoe, but there are several races. An Old World family with distribution through the temperate parts of Europe to southern Africa, Malagasy, India, Pakistan, Ceylon, Thailand, Malaysia and Sumatra. It is a strikingly beautiful bird with its shades of pinkish-brown, black and white, and has a spectacular crest, erectile at will. They are insect eaters and hole-nesters and have an extremely short tongue, taking all their food by probing with their long bill, grasping it and flicking it back into their mouth. The wings are rounded and the flight undulating.

The hoopoe is one of the birds that goes back centuries in literature, being referred to in the Bible as the lapwing, and illustrated in ancient Grecian and Egyptian murals. Legends were built around it, one being that, after King Solomon had been shaded from the glaring sun by the wings of a flock of hoopoes, he rewarded them with a crown of gold. This led to constant persecution of the birds by men who coveted the gold. Tired of this kind of life, the birds asked the King to take the crown back and to grant them a simple crest. This simplicity is symbolical of the splendour of Solomon for its beautiful fan-shape and striking markings make it one of the most attractive crests in the bird world.

. . . in ancient Grecian and Egyptian murals.

Another legend of eastern European origin, states that the hoopoe was the form assumed by Jerseus, King of Crete, in atonement for his sins. The fame of the species, however, was not confined to legends and murals, for many references have been made to it in magical and medicinal prescriptions. These were mainly for afflictions of sight and memory, and various parts of the bird's anatomy were recommended by scribes from the early Egyptian days down to the 18th century.

The nominate race, *Upupa epops epops*, has an extensive range, wintering in the Mediterranean countries and Turkey, spending the breeding season throughout Central Europe, including sometimes the south of England. There are at least four other races in Asia, these including the *U. e. orientalis* of northern India and Pakistan; *U. e. longirostris* of Burma and the neighbouring areas; *U. e. ceylonsis* of southern India and Ceylon and *U. e. saturata* from Mongolia. There also are two other races in Africa, the *U. e. africanus* of East Africa and *U. e. senegalensis* of the western parts.

We had but two of the races, one being *U. e. africanus* which has a range from the Congo to southern Ethiopia and southward over the entire continent to South Africa. About 11 inches (28 cm) in length, the sexes are very much alike, the female being duller and, in most cases, slightly smaller. The crest is russet brown with black tips; mantle earthy brown; wings and tail barred black and white; lower back barred black and buff; from chin to chest vinous buff; abdomen white with black streaks.

The other subspecies was the *U. e. longirostris,* which we received direct from Thailand. They are about 12 inches (30 cm) in length, $2\frac{1}{2}$ (6 cm) of which may be accounted for by the thin, slightly decurved bill. The head and fan-shaped crest pinkish brown, the crest feathers increasing in length from front to rear and broadly tipped with black. Back and sides of neck and the shoulders dull, ashy fawn; remainder of back broadly banded black and fawnish white, the bands extending across the wing-coverts. The quills of the wings and tail black; primaries with white tips; secondaries with several (three or four, it varies) white bands evenly spaced throughout their length. Chin whitish; throat and upper breast pale pinkish fawn; remainder of underparts white, extensively streaked with black and ashy-grey, except for the under tail-coverts which are clear white. The bill horny black, lighter at the base of the lower mandible; legs and feet slate-grey.

The main visual difference in the sexes lies in the length of the bill and the size of the crest, those of the female being slightly smaller than the male's. It had been observed with the birds in the Boehm aviaries that the males had nine pairs of black-tipped feathers in the crest, and the females seven. Whether this is a definite sex indicator or not I am not sure but, with all the young we reared over the years, the same difference did apply. The crest lies back over the head and is raised whenever the bird is excited and when they are feeding. It is quite a sight seeing a flock of them walking on a lawn, probing in the ground for insects, each probe being accompanied by an elevation of the crest. They have a soft, mellow call note, a repeated "hoop, hoop" which, although sounding pleasant when one is watching them, can become very irritating when one is endeavouring to rest in

. . . *"hoop, hoop"* . . .

the heat of the afternoon, as I experienced during my years in India.

We had a pair of them in a tropically planted aviary that they shared with many other species of birds and they selected, as their nesting site, a hole in a 12 inch (30 cm) thick tree stump about 8 feet (2.4 metres) above ground level. It was in May 1963 that the female was seen going in and out of this hole which led to a hollow about 9 inches (23 cm) deep and 8 inches (20 cm) across. Between May 18 and 22 four eggs were laid but they were all clear. They were pale blue and averaged 25 by 16 mm in size. A second round of five eggs was produced in June but only one hatched, on July 3, the others being clear. The nestling, sparsely covered with light down, had a minute bill, heavily margined in white. Its eyes were open at the eighth day and it then was feathering up in greyish fawn.

During the incubation and early brooding days, seemingly carried out by the female alone, the male was most conscientious in his attention to her, bringing food at regular intervals. This consisted mainly of live-food in the form of mealworms or crickets, supplies being placed before him hourly, and it was observed that he would take six to her, then eat two himself, and so on until the supply was exhausted. Thereafter he searched throughout the aviary for whatever he could forage, not just confining himself to ground level, but flying up to the roof of the aviary catching flies, moths or any other insects about. It was essential that fresh live-food was given hourly during the day for, if the male was a little tardy in taking something to the nest-hole, the female used to look out and give a most plaintive "hoop, hoop", and then he would get very agitated, flying up and down to see what he could find for her.

At 16 days old the nestling's feathering closely resembled that of the adult birds. Its bill was about an inch (2.5 cm) long now but still had the bulbous, white margins. The pictures at right and next page are of the adult male at the nest-hole and the young bird just prior to fledging at 23 days old. On leaving the nest it was a complete replica in general form of its parents, except that the colouring was softer, the crest smaller, and the bill shorter. It finally attained independence at one month and, from the number of feathers in its crest, was classified as a male. This turned out to be correct for it fathered several broods over the years following.

Contrary to my personal expectations, having scented many hoopoe nests in the wild in India, there was very little

Thailand
Adult Male
Hoopoe

Thailand Hoopoe: 23-day old young prior to fledging

odour from the nest. This I could only put down to the fact that there was but one chick as compared to the three or four in the wild but, from further breedings, when we had up to four chicks in one nest, it was exactly the same. This could well be due to the fact that birds in captivity are provided with fresh food all the time compared to whatever they can find for themselves in the wild; on the other hand it may be a form of a protective habit in the wild. In any case, whatever the reason, I am very glad we were spared that most unpleasant smell I experienced with a nest in the Punjabi Plains.

Family Phoeniculidae

This is a small family of birds generally known as wood-hoopoes, or tree-hoopoes, and it is confined to Africa. Mainly insect eaters, they also take berries and fruits. When handled they give off a musk-like smell which lingers on the hands for some time after they have been released; at least that was our experience with the three species we had.

*African
Green
Wood-Hoopoe
(See next Page)*

The WHITE-HEADED WOOD-HOOPOE, *Phoeniculus bollei,* is about 10 inches (25 cm) in length and is to be found in north-eastern Congo, Uganda, southern Sudan and Kenya. We only ever had one specimen and, since the sexes are alike in colouring, we surmised it was a female from the smallness of the bill. Head and throat white, remainder of body plumage iridescent green. Wings blue; central tail feathers mainly purple; abdomen black; bill, legs and feet red.

*It was a
most secretive
bird . . .*

It was a most secretive bird spending most of the time in a hollow tree stump, just coming out at feeding times to gather up a billful of mealworms and then back in its tree. We did manage to see it occasionally flying round the aviary provided we were well hidden but, as soon as it became aware that anyone was around, back it would dive ino the hole in the tree.

The GREEN WOOD-HOOPOE, *Phoeniculus purpureus*, has a general distribution through Malawi, southern Rhodesia, Kenya, and from Uganda to eastern and southern Congo. About 14 inches (36 cm) in length, the sexes are alike except that the males have longer bills. General colour iridescent green; wings dark blue with the primaries crossed with a white bar; wing-shoulders and tail purple and violet, white spots on the elongated tail; abdomen black; bill, legs and feet red.

We had a pair of them that selected a hole in the ground at the foot of a tree stump as a nesting site, but it was not revealed until the stump was uprooted by a gardener. There were two eggs in the nest, pale blue with minute white spots and they measured 25 by 18 mm., and they both appeared to be fertile. We had noticed prior to this that one of the birds always seemed to be on the ground in the vicinity of the stump whenever we went into their aviary but had not attached much significance to it. Although we put another stump in there and tried to simulate the same conditions, they did not go back to nest again during the remainder of their time with us.

The SCIMITAR-BILLED WOOD-HOOPOE, *Rhinopomastus cyanomelas,* is a smaller bird, about 10 inches (25 cm) in length, and the sexes differ. They are to be found in Malawi northward to Angola, eastern Congo, Uganda and Kenya. The adult male has head and body of iridescent bottle-green; steel blue wings; tail violet; legs and feet black; bill black, yellowish along the edges and it is long and decurved. The female is similar except that the head is brown and the bill shorter.

With all wood-hoopoes live-food is the most important item of their diet, but they all took the ground raw beef as well. With the exception of the White-headed Wood-hoopoe they were interesting to watch as they climbed up the tree trunks and the aviary framework in search of insects, probing away with their long, decurved bills. None of them could be said to have a song, just a series of chattering cries.

Mr. and Mrs. Boehm standing beside his porcelain sculpture of the Ivory-billed Woodpeckers

The members of this order are predominantly arboreal birds and their distribution is almost cosmopolitan except for the Australasian and the Malagasy regions. They feed mainly on berries, fruit and seeds with a modicum of insect life as a supplement, but some are almost solely insectivorous, this applying in particular to the woodpeckers, and others, such as the toucans, can be carnivorous as well.

The order is divided into two suborders, Galbulae and Pici, the suborder Galbulae being further divided into three superfamilies, and five families, the suborder Pici containing but one family, the Picidae—Woodpeckers, Piculets and Wrynecks. With Piciformes a specialised form of bill is a characteristic of each family. The only members of this order that we had at the Boehm aviaries were barbets, toucans and woodpeckers.

The barbets, Capitonidae, are all strongly built, with large heads and stocky bodies; a stout bill, heavy and conical with a sharp tip, and they range from $3\frac{1}{2}$ to 12 inches (9 to 30 cm) in length. Their flight is weak due to the rather short and rounded wings but they can fly swiftly for short distances, particularly when you are trying to catch them. Their legs are short and their feet zygodactyl, two toes forward and two toes back.

With most species the sexes are alike in colouring and their call mostly consists merely of a succession of single notes, harsh and shrill. A few do have clear, whistling calls, but these are in the minority. They are primarily vegetarians, but some do add insects to their diet. Most abundant in Africa, there are some species in both Asia and tropical America.

The DOUBLE-TOOTHED BARBET, *Lybius bidentatus,* is an African species to be found from Central Africa and the eastern parts of Congo to the Sudan, western Kenya and northern Tanzania. The sexes are alike, the general colouring being blueblack with a white lower back. Sides of face, chin and belly red; a rose pink wing bar; white bill with a deep groove on the upper mandible.

The WHITE-HEADED BARBET, *Lybius leucocephalus,* has a much more restricted range in Africa being more or less confined to the southern Sudan and northeastern Congo to Uganda and western Kenya. They are about 7 inches (18 cm) in length and the sexes are alike. The whole head, throat to breast, lower back and upper and under tail-coverts are white; belly, flanks, back, wings and tail black, with white flecks on the wing-coverts and belly.

The GIANT BARBET, *Megalaima virens,* is an Asiatic

bird and may be found from the Himalayan foothills through to Burma and China. As its name implies, it is a large bird, about 13 inches (33 cm) in total length, and the sexes are alike. Head and neck black with deep violet-blue edges to the feathers; back and shoulders brownish-olive, the upper back streaked greenish-yellow; broad patch above the base of the tail grass-green; wings blackish-brown, washed with blue-green and olive-brown; tail green above, blackish below washed with pale blue. Upper breast dark olive-brown; remainder of underparts blue down the centre, striped yellow and brown on the sides; scarlet patch under the tail. The bill is large, slightly flattened and swollen; the gape is wide, fringed with hair-like feathers.

The GOLDEN-RUMPED TINKER-BIRD, *Pogoniulus bilineatus*, is an African species to be found in Tanzania, Mozambique, Zambia and down into Malawi. It is a small bird, about 4½ inches (9 cm) in length, and the sexes are alike. Shining black glossed with green above; superciliary streak and a line from forehead under eyes to neck, white; ear-coverts and malar stripe black; edges of wing-coverts and flight feathers lemon-yellow; rump golden-yellow; throat to breast greyish-white; chest to belly pale lemon-yellow; bill black.

The LEMON-RUMPED TINKER-BIRD *Pogoniulus leucolaima,* is similar to the preceding species except that the rump is lemon-yellow and not golden-yellow. This species has a more restricted range from the Sudan through to Uganda, eastern Congo and north-western Tanzania.

The tinker-birds are amongst the smallest of the barbets and they feed on insects, especially ants, but they also eat fruit and berries. They have a peculiar call, a monotonous bell-like klunking, repeated four or five times, a pause, and then another series, this going on for five to ten minutes at a stretch—hence the name tinker-bird.

. . . a monotonous bell-like klunking . . .

The TOUCAN BARBET, *Semnornis ramphastinus*, is from western Ecuador and Colombia and is about 8 inches (20 cm) in total length. The sexes are much alike in general colouring. Forehead, crown, nape, area in front of the eye and at the base of the lower mandible, shining black; hind-crown bordered laterally by a broad white stripe; feathers of hind-crown of the male elongated so as to lay over the mantle like a pigtail, this feature being lacking in the female. Sides of head, ear-coverts, sides of neck, throat and breast, blue-grey, the ear-coverts bordered at the rear with black; mantle olive-brown, lower back and rump golden-yellow; wings and tail dark grey. A broad band of scarlet across the breast fading into reddish-yellow as it goes down the centre of the lower breast and abdomen; sides of body yellow. With the pair we had the scarlet breast band of the female was less broad than that of the male. They have a strong, heavy, swollen bill, yellowish-green with a black tip, and they use this in the manner of a woodpecker, hammering away at tree stumps. Their resonant call is similar to the noise of a very loud typewriting machine and can be heard for a considerable distance.

The YELLOW-BILLED BARBET, *Trachyphonus purpuratus*, an African species which ranges from Gabon through to the Congo, the Sudan, Uganda and Kenya, is a large bird, about $10\frac{1}{2}$ inches (26 cm) in length, and the sexes are alike. The subspecies we had, *T. p. elgonensis*, was received from Kenya. Neck and mantle iridescent blue-black; forehead, forecrown to over eye and down sides of neck a rich dark crimson; chin to throat black with shining tips; narrow crimson breast band; breast and abdomen pale yellow. Flanks black with large pale yellow spots; patch on wing-shoulder and underside of wing, white; bill yellow.

We always considered it best to keep the larger species such as the Double-toothed, Giant, Toucan and the Yellow-billed Barbets in accommodation by themselves for they all possess strong heavy bills that could easily inflict mortal damage to any of the smaller birds. The tinker-birds were with mixed collections and they settled down very well but did not go to nest. As the aviaries were all of large dimensions and there being plenty of birds that would live amicably together, we never gave any of them over to the larger barbets and eventually disposed of them to zoos. In addition to fruit and live-food, they also consumed a considerable amount of ground raw beef and we never had any trouble with any of them.

The toucans, Ramphastidae, are much larger birds, 12 to 14 inches (30 to 60 cm) in length, and are confined to the tropical parts of America. In most cases the sexes are alike in colouring but the adult males normally are larger than the females of the same age, the females normally have shorter bills. The wings are short and rounded, the tails lengthy, but the main characteristic is the oversize bill which, in some cases, even exceeds the length of the body. They have very strong legs and feet, these being zygodactylous as with the barbets. Their food consists of berries, fruits and insects, and they are not averse to small birds and rodents. They have practically no vocal powers, their call being more like a frog croaking or puppies yelping.

They have strong legs and feet . . .

114

The GREY-BREASTED TOUCAN, *Andigena hypoglauca*, is to be found in the mountains of Ecuador, Peru and Colombia and is sometimes known as the Mountain Toucan. About 18 inches (46 cm) in length, the sexes are alike in colouring but there is a slight difference in the bill, that of the male being larger. The crown, nape and ear-coverts glossy black; bare skin round the eye light blue; back olive-brown; rump golden-yellow; wings and upper tail-coverts slaty-olive; tail blackish, central feathers tipped rufous. Chin blackish; throat, breast, centre of belly and collar on hind-neck, blue-grey; flanks chocolate-brown; under tail-coverts and sides of rump crimson cherry. The bill is 3½ to 4 inches (9 to 10 cm) in length, extreme base and frontal portion of lower mandible bright yellow followed by a black band; base of upper mandible black; middle portion of both upper and lower mandibles orange-red, separated from the greenish-yellow by a black line.

The WHITE-THROATED TOUCAN, *Ramphastos tucanus*, is a larger bird, some 19 to 22 inches (48 to 59 cm) in length, and may be found in Venezuela, eastern Colombia and the Guianas, south to eastern and central Brazil, northern Argentina and Bolivia. The sexes are alike, the upperparts, wing and tail black, mantle tinged maroon; ear-coverts golden-yellow; bare skin around the eye light blue; upper tail-coverts yellow. Throat and breast white, tinged pale sulphur-yellow; under tail-coverts crimson. The bill is 6 to 7 inches (15 to 18 cm) in length, base of the upper mandible orange-yellow; base of the lower mandible light blue; ridge of upper mandible yellowish-green; tip of bill yellow, remainder dark red.

They consumed considerable amounts of fruit whilst with us and readily took dead white mice of which they got about four a week. The second mentioned pair, the White-throated, became exceptionally tame and would climb all over us. This could be quite embarrassing at times for they are not particularly careful when or where they excrete and, being mainly fruit-eaters, we alone took the chances, never letting any of the visitors retain stained memories of their tour through the aviaries.

. . . and would climb all over us.

SUBORDER PICI

The woodpeckers, family Picidae, are world-wide in distribution except for the extreme latitudes and the Australasian and Malagasy Regions. They vary from 3¼ to 22½ inches (8 to 58 cm) in length and the sexes are closely alike in colouring.

They have wedge shaped tails, the stiff tail feathers of the true woodpeckers serving as a support when they are climbing trees, etc. The bill is stout, fairly long, and very strong. Their tongues also are very long and worm-like in the way they use them to search out grubs in the bark of trees, licking out ants and other insects. Short legs with strong feet, the mobile toes being capable of being directed in various directions when climbing although, at normal times, they are the same as the barbets and the toucans. Although they do eat berries, insects and grubs are their main diet.

The GOLDEN-BACKED WOODPECKER, *Dinopium shorei*, is an Asiatic species to be found in the Himalayan region through to Burma. About 11 inches (28 cm) in length, the sexes are very much alike. There are five species bearing the name golden-backed, three of them having four toes, the others having but three. The *D. shorei* is of the latter type and is often referred to as the Three-toed Woodpecker. The forehead, crown and hind-neck black, feathers tipped crimson; crimson patch on chest, that of the female being slightly smaller than the male's; sides of head and neck white, streaked black; upper back and shoulders golden-yellow; wing-coverts black at the shoulders changing to golden-olive-yellow. Flight feathers whitish-black, spotted white, all but the outer feathers which have the outer webs washed golden-olive-yellow. Lower back and tail black; rump red; underparts white with two black lines down the centre of the throat, divided by a narrow brown stripe.

The FLAME-CROWNED WOODPECKER, *Melanerpes pucherani*, is from Central and South America with a range from southern Mexico in western Ecuador and coastal Colombia. They are about 8 inches (20 cm) in length and the sexes differ. The forehead and forecrown of the adult male golden-yellow; hind-crown and nape scarlet; eyebrows and ear-coverts black with a white streak behind the eye. Mantle and inner flight feathers black, barred white; lower back and upper tail-coverts white; tail black, central feathers notched with white. Throat whitish; breast dirty olive; centre of abdomen crimson; remainder of under-parts yellowish-olive, barred black. With the female the crimson of the head is confined to the nape, the centre of the crown being black, nottled white.

The only trouble with woodpeckers in aviaries such as Mr. Boehm laid out was their destructiveness to the trees and the wooden framework. The repairs they necessitated were the main reason why, after having been with us but some six months, they were presented to a zoo. During the time we did have them they ate the fruit mixture, the ground raw beef and a plentiful supply of live-food.

Downy Woodpeckers
porcelain sculpture by
Edward Marshal Boehm
—one of his favourites

American Song Sparrows porcelain sculpture by Edward Marshall Boehm

The Passeriformes, or Perching Birds, is the largest order including more than half of all species of birds and more than a third of the recognised families. It is comprised of the following suborders and, with the exception of the third named, representatives have been kept at the Boehm aviaries.

Eurylaimi _____ Broadbills.
Tyranni _____ Pittas, Cotingas etc.
Menurae _____ Lyrebirds and Scrub-birds.
Oscines _____ "Song birds."

SUBORDER EURYLAIMI

Family Eurylaimidae

This is a group of mainly brightly coloured birds inhabiting the Old World tropics from Africa to the Philipines. They vary from 5 to 11 inches (13 to 28 cm) in length, have short rounded wings, rounded or graduated tails, strong feet and flat, wide, slightly hooked bills. The head is broad, eyes large, gape wide and body cobby. Most of them are mainly insectivorous, even taking insects on the wing, but some of those from Asia are principally frugivorous. We had but two species, one from Africa, the other from Borneo.

The GREEN BROADBILL, *Calyptomena viridis*, resident in South-eastern Asia, is about 6 inches (15 cm) in length and the sexes differ. The male is iridescent grass green with black bars and patches on the wing, whereas the female is a dull green without black markings. The bill is black above, greenish below and at the tip, and yellow along the edges. Feet and legs dull green, undersides of feet yellowish. This species is almost entirely frugivorous and, when kept in captivity, it is essential that, particularly in the hot weather, the fruit is always fresh. Berries, such as blueberries are taken avidly as are chopped up grapes, cherries and diced apple. An occasional mealworm was accepted but the birds were never seen to touch the ground raw beef or the soft-food mixture. They have a most peculiar call, a series of short, soft, warbling notes.

They have a most peculiar call . . .

The AFRICAN BROADBILL, *Smithornis capensis*, is to be found practically throughout the southern parts of Africa from the Congo across to Mozambique and down to Angola in the west, to Lesotho in the east. They are about 6 inches (15 cm) in length and the sexes are almost alike in colouring. The top of the head of the adult male is black; remainder of upperparts olivaceous-grey to olivaceous-brown; feathers of mantle and back with the basal portions two-thirds white and some black markings on the ends. Underparts white with black streaks; upper mandible black, lower white. The top of the head of the female is grey, streaked blackish. The call of the male is a loud, jarring, vibrating noise, like a wooden rattle being twirled at a medium pace. This species is purely insectivorous, taking insects on the wing as well, but they did consume a considerable amount of ground raw beef whilst with us. They were constantly on the look-out for insects either in the air, in the shrubs, or on the ground, and were one of the few species we had that ate ants.

THE SUPERFAMILY TYRANNOIDEA

This superfamily is comprised of the following families:

Pittidae	Pittas
Philepittidae	Asities
Xenicidae	New Zealand Wrens
Tyrannidae	New World Flycatchers
Pipridae	Manakins
Cotingidae	Cotingas
Phytotomidae	Plantcutters

of which we had specimens of all except the second, third and last.

Family Pittidae

There are some 23 species of this family of mostly brightly coloured birds found in the Old World tropics from Africa to the Solomon Islands, the main centre of distribution being in Indo-Malaya. They are mainly ground birds, feeding mostly on insects but also taking small berries. Although they usually proceed on the ground by long hops, they are very strong flyers with a most direct flight. We fed them ground beef, soft-food mixture and live-food in the form of mealworms, crickets and gentles. Absolutely fearless, when roosting they remain perfectly motionless and, provided one approaches with caution, can be picked off their perching sites by hand. This fact leaves them an easy prey to night predators such as rats, weasels etc.

. . . very strong flyers.

Plump, cobby birds, ranging from 7 to 11 inches (18 to 28 cm) in length, with strong legs and short stubby tails, they are very thrush-like in shape and movements and, in their places of origin, are often referred to as 'painted thrushes,' 'jewel thrushes' and 'ground thrushes.' Although sociable with other species we found that all pittas are inclined to be quarrelsome amongst their own kind. Except at breeding time we were not able to house two in the same aviary or room, and even with the one pair that did breed, we had to separate them during the off season.

The BENGAL or INDIAN PITTA, *Pitta brachyura,* is to be found throughout the Indian peninsular down to Ceylon; the breeding range the Himalayan foothills to the Central Plains, wintering in the southern regions. The sexes are practically identical it being extremely difficult to sex an individual specimen. Top of head pale fulvous with a black band through the centre of the crown, running from the forehead to back of the head, this joined at the rear by two other black stripes that run from below each eye. Above the eye a narrow white strip. Chin and throat white, remainder of the underparts bright fulvous, except for a bright red vent patch. Back and shoulders green, lower rump pale blue, wings black with green and blue coverts. There is a white patch on the flights which is most conspicuous when the bird is in flight. Tail black, tipped with blue, legs pale purplish flesh colour and the bill is black at the tip, shading to orange at the base.

The call, heard mainly at dawn and dusk, clear and far reaching, sounding like "wheet-pee-u", and a scolding note "che-e-e-r". When giving vent to this they adopt a menacing pose with neck extended and wings partly open and drooped. It is at such times that the beauty of their colouring can best be appreciated. As stated above, the sexes are very much alike but, when a true pair are seen together it is possible to notice slight differences such as the intensity of colour of the vent feathers, the female's being paler, and the bill, the female's slightly longer and slimmer.

By trial and error, working with three birds, a pair was sorted out and early in May 1961 they constructed a large globular nest in a white pine about six feet (2 metres) above ground level. The exterior was of dried leaves and grasses bound together with reeds, twigs and rootlets, the interior being lined with fine rootlets, grass and green leaves. The entrance hole was low down leading to a tunnel-like aperture about nine inches (23 cm) in depth. Both birds took part in the building, the female doing most of the constructing, the male furnishing the materials.

Five eggs, broad and almost round, measuring 23 by 22 mm., of a china white colour with speckles, spots and hair lines of brownish purple were laid between June 3 and 7. Both shared the incubating which apparently began with the laying of the second egg for, with this round and subsequent rounds, two chicks hatched at the end of seventeen days, with one more each on the next two days. The fifth egg in each instance was clear and it was from this that the data given above was obtained. During the incubation period it was noted that each day they took a few fresh green leaves up to the nest, discarding some of those from the lining. It was considered that this may have had the effect of retaining humidity in the nest but nothing definite can be said on this point.

Little could be seen of the nestlings owing to their being well back in the nest but it was observed that their gapes were bright orange red, they were dark skinned, almost bare of body down, and had very flat heads. As with the incubation, the rearing was shared, live-food being the sole diet. This consisted of the grubs and insects they got for themselves plus hourly supplies of mealworms, crickets and gentles. In addition, a tray of fresh leaf-mould was placed below the tree every day. The chicks left the nest on July 7 and 8, two on each day, and they were dark grey on the underparts with bottle-green upper plumage. The head markings were similar in pattern to those of the adult birds but not as distinct. Within five days the fulvous of the underparts had begun to show down the centre of the abdomen and, by now, the young birds were entirely independent of their parents. This appeared to be remarkably early, but there was no doubt about it and the same thing happened with the second round. By the end of a further three weeks the underparts were identical to those of the parent's, even to the under-tail red feathers, and, by the time they were seven weeks old, all that could have distinguished them would be their paler legs. They had been moved from their parents when independent as the male had started to chase them around, and each chick was placed in a separate aviary that was pitta free. The second round followed the exact same pattern although a new nest was built, the old one being stripped down, much of the material used for the second nest which was sited about two feet (61 cm) higher in the same tree. Incidentally, about a further two feet (61 cm) up, and on the other side of the tree, White-cheeked Touracos raised their families at the same time as the pittas were busy with theirs.

The HOODED PITTA, *P. sordida cucullata*, is slightly

. . . the rearing was shared . . .

123

larger than the preceding species and is to be found in the eastern Himalayan foothills right through to Burma and Malaysia. Again the sexes are so similar that one description suffices for both. Forehead to nape rufous brown, the rest of the head, sides of neck, throat and a broad collar on the hind neck black. The back and rump dark green, upper tail-coverts bright blue, and the tail black tipped with dull blue. The breast pale green and the under tail-coverts crimson. We had several purported pairs of this species over the years but could never get any two to agree.

. . . could never get any two to agree . . .

Another S. E. Asian species is the BLUE-WINGED PITTA, *P. moluccensis,* the same size as the Hooded and sexes similar. Top of head light brown with a black line down the centre and a black eye-streak continued round the nape. Rump shining blue, tail black with blue tips. The wings green with a large central patch of shining blue and a patch of white in the middle of the black edges. The rest of the upperparts green. Black chin and white throat, remainder of the underparts buffish brown except for a crimson streak above the belly extending into the under tail-coverts.

The BLUE-BREASTED PITTA, *P. mackloti,* is to be found in Malaysia, New Guinea and Australia, and is about 7½ inches (19 cm) in total length. The back and wings green, crown rust brown with a black stripe, sides of head and nape are black edged with buff, the hind neck red. The shoulders and rump light blue, throat black, breast blue with a black band across the lower breast. The abdomen through the under tail-coverts red.

The fifth species was the NOISY PITTA, *P. versicolor,* which is to be found in New Guinea and Australia. Larger than any of the preceding, it is some 8½ inches (22 cm) in length. The back and wings green, crown rust brown with a black stripe, throat, sides of head and nape black edged with buff. Shoulders and rump light blue, breast buff and the abdomen black centred with buffish edges, under tail-coverts red.

All the pittas we had had similar call notes to those described under the Bengal Pitta and the only difference we ever detected between the sexes was that the female's call and scold were slightly softer in tone.

Family Tyrannidae

This is the family of the tyrant-flycatchers, comprising over 500 species and subspecies, and is confined to the New World with 41 in North America, nine of them resident, and the remainder in Central and South America. They are the counterpart of the subfamily Muscicapinae of the Old World, with whom they show a great similarity in their feeding habits. However, they show a wider range of habitat and variety of form than the Old World flycatchers.

We only ever had the following three species of the Tyrannidae family.

The YELLOW-BELLIED ELAENIA, *Elaenia flavogaster*, has a range from Mexico, Central America, Venezuela, and down through the Guianas to Brazil, Ecuador, Peru, Bolivia and Argentina. It is about 7 inches (18 cm) in total length, and is one of the more conspicuously crested of the elaenias, the centre of the crown having a concealed white patch. The upper plumage is olive, the wing-coverts edged with yellowish-white forming a double bar. The throat is whitish, the breast grey, sharply defined from the pale yellow abdomen. Feeding did not present a problem as, not only did it take readily the soft food and ground meat, but chopped fruit also was accepted liberally. Lack of accommodation prevented us from keeping it so we were not able to really study its habits but, during the time it was there, all we ever heard were chittering alarm notes.

The DERBY FLYCATCHER, *Pitangus sulphuratus*, also known as the Kiskadee and the Tyrant Flycatcher, is one of the larger members of the Tyrannidae. It has an extensive range from southern Texas to as far south as the northern parts of Argentina. About 10 inches (25 cm) in total length, it is easily identifiable by its bright yellow underparts, and the chestnut-brown wings and tail. Its bold upright stance, and habit of perching in open spaces are further aids to identifying it in the field.
Its bold upright stance . . .
Sexes are distinguishable in so far as that the colouring of the female is a paler counterpart of that of the adult male whose head is adorned with a broad black band on either side which runs from the base of the bill, through the eye, and round the nape. Above this is a narrower white stripe also extending round the head, the actual crown is in the form of a flat crest of black over yellow, the latter colour only being visible when it is erected. The chin and throat are white, the upper chest through to the under tail-coverts a bright primrose-yellow. Upperparts, including the wings and tail, are bright chestnut. The strong, powerful bill is black, as are the legs and feet. As mentioned earlier, the female resembles the male except that the underparts are pale yellow, and the wings, back and tail a duller shade of

brown. Further, the bill is smaller, as is the overall size. They have a most distinctive call, a loud single 'geep', usually followed by 'career', the whole cry thus becoming 'geep career' most clearly enunciated. It is from this cry that it is reputed the name Kiskadee was derived, but, personally, I could never attune my ear to that interpretation. They are very insectivorous and do well on a good insectile mixture, strips of raw beef, live-food and a little fruit. Their habit of perching near streams in the wild is so that they can locate small fish on which they swoop down. We used to demonstrate this in their aviary, which had a very large pool, by tossing mealworms on the water and they would dart down and seize them before they had a chance of sinking. Despite their temperate and tropical habitats, they are very hardy as we have kept them in an outside aviary the year round, the winter temperature often dropping well below the freezing level. They are very compatible with birds of a similar size, but never have more than one pair of them in an aviary

. . . or there will be trouble.

or there will be trouble. After the wintering out referred to above they decided to build a nest in a pine tree overhanging the pool. It was a large, globular affair, rather untidy so far as the exterior was concerned, of about 8 inches (20 cm) in breadth and height, and 10 inches (25 cm) deep. The outside was constructed of twigs, reeds, and coarse grasses, the interior, however, the entrance to which was low down, was very neat and lined with soft grasses, feathers, wool etc. The female prepared the entire interior whereas the pair of them had built the outer shell, the male doing most of the fetching of materials. Four eggs, pale buff with brown fleckings, denser at the thicker end, were laid, and they measured 23 by 17 mm. Incubation began with the laying of the second egg and lasted for 21 days. By this time they had become very territorial regarding the nesting site and no other bird dared venture near. In fact it was hazardous for any of us to go too near for they would swoop down and drew blood more than once. A rule was made that anyone having to go to that part of the aviary was to wear a peaked hat to protect the eyes, a favourite attack spot of theirs. I did brave them so as to see the chicks, three of them, and found they were covered with white down and had orange-red gapes. However, due to the persistent aggressiveness of the male it was not possible to follow their development in the nest. They fledged 18 days after my first sight of the young and were flying strongly within the hour. At this stage they were replicas of the adult female, even to the tail which was fully formed. As with the incubation, the rearing was shared and appeared to be almost entirely on live-food. They were independent at 12 days after fledging and were sexable at about ten weeks of age. One was a male and it had to be caught up and transferred to another aviary since the adult male would not permit it anywhere near the feeding stands.

The third species we had was the VERMILLION FLY-CATCHER, *Pyrocephalus rubinus*. There are several races located from the south-western United States through Mexico and Central America to the Guianas, Brazil, Ecuador, Uruguay, Paraguay, Chile, northern Argentina and eastern Bolivia. There is little difference in the races, mainly consisting of size variations, $5\frac{1}{2}$ to $5\frac{3}{4}$ inches (14 to 15 cm) in length, and the extent of the red and black markings. The adult male has the crown and underparts of scarlet, the lores, ear-coverts, back, wings and tail dark smoky or blackish-brown. The margins of the inner primaries and wing-coverts, and the outer webs of the outer tail feathers are white. In the female the upperparts are pale smoky brown, the underparts are white with the breast and belly streaked greyish-brown. There are more variations in the females than the males, some having the crown tinged with scarlet, the throat white, upper breast white streaked greyish-brown, and the lower parts pinkish-scarlet. A third variation is one in which the throat, breast and centre of the abdomen are white, the breast finely streaked greyish-brown, the rest of the underparts salmon-pink. The pair we had came from Ecuador but, during their time with us they were confined to a spacious cage and we had no opportunity of studying them in the open. Nevertheless they went through a complete moult with no loss of colour and appeared to be a very straightforward bird to cater for, taking well to the soft food mixture and ground beef, but also requiring an ample supply of live-food.

. . . more variations in the females . . .

Family Pipridae

Manakins are confined to tropical South and Central America and there are some 54 species in this group. Feeding mainly on small fruits and insects, their normal habitat is in forested regions. As caged birds we found they did well on blueberries and diced fruits, but showed no interest in either mealworms or gentles, but occasionally helped themselves to raw ground beef. However, once released into aviaries they were then seen to take small flying insects, mostly snapping at them as they passed by and not taking them on the wing in flycatcher fashion, but most of their time was spent foraging through the foliage for insects. They are small, ranging in size from 3½ to 6 inches (9 to 15 cm), the males usually brightly coloured, the majority of females being varying shades of green.

We only ever had three species, all from Ecuador, but were not fortunate enough to breed them, this being contributed mainly to the fact that we never had more than one female of each. Since most manakins are polygamous in the wild, we tried to obtain extra females so as to introduce the spirit of competition, but we could not get hold of any more.

The BLUE-BACKED MANAKIN, *Chiroxiphia pareola*, adult male is about 5 inches (13 cm) in total length, the centre of the crown scarlet, forehead, sides and back of head greyish-black. The mantle light blue, wings and tail black, and the underparts deep black. The upperparts, wings and tail of the female are green, throat greyish-green, breast olive-green, the remainder of the underparts yellowish-green. Their range is from eastern Colombia through to the Guianas, southward to Bolivia and southeastern Brazil, and on the islands of Tobago and Trinidad.

The YELLOW-HEADED MANAKIN, *Chloropipo flavicapilla,* is larger than the Blue-backed, and is from the subtropical zone of the Western and Central Andes and the southern end of the Eastern Andes on their western slope in Colombia. It was with this species that we were able to witness the interesting dance routine. The two males would be side by side on a branch and, after one or two little piping notes would begin to bob up and down. Then one would jump right up off the perch in a sideways direction toward the other bird which would slide along and take up the position originally occupied by the other, the 'acrobat' landing where that one had been. They would go through the same movements alternately, continuing this sideways leapfrogging for ten minutes or so at a time, accompanied by loud clicking and snapping of their wings. As I mentioned earlier, we only ever had but one female and no matter how long or frequently the males displayed, she was never attracted to them. The male has a crown and nape of bright golden yellow, the feathers forming a flat, broad crest. The upperparts, wings and tail golden olive, throat and breast olive, remainder of the underparts pale yellow. The upperparts of the female olive-green, throat and breast olive, rest of the underparts dull yellow.

The final species, the WHITE-BEARDED MANAKIN, *Manacus manacus,* is about 5 inches (13 cm) in total length, and

. . . this sideways leapfrogging . . .

again the sexes differ. They have a much more extensive range than the preceding species being found from Colombia through to the Guianas and Trinidad and southward into Peru, Brazil, Paraguay and Argentina. The crown, nape, mantle, wings and tail of the male black, remainder of the back grey. Sides of head, collar and hindneck, throat, breast and lesser wing-coverts white, the feathers of the throat lengthened. The upperparts of the female bright olive-green, underparts pale olive-green, paler on the abdomen and greyish on the throat. This species has a peculiar wing feather structure that causes a loud whining sound to be emitted as they fly. On the daily check of birds it was this sound that invariably confirmed their presence in the aviary for they had a habit of keeping to the denser parts and were most elusive.

*. . . keeping
to the
denser parts . . .*

Family Cotingidae

The Cotingidae family of birds is confined to the New World and, although they are to be found mostly in the Amazonian region, they live as far northward as the borders of the United States and southward to northern Argentina. There are some 90 species in all, embracing such birds as Cocks-of-the-Rock, Bell Birds, Umbrella Birds, Fruit Crows, etc, their size varying from 3½ to 18 inches (9 to 48 cm). Some of the species are known as Chatterers and are recognised under the common name of Cotinga.

They are arboreal, taking fruit and insects as their main diet and require careful acclimatization to be kept alive in captivity. In addition to our normal fruit, soft food, ground meat, fish and mice, an ample supply of live-food in the form of mealworms, crickets and moths was provided to suit the needs of the particular species.

The ORANGE-BREASTED COTINGA, *Pipreola jucunda*, is about 8 inches (20 cm) in total length, comes from western Ecuador, and the sexes are dissimilar. The adult male's head, including the throat, is shiny black, upper breast orange margined in black, lower breast through to the abdomen yellow. The back, wings, tail and sides of breast grass-green, with the flanks mixed grass-green and yellow. The bill orange, legs and feet greyish-green. The female is much like the male except that the breast is streaked with green. Mr. Boehm brought two pairs back from Ecuador and we were forced to keep them in cages for some four months due both to inclement weather and lack of aviary accommodation. They were quite a problem to feed under such conditions and only one pair survived. This pair eventually was released into a planted aviary and made several attempts to raise a family but none lived longer than sixteen days. Their nest was an open cup of twigs and grasses, a very clumsy and flimsy affair, and they positioned it in the upper branches of a tree, about 8 feet (2.5 or 2½ metres) up. No more than two eggs were ever laid in the three rounds they had, and the incubation time was estimated at 18-19 days. As far as we could tell the female only sat on the eggs, the male taking up tid-bits to her throughout the day. Although live-food was supplied several times daily in the aviary that they shared with Fairy Blue Wrens, Hoopoes and Roulroul Partridge, it was not until they were with eggs that they took any of it. We tried everything that had been used in the diet of the Black-throated Cotinga when rearing their young, and even added soaked currants, sultanas and elderberries, but all to no avail. They did take mealworms and crickets both for themselves and to feed to the young. The eldest chick we ever had was well feathered with green in the wings and back, black head, yellow underparts and rump, and a red gape, all at sixteen days of age.

. . . the male taking up tidbits . . .

The BLACK-THROATED COTINGA, *Pipreola riefferii*, also known as the Green-and-black Fruiteater, is the same size as the former species and again the sexes are distinguishable. They have a wider range, however, through Venezuela, Ecuador, Colombia and down to Bolivia. These also Mr. Boehm brought back from South America. The adult male has a black head and throat with a yellow collar extending from the base of the neck round to the upper throat, where it blends in with the yellowish-green underparts. The upper plumage is dark green from the back of the head through to the tail, including the wings, the upper coverts white tipped. The tail green tipped with yellow, the undersides dark grey, almost black. The upper surface of the flight feathers is green edged with yellow, the undersides dark grey. Bill, legs and feet bright red, the claws black. The female is green throughout, with slight yellow fleckings, and the upper wing-coverts are white edged. The eye is brown, as is the male's, but has a fine yellow eye-ring. The legs and feet are similar to the male's, even to the black claws, but the red is a lighter shade. The bill is red but has a black tip, a feature lacking in the male.

We had one male and two females in the same aviary and, in April, 1962, one of the females began nest building in a hemlock. An open-cup nest made within a basket originally positioned there as an encouragement for any of the seven different species occupying the aviary. The materials employed were dried grasses, rootlets and horsehair, the latter being woven into the other materials to bind it all together. The first egg was laid on the 17th, with a second the following day, incubation by the female commencing with the first egg. The eggs were pale brown, spotted with sepia, heaviest at the bolder end, and measured 25 by 18 mm. Incubation was by the female entirely and it was noticed that whenever the other female approached the nesting site, the male drove her away. To avoid trouble, she was transferred to another location.

The male fed his mate on the nest and, when she vacated it for a bath, they are ardent bathers, or for any other reason, he stood on the edge of the nest, made no attempt to cover them, just standing on guard. Unfortunately both eggs were clear and it was not until June 12 that another was laid. This time there was a three day interval before the second egg was produced. One chick hatched on June 30, the second on July 2, but this one died three days later. Both parents fed the nestling, the initial diet consisting entirely of live-food in the form of mealworm pupae, moths, flies and other insects. At ten days old, fruit and ground raw beef were included in their feeding and the male even caught small minnows out of the pool and fed them both to the female and the young bird. They did not kill the fish in the manner normal with kingfishers, but just swallowed it whole, head first. Having very little reference literature on this species of bird it was enlightening to learn that they are live-fish eaters. Owing to the location of the nest it was not possible to follow closely the progress of the nestling but, at fourteen days old, it was found dead on the ground immediately below the nest. It appeared to be well fed, had a fair amount of green and yellow feathering, and its eyes were open. No definite cause for the young bird to have fallen out could be decided upon since the nest was quite deep. It was felt that the female may have accidentally pulled it out when disturbed by some other bird. To obviate any recurrence, a portion of the aviary was divided off for the sole use of the Cotingas. On July 24 another egg was laid with a second on the 26th. Even this effort was fruitless for one egg was clear, and the chick from the other died two days after hatching. Again the female got busy with another nest but this time she got entangled in a strand of horsehair and strangled herself.

When attempting to breed softbills one gets accustomed to

. . . ardent bathers . . .

setbacks and we felt we certainly were having our share now. However, never daunted and ever hopeful, we introduced the other female to the widowed male. Close observation of his reactions was maintained and, although he was inclined to chase her around for the first few days, by the fifth day they had settled down together. It was on September 20th that this female was seen taking nesting material up into a shallow, open box fixed on a beam just inside the entrance to the aviary. Although horsehair was still distributed, it was cut into lengths not exceeding four inches (10 cm). The first egg was laid on the 29th., with a second the following day. It was noted that the basic colour of the second egg was much lighter than the first, in fact paler than any of the previous eggs. As on prior occasions, the entire incubation was carried out by the female, the male feeding her on the nest as he had done with his first mate. In addition to this bedroom service, she would accept fruit, ground meat and mealworms from any of us when offered to her on the nest, but nothing from our fingers when she was off. Passage of time revealed that the first egg was clear, the second hatching on October 19. The female had become so used to us approaching her nest that it was fairly easy to keep a close watch over the nestling. The bright pink little body was sparsely covered with black down, and the gape was bright orange. At six days quill feathers were beginning to show and, by the 28th, its eyes were open, and green and yellow feathering could be discerned. The bill was black, wide and squat as compared to the fine, red bills of the parents. At twelve days, yellow tips were visible in the primaries and tail, and the white edges to the wing-coverts were most distinct. At this age it was left to itself for periods of up to an hour at a time, so, to avoid any chance of it clambering out of the nest, a 4 inch (10 cm) strip of cardboard was stapled to the outside of the box containing the nest. Fledging on November 9, 21 days old, it was a strong flyer from the outset and soon was perching with its parents in the top of a 16 feet (5 metres) tree. The entire feeding had been shared by the parents, live-food and live-fish again being one of the regular ingredients. Once it had left the nest the male took over any feeding necessary. By the second day the fledgling's bill had lost its flat appearance and, although still black, had taken on the slender shape of the adults. The basic feather colour was dark green with yellowish underparts, orange-red legs and feet with black claws. By 25th November the tail feathers were fully down and it was feeding itself three days later, that is, at forty days old. The bill com-

. . . was perching with its parents . . .

menced to change colour from the base outwards at 48 days and black feathers were showing at the throat indicating that it was a male. It obtained full adult plumage at about five months of age by which time it had been separated from its parents since the adult male was showing marked aversion to it.

It was most frustrating that, after all we thought we had learned from this breeding, we still had not been able to raise the Orange-breasted Cotingas.

The NAKED-THROATED BELL BIRD, *Procnias nudicollis*, of south-eastern Brazil, is a large bird, about twelve inches (30 cm) in total length, the adult pure white with a bare verdrigris colour throat and face. It is not just bare skin for it is covered with scattered bristles. We had two of them at different times, one fully adult, the other a young bird which was brown with white fleckings. By the end of the year, however, it was pure white. How long this colour change takes we did not know for we did not know the age of the bird on receipt. Their resonant bell-like call can be heard for miles and becomes quite shattering in an enclosed area. The most 'bells' we ever had one make in succession was seventy-two, the normal being about forty. Having but one at a time we learned nothing of their nesting habits but did find that they are very partial to new born mice, of which they got one every other day once we had noted their liking for them. They also took a large quantity of fruit, fair portion of ground meat and soft-food, and as many mealworms and crickets as they could get hold of.

. . . resonant bell-like call . . .

Cocks-of-the-Rock form a small group of birds found only in South America. Due to their remarkable appearance and habits they were classified in a separate subfamily, Rupicolinae, but are now recognised as members of the Cotingidae. Over the years we had pairs of the *Rupicola rupicola,* Orange, and the *R. peruviana,* the Scarlet. These were sent to us by South American dealers but, during his bird-watching trip to Ecuador and neighboring countries, Mr. Boehm did acquire a male of the rarer *R.p. sanquinolenta,* also referred to as Scarlet. Unfortunately he had to entrust it to someone else to ship back to the States and, on arrival, it was a very, very sick bird and died two days later.

In addition to fruit, soft food and ground meat we found they are great insect eaters, preferring crickets to mealworms, and are also very partial to a mouse. One aviary was specially fitted up with a rock cave in the hope of providing them with a nesting site but it was never taken to. However, none of the males ever lost their colour and we had them for well over six years.

The adult male Orange, *R. rupicola,* is almost completely orange, its head with its large, front-to-back circular crest from the tip of the bill to the back of the head, being typical of the genus. The crest is bordered dark brown. Wings brownish-black, bordered broadly with white, the outer edges and broad tips of the secondaries pale orange. The outer secondaries have the outer webs prolonged into long filaments. The short tail is dark brown, edged and tipped pale orange, bill, legs and feet yellow. The female is mainly dark brown all over, the rump, tail, abdomen and under wing-coverts washed orange-brown. The crest is much reduced in size, the bill almost wholly uncovered. This species varies from 12 to 14 inches (30 to 36 cm) in length, the males generally slightly larger than the females.

The Scarlet, *R. peruviana,* ranges up to 15 inches (38 cm) in total length, and the adult male is scarlet where the previous species is orange. The same shaped crest, but slightly smaller. The wings make a striking contrast to the scarlet body for the very broad, innermost secondaries are silver grey, the rest of the feathers black, as is the tail. The female is dark maroon-red with greyish olive-brown wings and a dull maroon-brown tail.

. . . bobbed, danced and called to each other . . .

We housed the pairs in adjoining aviaries and it was interesting to note how the males bobbed, danced, and called to each other through the dividing netting. They have a raucous call note and keep it up for quite long periods at a time as they appear to challenge each other. It had been hoped that their proximity might stir up some breeding instincts, but no. Actually the males and their respective females were seldom close together, each seeming to prefer its own end of their particular aviary, but we never experienced any fighting between them the entire time we had them.

THE SUBORDER OSCINES

This suborder embraces the 41 different families listed below and it is often referred to as the song-bird suborder for it most certainly includes the best musicians in the feathered world. Further, it is the only passerine suborder represented in the Palaeartic Region. Only those families actually kept at the Boehm aviaries over the years are covered in this work, these families being marked with an asterisk.

Alaudidae	Lark	Hirundinidae	Swallow

*Motacillidae	Wagtail	*Campephagidae	Cuckoo-shrike
*Pycnonotidae	Bulbul	*Irenidae	Leafbird
*Laniidae	Shrike	Vangidae	Vanga
*Bombycillidae	Waxwing	Dulidae	Palmchat
Cinclidae	Dipper	Troglodytidae	Wren
*Mimidae	Mockingbird	Prunellidae	Accentor
*Muscicapidae	Thrush, Babbler, Parrotbill, Warbler, Wren, Flycatcher, Thickhead		
*Paridae	Tit	*Sittidae	Nuthatch
Certhiidae	Treecreeper	Climacteridae	Treecreeper
*Dicaeidae	Flower-pecker	*Nectariniidae	Sunbird
*Zosteropidae	White-eye	*Meliphagidae	Honeyeater
*Emberizidae	Bunting, Cardinal, Grosbeak, Tanager, Swallow-tanager, Honeyeater		
Parulidae	Warbler	Drepanididae	Honeycreeper
Vireonidae	Vireo	*Icteridae	Oriole
*Ploceidae	Weaver, Sparrow	*Sturnidae	Starling
*Oriolidae	Oriole	Dicruridae	Drongo
Callaeidae	Wattlebird	Grallinidae	Magpie-lark
		*Artamidae	Wood-swallow
Cracticidae	Magpie	*Ptilinorhynchidae	Bowerbird
*Paradisaeidae	Bird-of-Paradise	*Corvidae	Crow

Family Motacillidae

. . . often
with
undulations.

This family is world-wide in distribution but does not breed in New Guinea or Oceania. A characteristic is their strong feet and relatively long toes. In some species the hind claw is elongated and spur-like. They are mainly terrestrial in habits, walking or running on the ground, many not as a rule alighting on trees or bushes. Their flight, however, is strong, often with undulations. Mainly insectivorous, they also take spiders, small molluscs and even small seeds and other plant material.

The ROSY-BREASTED LONGCLAW, *Macronyx ameliae,* is an East African species, ranging from Kenya down to Rhodesia. They are about 8 inches (20 cm) in length, and the sexes differ. The adult male is black above with tawny edges to the feathers; below, rich salmon; a broad black collar across the chest and curving upwards to the base of the mandible. Hind claw curved and very long. The female is buffish-brown below, with the salmon colour much paler and confined to the abdomen and a few spots on the throat. The chest band is replaced with black streaks.

The WHITE WAGTAIL, *Motacilla alba,* is an European species of about 7 inches (18 cm) in length. We had specimens of both the British subspecies, *M. a. yarrelli,* and the continental subspecies, *M. a. alba.* They have a summer and winter dress, the summer plumage of the male British subspecies having a black back, crown, throat and breast; blackish wings with a double white bar; black tail with white outer feathers; white forehead, sides of head and abdomen. The female is greyer above, with less black on the head and breast. In winter both sexes have black on the crown; white throat with crescent-shaped black bib and grey back. The continental subspecies, often referred to as the Pied Wagtail, is similar but, in the breeding season, has a light grey back and rump.

The YELLOW WAGTAIL, *M. flava,* another European species with subspecies extending into Asia. There are several subspecies and those we had were the Yellow, *M. f. flavissima,* from England and the Blue-headed Yellow, *M. f. flava,* of Central Europe. They are about 6½ inches (16.5 cm) in length and the sexes are very much alike, the female being slightly duller. They also have summer and winter dress. The Yellow adult male in summer dress has a bright yellow eye-stripe, throat and underparts; cheeks and upperparts yellowish-green. The female in summer dress, and both sexes in the winter, is duller and browner above and paler below. The Blue-headed adult male has a bluish crown; hind-neck and cheeks bluish-grey; white stripe over the eye, remainder of plumage as with the Yellow. The adult female is much duller and has a white chin. Again there is a winter plumage when the male resembles the female except for the white chin.

We found wagtails to be perfectly sociable with all other birds but inclined to be quarrelsome amongst themselves, demanding their own territory and driving off all other wagtails irrespective of the season. It was our experience that, until ready to breed, it was better not even to keep a true pair together. If housed in cages they should be provided with peat moss, dampened daily, or fresh sods of grass as the floor covering together with little logs to perch on. Most of the regular cage-perching is unsuitable for the long feet of the birds of this family. They do very well in cages on a ration of meal-worms, ground raw beef and soft-food mixture. In aviaries they take the same, supplemented by whatever they can forage for themselves.

Family Campephagidae

This family has a palaeotropical distribution and is made up of two distinct groups, the rather drab cuckoo-shrikes proper and the lively and colourful minivets. They are all arboreal, but not forest dwellers, and their main food is insects, supplemented by berries and soft fruits.

The BLACK CUCKOO-SHRIKE, *Campephaga sulphurata,* is an African species, mainly below the Equator but also found in Ethiopia and the Sudan. They are about 8½ inches (21.5 cm) in total length and the sexes differ. The general colour of the adult male is glossy black. Wings and tail black edged with glossy blue-black, shoulders either glossy blue-black or bright yellow. The under wing-coverts blue-black or blue-black and yellow, the inner webs of the flight feathers washed with yellow. The female is brown or yellow-brown above, barred with black on the rump and upper tail-coverts, and more distinctly barred on the lower mantel. The wings brown with bright yellow edges to all feathers, tail brown and blackish, outer feathers tipped with bright yellow. The underside is white with a yellowish wash and black bars and crescent-shaped markings. They were not very interesting aviary birds for, although always on the move searching for insects, they kept themselves very well concealed in the bushes.

. . . not very interesting . . .

The WHITE-WINGED TRILLER, *Lalage tricolor,* is an Australasian species about 6½ inches (16 cm) in total length. The sexes differ, the crown, hind-neck and upper back of the adult male black, shoulders and a line on the wing white, rest of wing black. The lower back grey, tail black with the outer feathers tipped white. The underparts, including the throat, white. The female is brown on the upperparts with lighter lines on the wings, the underparts dusky white. They are very insectivorous and the male is a fine songster with a canary-like song. Mainly keeping to themselves, they were very good aviary inmates.

The SHORT-BILLED MINIVET, *Pericrocotus brevirostris,* from the Himalayan foothills through to Eastern China, normally found above the 3,000 feet level (900 metres) is 7 inches (18 cm) in total length and the sexes are unalike. The upper plumage of the adult male is black, chin and throat glossy black. The wings are black with a broad band of scarlet running through them. The central tail feathers black, the next pair black with the outer webs scarlet, and the remainder all scarlet with a black patch at the base. The rest of the body plumage scarlet. The female's upper plumage is light grey tinged with olive, forehead greenish-olive, rump and upper tail-coverts olive-yellow. The wings are blackish brown with a broad band of yellow running through them. The central tail feathers black, next pair yellow with black on the inner webs, the remainder all yellow with a black patch at the base. They are purely arboreal but we found them difficult to keep even in planted aviaries. They appeared to be mainly insectivorous, taking but little of the other food.

The SCARLET MINIVET, *P. flammeus,* is to be found practically in the same regions as the preceding species but is a larger bird, some 9 inches (23 cm) in total length. There are several subspecies, the ones we had being *P. f. elegans* from Assam. The upper plumage to the middle back, chin and throat of the adult male are glossy black, remainder of the body plumage scarlet. The wings black with a broad band of scarlet and large round scarlet spots on the secondaries. The tail is scarlet with the central feathers black. The female's upper plumage is deep grey; the forehead yellow, fading on the crown; rump and upper tail-coverts olive-yellow. The wings blackish-brown with a broad band of yellow and round yellow spots on the secondaries. Central pair of tail feathers black, next pair black with the end of the outer web yellow, remaining feathers yellow with a black patch at the base. The lower plumage yellow. Similar in habits to the Short-billed and difficult to keep as cage or aviary birds.

The SMALL or LITTLE MINIVET, *P. peregrinus*, is found throughout the Indian peninsula, including Ceylon, extending on the east to Burma, Thailand and the neighbouring countries. It is about 6 inches (15 cm) in total length, the adult male having upper plumage grey except for the rump which is flame-coloured. The wings blackish-brown with a central patch of flame-colour, tail blackish-brown, long and graduated, all but the central pair of feathers tipped flame-colour. The sides of the head, chin and throat blackish-grey, breast flame-colour gradually paling to white at the vent. The female is paler throughout, the lower plumage white tinged with yellow. We only had one pair which, due to lack of accommodation were passed on to a zoo. During the period they were with us it became apparent that cage life was not to their benefit.

. . . passed on to a zoo.

Family Pycnonotidae

This is the family of bulbuls and greenbuls, an Old World and largely tropical group of birds of some 50 species of varying moderate sizes. In all bulbuls the males and females are alike in colouring, and usually also in size. They are forest birds and have a feeble flight for their wings are short and concave. Their tails normally are long, square, rounded or slightly graduated. Fruit and berries form their basic diet in the wild but many of them are insectivorous, collecting insects from the trees and shrubs, not catching them on the wing. Gregarious at normal times, when the breeding season comes round each pair will select its own territory and this area is then taboo to all comers until such time as the family has been reared and left the nest. Even then they follow the young ones around making passes at any other birds that might come near to them.

The JOYFUL GREENBUL, *Chlorocichla lattissima*, an African species from a comparatively restricted area from northern Congo, through the Sudan to Kenya, is about 10 inches (25 cm) in length. The upper plumage is golden-green the head feathers dark centred giving a scaly effect; underparts golden-yellow, more intense at the throat, forming a distinct patch. The only differences we could detect in the sexes was that the throat patch was less extensive and the underparts were not as bright with the female. They have a most melodious, soft song, more varied with the male, but also possess a harsh, staccato alarm note which they are subject to give vent to at the slightest provocation.

We had a pair housed with Spreo and Royal Starlings and Variegated Tits in a densely planted aviary and it was not until there was a nestling that we had any idea they had even gone to nest. It was noticed late one July that they began to get very excited whenever anyone entered the aviary, flying up and down and chattering incessantly, but they never came down for any form of live-food be it mealworms, gentles, moths or crickets. About two weeks later, from an adjoining aviary one of them was observed carrying a moth into one of the dense bushes and coming out empty billed. Then, during a temporary lull in the general bird noises, a faint cheeping was heard. On examining the bush under a veritable bombardment of protest cries by the greenbuls, an open-cup nest containing a nestling was discovered. It was obvious at a glance that it was a young greenbul, for its colouring so closely resembled that of the adults. It was almost fully feathered, with a gape of bright orange margined in pale yellow. We hazarded a guess that it was just over a week old. When it vacated the nest six days later the upper plumage was green with a brownish wash, the underparts pale yellow washed with green. Both parents fed the fledgling varying the diet between live-food and fruit. Full independence was attained two weeks later and, at six months of age, it was identical to the parent birds, favouring the male with its soft call note and colouring. The following year the nest was built in a more accessible spot, but, although one egg was laid on three separate occasions, well spaced apart, they were all clear. The nest was built entirely by the female and was an untidy, open-cup-shaped affair, mainly constructed of Spanish moss, rootlets and fine grasses, and was about 9 inches (23 cm) across the top, with a central depression of some $2\frac{1}{2}$ inches (6 cm). The eggs were of greyish colour, with dark brown speckles and hair-lines and averaged 20 by 15 mm. Although the data gathered from this breeding is not fully complete, since we only saw the chick from about 8 days old, it does appear likely that they do lay but one egg. This was a first breeding ever in captivity at that time and any information, no matter how little, was important.

. . . this was a first breeding . . .

The BROWN-EARED BULBUL, *Hypsipetes flavala,* from the Himalayan foothills through to Burma, is about 8 inches (20 cm) in length. Ashy-grey above with yellowish-green edges to the wings and tail; head, including crest, ashy-grey; cheeks and lores black; ear-coverts greyish-brown; chin, throat and middle of abdomen white; remaining underparts pale grey. A very musical bird with a variety of calls often associable to common phrases.

The RED-VENTED BULBUL, *Pycnonotus cafer*, is to be found throughout Ceylon, India, Pakistan, Burma, Thailand and the adjoining countries. It is one of the least musical of the family but, nevertheless makes a good aviary or cage bird. There are two species that are accorded the common name of Red-vented, the difference being in the colour of the ear-coverts, throat, breast and under tail-coverts. The *P. cafer* has blackish ear-coverts, throat and breast, and scarlet under tail coverts and their range is limited to Ceylon, India, Pakistan and eastern Burma. The other species, *P. aurigaster*, is from western Burma, Thailand, Cambodia and Laos and has whitish ear-coverts, throat and breast, and the under tail-coverts vary from vermillion, through orange to yellow. The species we had, *P. cafer*, is about 8½ inches (21.5 cm) in length and their main colouring is black and brown, relieved by the red on the vent and the white tips to the tail feathers. The largish erect crest is black, and the bill, legs and feet dark coloured. The only differences we could detect in the sexes was that the crest of the female was slightly smaller and the head was flatter. It is only when a number are together that even these can be seen but they cannot be taken as a definite sex indicator since, up to six months of age, young birds are identical to the adult female.

We had three of them in a very large aviary with about 20 other different species and it was noticed that two of them were busily engaged building a nest in the uppermost branches of a Canadian hemlock. It was about 10 feet (3 metres) up and totally inaccessible for the tree was not sturdy enough to be climbed or even to bear a ladder against it. However, whilst some repairs were being made to the top wiring of the aviary it was seen that there were three pinkish-white eggs, heavily blotched with reddish-brown, in the nest. This was fairly deep, suspended in the branches, and appeared to be made of woven grasses, lined with feathers. By careful observation it was learned that the incubation was shared. All further watching was made from ground level which restricted the data obtainable regarding the development of the chicks. The first sight was of three red-lined gapes as the nestlings reared themselves up for the parents to feed them. Live-food only was used for about the first week, after which blueberries and ground raw beef was

. . . least musical . . .

141

taken. All three vacated the nest on the same day and, when caught for ringing, it was seen that they had the dark feathering and crest of their parents but lacked any red colouring underneath. Ten weeks later the feathers of the vent began to change colour and two days after that it was only the colour of the leg-bands that distinguished them from the adult female. It was not until a year had elapsed that any appreciable differences in the heads could be detected but, by then, it did appear that we had four males and two females from two broods.

The RED-WHISKERED BULBUL, *Pycnonotus jocosus,* has a wide distribution from India to China and there are several races. About 8 inches (20 cm) in length, there is a conspicuous white patch on the sides of the face above which is a small crimson tuft springing from below the lower eyelid; upstanding crest, top of head down to nape and around and below the white face patch, black, merging into a broad blackish-brown gorget, broken in the centre by the white of the throat and breast; reminder of upperparts brown, darker on the wings and tail, the latter tipped with white except for the central pair of feathers; underparts white washed with brown at the flanks; under tail-coverts crimson red. This species is very similar in habits to the Red-vented Bulbul but does have a more melodious song.

. . . the Himalayan foothills . . .

The WHITE-CHEEKED BULBUL, *Pycnonotus leucogenys,* is an Asiatic species to be found from Iran to eastern Pakistan and India. There are three races in India, the nominate race being confined to the Himalayan foothills where it can be found up to elevations of 9,000 feet (2800 metres). The species we had, *P. l. leucotis,* ranges through the Punjabi Plains, the Sind and Central India. About 8 inches (20 cm) in length, they have a short, forward curving crest of black, narrowly edged with white; chin, throat, parts of the sides of the neck and a patch around the eye extending to the bill, black; a conspicuous white patch on the ear-coverts; whole body and wings olive-brown, darker above and paler below, becoming whitish at the vent; tail, brown at the base getting darker towards the end, all feathers except the central pair broadly tipped white; under tail-coverts saffron. They have a most melodious song. There was a pair of them in the same aviary as the Red-vented Bulbuls and they built an open-cup nest of stout grasses and twiglets in the centre of an azalea bush. The nest was lined with fine grasses, wool and dogs' hair, and two eggs were laid. Measuring 22 by 16 mm., they had a ground colour of pinkish-white, thickly speckled and blotched with purplish-red. The sexes being alike, it was only by virtue of the fact that they wore different coloured leg-bands that we could tell the incubating, lasting 14 to 15 days, was shared. The rearing also was shared, the female doing most of the feeding to the nestlings, the male collecting food for the entire family. The decision as to which was the male and which was the female was based on the bird that did the nest building, the other gathering materials. Prior to vacating the nest, nothing but live-food was fed to the young birds but, when they fledged at 14 days old, the parents then began to add ground raw beef and fruit to their diet. The white cheek patches and the yellow under tail-coverts were plain on the young birds and there was also signs of the short crest. Independent at five weeks old, their crests were not fully formed and their tails were all brown. Full adult colouring was attained at about ten months of age.

Independent at five weeks . . .

The RED-EYED BULBUL, *Pycnonotus nigricans,* is to be found in the dry, inland areas of Africa, more or less following the track of the Kalahari Desert from eastern South Africa, through south-west Africa, and up into Angola. Although the sexes are alike in colouring, the female generally is smaller, and her song less varied than that of the male. Eight inches (20 cm) in length, the upper plumage, from the nape through to the tail, is dark greenish-brown, as is the upper chest; head, face and throat dark brown, this colour blending in with that of the upper chest with no clear line in between; abdomen greyish-white flecked with brown; lower belly and under tail-coverts yellow. Their distinctive feature is a red wattle round the eye, the iris of which is orange to reddish-brown; bill, legs and feet black.

A pair of them selected a rhododendron bush as a nesting site and built an open-cup nest, rather untidy in general construction, and two eggs were laid. These were pinkish-white, heavily flecked and spotted with reddish-brown, and measured 21 by 15 mm. It cannot be said whether the incubation was shared or not for both birds were always in the vicinity of the nest, leaving there as soon as anyone approached the aviary. Incubation time was calculated at about 12 days and it appears to have started with the laying of the first egg for, one morning, on inspecting the nest, two nestlings were discovered. One of them obviously had just hatched as it was still damp and there were pieces of eggshell in the nest, whilst the other was completely dried out and looked larger. They were devoid of all body fluff and had bright pink gapes margined in yellow. The rearing was shared, live-food in the form of moths, insects and mealworms being the diet for the first few days but, as soon as their eyes were open on the fifth day, fruit was added to this by the parents. At ten days old their upperparts were fully feathered in dark greenish-brown. Vacating the nest at 12 days, they resembled their parents in general colour, even to the dark face, head and throat. The underparts, however, were clear of all fleckings, being yellowish-white, under tail-coverts pale yellow. The eye was dark and there was no sign of the surrounding wattle. Independent at four weeks old, it was a further six weeks before a yellowish wattle made its first appearance. At 13 weeks it had taken on a pinkish tinge but full adult colouring was not attained until they were some 8 months old. From their song and general appearance it was concluded that they were one of each sex.

. . . easy to cater for . . .

All the bulbuls we ever had were excellent aviary birds, easy to cater for, sociable and, with the exception of the Red-vented, most pleasant songsters.

Family Irenidae

This is a small Oriental group of three very distinct genera, *Aegithina* the ioras, *Chloropsis,* leafbirds or fruitsuckers, and *Irena,* the fairy bluebirds. They are purely arboreal and the majority feed on nectar from flowers, fruit and berries supplemented with live-food. It was only specimens of the last two genera that we had in the aviaries.

The GOLDEN-FRONTED FRUITSUCKER, *Chloropsis aurifrons,* is about 7½ inches (19 cm) in length and is to be found in the Himalayan foothills through to Malaysia and the neighbouring countries. The adult male is bright shining green with a blue patch in the fold of the wings; forehead and front of head orange-yellow; chin, throat and cheeks deep blue encircled with black, this black extending to the lores, sides of neck and base of throat, the whole surrounded from the eye with yellow. The female is similar but not as bright and it is difficult to sex a single bird.

The ORANGE-BELLIED FRUITSUCKER, *C. hardwickii,* is smaller than the previous species but is to be found in the same areas. The male is grass green above; yellowish on forehead and above the eye; shoulders light blue; rest of wing green with dark blue edges; tail blackish-brown washed with blue. Moustachial streak blue; chin, throat, lower part of face and upper breast black; rest of underparts orange-yellow. The female resembles the male but the chin, throat, face and tail are green, and the blue is a lighter shade.

JERDON'S FRUITSUCKER, *C. jerdoni,* about 7 inches (18 cm) in length, is a resident species in the Indian peninsula from the Himalayan foothills through to Ceylon. The male's general colouring is bright green. A black mask extends from the base of the bill to the eye and on to the lower throat, broken by a broad moustachial streak of bright purplish-blue. The forehead and a broad band behind the face-mask greenish-yellow; a patch of bright blue at the bend of the wing. The female is similar except that the black mask is replaced by pale bluish-green and the moustachial streak is bright greenish-blue.

We found all the fruitsuckers peaceful birds, quickly becoming hand tame. Not having had any go to nest, or even attempting to, no comments can be offered as to their nature at breeding time.

The FAIRY BLUEBIRD, *Irena puella,* is to be found in the northeastern parts of India and Burma, extending as far south as Ceylon and eastwards to Malaysia and Java. The species we had, *I. p. puella,* is from Thailand and is just over 10 inches (25 cm) in length, the adult male from the crown to tail-coverts,

*Thailand
Fairy
Bluebird
nestlings*

scapulars and under tail-coverts is a brilliant, shining pale ultramarine with a pinkish sheen. Remainder of plumage velvety black; bill, legs and feet black; iris a brilliant red. The female is basically dull peacock-blue with brownish wings and tail. The two central tail feathers have a tinge of ultramarine as do the tips of the two pairs of feathers on either side. The greenish-blue feathers of the back have dark shafts, giving an impression of streaked feathers. Bill, legs and feet black; iris orange to reddish-brown.

A pair were housed in a planted aviary for over a year before the female began building an open, cup-shaped nest of coarse grasses, twiglets and dogs' hair in a hemlock. The nest was very thrush-like in its general structure except that no mud was used, it just being kept together by the grasses and the twigs. All the construction was carried out by the female and we did not witness the male even fetching materials. The clutch consisted of three eggs laid on consecutive days and they were greenish-white, heavily blotched, spotted and mottled in reddish-brown and grey. They averaged 28 by 21 mm in size. Incubation was by the female only and began with the laying of the first egg. At thirteen days the first hatched, the other two hatching on the following two days. The nestlings were pink skinned, thickly covered with dark brown fluff, had pink gapes externally margined white, internally margined black. Both parents fed the young, live-food only being employed for the first four days and their progress was rapid. One was thrown out of the nest at two days but the other two had their eyes open and quill feathers showing at five days. By nine days the nestlings' backs were completely feathered, the wings blackish-brown, the remainder of the upperparts bluish. Their heads were the last to be feathered and, when they vacated the nest at thirteen days old their heads were just a mass of pen feathers. They were comparatively strong on the wing for such young birds and soon selected perching sites from which they kept up an incessant cry for food. Now the male did most of the feeding, fruit, ground beef and live-food being used and, if their growth in the nest had appeared to be swift, once they were out it was even more so. At four weeks of age they were completely feathered up, similar in colour to the adult female, and were about 9 inches (23 cm) in length. However, it was another two weeks before it could be said that they were fully independent. I do feel that they could have looked after themselves prior to this but, so long as the male offered them food, they took it. The parent birds had two more rounds that year, rearing two from each to maturity. It was at about six months of age that the young males began to show the ultramarine colouring, mature plumage being attained at one year.

. . . the male did most of the feeding . . .

We found them to be very good with any other birds, comparatively easy to cater for since they took fruit, meat and live-food with no problems at all, in fact, one of the easiest birds we ever had to acclimatize. Next to the Black-headed Sugarbirds they were one of the most prolific breeding species, rearing four, five or six young regularly every year.

Family Laniidae

This widespread but mainly Old World family is comprised of four subfamilies; Laniinae, true shrikes, Malaconotinae, bush-shrikes, Prionopinae, helmet-shrikes, and Pityriasinae, the Bornean Bristlehead. They are all characterised by a strong, hooked bill, often with a distinct 'tooth' on the upper mandible and a corresponding notch in the lower. They have strong legs and feet, the claws being particularly sharp, and they all have well developed rictal bristles. They are bold, aggressive and essentially carnivorous, some catching only insects, others small reptiles, birds and rodents. Their usual haunts are at the edges of woods and forests where they can perch and swoop on prey as it passes.

Subfamily Laniinae

This subfamily is widely distributed in Europe, continental Africa and Asia as far as New Guinea, and also has a small representation (two species) in North America.

The FISCAL SHRIKE, *Lanius collaris,* is an East African resident species ranging from Ethiopia down to Rhodesia. About 9 inches (23 cm) in total length, the sexes differ slightly. The upperside and sides of face of the adult male slightly glossy black; rump and upper tail-coverts grey; scapulars, basal part of primaries and underside white; axillaries black and white; tail black, except central pair of feathers which have white ends and the outermost feathers which are mainly white. The female has chestnut flanks and is more brownish-black above.

The RED-BACKED SHRIKE, *L. collurio,* is an European and Asiatic species, migrating to Africa, Arabia and India during the non-breeding season. About 7 inches (18 cm) in length, the sexes differ. The adult male has a narrow band of black on forehead, this colour also on the lores to the ear-coverts. Head, neck, rump and upper tail-coverts grey; mantle, scapulars, edges of wing-coverts and inner secondaries, chestnut; base of primaries white. Tail white, with broad black ends except for the central feathers which are all black. The female's head and ear-coverts ashy-brown; mantle, scapulars and wing-coverts brown; outer tail feathers dusky bordered and tipped with white. The underparts pale buffish-white with crescent-shaped blackish markings on sides of neck, chest and flanks.

The LOGGERHEAD SHRIKE, *L. ludovicianus,* is an Eastern North America species about 9 inches (23 cm) in length and the sexes are alike. Above plain slate-grey, darkest on the crown fading into paler grey on upper tail-coverts and into white on outer shoulder region. Eye region, ear region and lores, black, forming a conspicuous patch on sides of head; wings and tail black, secondaries tipped white. Entire underparts white, the sides and flanks faintly shaded with grey. They are a common bird in the Florida Everglades, perching on the telephone wires along all the roads on the look-out for unwary prey.

. . . perching on the telephone wires . . .

We fed mealworms, crickets and day-old mice to the above species and they also took a considerable amount of ground raw beef.

Subfamily Malaconotinae

This is a wholly African group of birds of medium size where the bill varies from strong, to moderately strong, to relatively weak but they all have the characteristic hook with the 'tooth' and notch. Their other distinction is that the feathers on the rump are soft and elongated.

The SULPHUR-BREASTED BUSH-SHRIKE, *Chlorophoneus sulfureopectus*, is about 7 inches (18 cm) in length, and the sexes are similar. It is to be found in the eastern parts of Africa from Ethiopia down to Cape Province and across to Angola. The adult male has forehead yellowish-green; crown to mantle grey; yellow stripe over eye; lores to ear-coverts black; the rump, wings and tail, green, the tail feathers having yellow tips; chest bright orange; remainder of underparts yellow. With the female the lores and ear-coverts are a greyish-black.

The PUFF-BACK SHRIKE, *Dryoscopus gambensis*, about the same size as the preceding species is more localised to Central Africa, north-eastern Congo, Uganda and Kenya. The sexes differ, the adult male's head, sides of face, wings and tail glossy blue-black; edges of wing-coverts white; edges of outer tail feathers paler as are the tips of the other feathers. Mantle greyish-black; rump and lower back greyish-white; underparts white with a greyish tinge. The female is earth-brown above, darker on head, and has buffish edges to wing-coverts and scapulars. Underparts tawny-buff, darker from chin to breast.

The GREY-HEADED BUSH-SHRIKE, *Malaconotus hypopyrrhus*, is a much larger bird, about 10½ inches (27 cm) in length, and has a very strong, powerful bill. Another African species extending from Kenya southward to South Africa. The sexes are alike, head, sides of face and upper mantle, grey; lores white; remainder of upperparts green with pale yellow spots at ends of inner secondaries and tips of tail feathers. Underparts bright yellow; chest and breast saffron; bill black.

. . . a very strong powerful bill.

The BROWN-HEADED BUSH-SHRIKE, *Tchagra australis*, also from East Africa, is about 8 inches (20 cm) in length and the sexes are alike. They are distinguished in having the centre of the head from forehead to nape, brown, with a black stripe between this and a buffish stripe over the eye. Mantle brown; rump greyish-brown; wings chestnut with blackish ends to primaries and greater part of inner secondaries; tail black with white tips except for the central feathers which are brownish-grey, more or less distinctly barred. Chin white; remainder of underparts buffish.

The GORGEOUS BUSH-SHRIKE, *Telophorus quadri-color,* is about 7½ inches (19 cm) in length and the sexes are very similar. It has by no means as large a range as any of the preceding species being mostly confined to Mozambique, Rhodesia and Malawi. Above bright green; base of bill and over eye, yellow; lores to under eye and on side of neck black; ear-coverts green; tail, black and green. The chin and neck, rich scarlet tinged with orange; a broad black band across the chest joining up with the black stripe from the lores to neck; breast to under tail-coverts golden-yellow; flanks and under wing-coverts green. The female is less bright on the breast and abdomen, and has a narrow black chest band.

The Grey-headed Bush-shrike was fed on the exact diet of the normal shrikes, but the day-old mice were not taken by any of the other bush-shrikes, these being content with the insects and ground raw beef.

Subfamily Prionopinae

This subfamily also is wholly African and the members are noted for their sociability, a trait lacking in the other subfamilies. They are strictly insectivorous and have relatively weak bills.

The CURLY-CRESTED HELMET-SHRIKE, *Prionops cristata,* is to be found in Ethiopia and south-eastern Sudan. They are about 7½ inches (19 cm) in length and the sexes are alike. Head grey; crest from forehead to over crown distinctly curly and white, tinged with grey; blackish bar behind ear-coverts; broad white bar on hind-neck. Mantle jet black with a bottle-green sheen; wings black with white tips to the middle coverts and white edges and tips to the innermost secondaries forming a narrow longitudinal bar. Tail black, outermost feathers and ends of others white; throat greyish; remainder of underparts white.

The STRAIGHT-CRESTED HELMET-SHRIKE, *P. plumata,* is a South African species about 8 inches (20 cm) in length. The sexes are alike and they are very much like the Curly-crested except that the crest is short, straight and grey. The mantle is not as deep a black and it has a greenish gloss. Further, the longitudinal bars on the wings are broader.

In addition to live-food we also had the Helmet-shrikes feeding on ground raw beef and eating the soft-food mixture.

They would take insects from our fingers and although they often picked up small pieces of fruit they invariably discarded it.

Family Bombycillidae

Although three species of waxwing, one species of hypocolius and four species of silkyflycatchers make up this family, it was only with two species of waxwing that we were concerned. These were of the subfamily Bombycillinae, which breed in the sub-Arctic regions and move south for the winter. They are mainly berry and fruit eaters, but also partake of insects, mostly beetles. However, when rearing young, insects are the main diet, this fact being disclosed by the examination of the stomach contents of some young birds found dead in a nest.

The CEDAR WAXWING, *Bombycilla cedrorum*, is a temperate North American bird in general, breeding from British Columbia across to the Hudson Bay and down to Arizona and New Mexico. They winter in the entire United States in wooded districts, and migrate to the West Indies and Central America with accidental visits to Bermuda. We obtained seven specimens as they passed northward through New Jersey but were not fortunate enough to breed them ourselves. About 7¼ inches (18 cm) in total length, the sexes are almost identical. The lores and a wedge-shaped patch behind the eye velvety black, chin dull black, and the rest of the head, together with neck and chest soft pinkish-brown or brownish-fawn, darker on the throat and slightly greyer on the hind-neck. The back and shoulders similar to the hind-neck but slightly greyer, the wing-coverts still greyer and the secondaries and primary-coverts slate-grey. The secondaries have terminal appendages of scarlet, like red sealing-wax. The rump, upper tail-coverts and basal portion of the tail paler grey, deepening towards the end of the tail into blackish-slate, all feathers tipped with a sharply defined band of yellow. The underparts go from vinaceous brown on the chest to a paler hue on the breast and front portion of sides into a light yellowish-olive on the flanks, paling almost to white through the abdomen. With the female, the scarlet terminal appendages generally are smaller than those of the male.

The BOHEMIAN WAXWING, *B. garrulus*, is slightly larger than the Cedar and is a circumpolar bird being found in practically all northern parts of the northern hemisphere, breeding in coniferous forests. The sexes are very similar, the general colour soft drab, becoming wine-coloured forward. It is readily

American Cedar Waxwing Fledgling porcelain sculpture by Edward Marshall Boehm

identifiable by its pinkish-chestnut crest and short, yellow-tipped tail. Like the Cedar, the lores, chin, upper throat and a streak behind the eye are velvety black. The upperparts are chestnut with a grey rump, the underparts pinkish-brown with chestnut under tail-coverts. The dark wings are boldly marked white and yellow, and the secondaries have scarlet, waxy tips, these being less conspicuous in the female. We found them most peaceful with any species whatever, and they made excellent aviary birds.

Family Mimidae

This is a New World family of birds which in appearance are suggestive both of thrushes and the larger wrens. Various fruits, berries and ground-dwelling invertebrates are their main sources of nourishment for most of them. Renowned for their strong and versatile songs, seldom keeping to a definite pattern of notes, they range from southern Canada through Central America to the West Indies and South America to southern Argentina and Chile.

We only ever had two species in the aviaries, both kept purely for modelling purposes, being released as soon as the necessary data had been collated. However, in the grounds, as one was on one's way from aviary to aviary with mealworms, either specimens of one or the other would follow hoping for a handout, which they invariably got.

The CATBIRD, *Dumetella carolinensis,* about 8½ inches (21 cm) in length, is a temperate central and eastern North American species, wintering from the southern States through Central America to the West Indies. The sexes are alike, forehead slate-grey; crown black or slate-black; nape more sooty. Wings, slate-black with broad slate grey edges; tail, black, feathers edged slate-grey basally; under tail-coverts chestnut; remainder of plumage plain slate-grey, darker above.

The MOCKINGBIRD, *Mimus polyglottos,* is a larger bird, some 10 inches (25 cm), and is to be found in the Eastern United States, breeding and resident throughout its range. It also goes southward to Florida, along the Gulf Coast to Texas, *. . . the king* and also to the Bahamas. It stands unrivalled in the States as the *of song.* king of song. During the breeding season the song is incessant, and on a moonlit night, it is nothing to hear the trills of their liquid and sweet song for hours on end. A sociable bird with humans, nesting in back gardens, but zealously guarding their territory from all other birds. They will even swoop down on dogs and cats that venture too close to the tree or bush in which they are nesting, or into any area where recently fledged young may be. The upperparts brownish-grey; wings and tail dull blackish-slate with pale slate-grey edgings, broadest on the secondaries; middle and greater wing-coverts narrowly tipped greyish-white forming two narrow bands; primary-coverts and base of primaries white. Outermost tail feathers white; chest and sides of breast pale smoke-grey, passing into a more buffy hue on sides and flanks; centre of breast and abdomen white; under tail-coverts pale buff.

. . . swoop down on dogs and cats . . .

The ones we kept of both species were easy to cater for since they took the soft-food mixture, ground raw beef, the fruit mixture and any live-food we cared to offer them in the insect form.

Family Muscicapidae

The family muscicapidae of the suborder Oscines is commonly regarded now as embracing a great assemblage of mainly Old World, largely insectivorous, ten primaried song birds and they are grouped in the following subfamilies:

Turdinae	Thrushes, robins, chats.
Timaliinae	Babblers, Picathartes, wren-tits.
Cinclosomatinae (Orthonychinae)	Rail-babblers, log-runners, quail-thrushes.
Paradoxornithinae	Parrotbills, reedlings.
Polioptilinae	Gnatcatchers, gnatwrens.
Sylviinae	Old World warblers.
Malurinae	Australian wrens or warblers.
Muscicapinae	Old World flycatchers, fantails.
Pachycephalinae	Thickheads or whistlers

Only the subfamilies Cinclosomatinae and Polioptilinae had no representatives in the Boehm aviaries.

Subfamily Turdinae

This subfamily is comprised of thrushes, wheatears, chats, robins, redstarts, akalats, alethes, bluethroats and nightingales, thus being made up of species of widely differing habits, appearances and habitats, but all fairly closely related. Some 306 species, with subspecies totalling over 580 have been recognised and, with the exception of the Antarctic regions, and some Polynesian islands, are now spread throughout the world. Originally there were no thrushes in New Zealand but importations of the European Blackbird and Song Thrush have established themselves there.

The Ethiopian region—Arabia and Africa except the north—is the most abundant in thrushes, there being over 190 species of which some 160 are confined to that area. The second largest, so far as species is concerned, is the Oriental or Indian region which has over 150 species listed within its bounds, a third of them being migratory. The Neotropical region boasts of some 130, of which very few are migratory. Europe, north-west Africa and northern and western Asia—the Palaearctic region —has recognised over 120 species but less than half are confined thereto. The Australasian region, so rich in so many birds, is low with the subfamily Turdinae there only being 40 recognised there but, of these, only 4 are migratory. Last of all comes North America, the Nearctic region, there being about 30 different species of which half are purely migratory.

Thrushes, using this term to cover all the species in the Turdinae group, feed mainly on insects, with mollusca, spiders, millipedes and earthworms forming part of their diet. Some species consume a great amount of fruit and berries also. They all build open nests although the location of them varies from bushes to trees, on the ground, in crevices, and even in holes in trees. One species we had the pleasure to breed had their first nest in an old woodpecker's nest hole but, in subsequent years, they built in bushes.

. . . all build open nests . . .

Over the years we had over 40 species of this subfamily, seven of them producing young. The feed supplied to them consisted of mealworms, gentles, crickets, moths and other flying insects caught in night-traps. Further, the majority were housed in large planted aviaries so they were able to supplement by their own foraging. Their basic feed consisted of ground raw beef, lightly dusted with bonemeal, this being served with the home-made soft food mixture mentioned in the chapter on feeding. To meet the requirements of the fruit and berry-eaters, diced apples, grapes, cherries, plantain, sultanas and blueberries were given also.

I will commence the details of the various species with the SHAMA THRUSH, *Copsychus malabarica*, which is an Asiatic bird, and is one of the most melodious, if not the best, of the Turdinae. It is widely distributed in India, Pakistan, Ceylon,

Burma, Thailand, Malaysia and China, and is divided into various races. Those we had were from India, the sexes being readily identifiable. They are about 11 inches (28 cm) in total length, the adult male having upper plumage, wings and lower plumage to the lower breast of black, the remainder of the lower plumage bright chestnut, except for the thighs which are whitish. A patch on the rump is white and the long tail is black and white except for the two central pairs of feathers which are wholly black. The female in conformation is like the male but the black is replaced with slaty-brown, and the chestnut by rufous. Further, the feathers of the wings are narrowly edged with rufous and the tail is not as long. The males tend to be very belligerent towards any species of thrush, in fact it was our experience that they had to be watched when housed with pretty well any other insect eaters, such as flycatchers etc. They have been bred many times in captivity, the most successful results being obtained when they are allowed to fly free once the young are hatched. We only had a female for a short while and did not retain the males owing to their incompatability, our aim being to get birds to socialise, and live and breed in harmony.

The DHYAL THRUSH, MAGPIE ROBIN, STRAITS ROBIN, what you will, *Copsychus saularis,* is like a cousin to the Shama being found throughout India and Pakistan, right through to the Malayan peninsula. Hence the name Straits Robin, that was accorded it as a common garden bird of the original Straits Settlements. They are usually to be found in the higher regions—anything up to 5,000 feet (1500 metres)—but occasionally, as in Singapore, they do frequent the lowlands. There are numerous subspecies, the best known being the nominate race. They are about 8½ to 9 inches (21 to 23 cm) in total length, and, as adults, are sexable at sight. The adult male has a head, back, throat and breast of glossy black, the central tail feathers being the same colour with the outer feathers white. The wings also are black and white, and the bill, legs and feet black. The remainder of the underparts are white. The female is of the same colour pattern except that the glossy black is replaced with dark grey, the throat and breast paler than the other portions. Further, the under tail feathers of the female are a pale buffish shade. They also are good songsters, as musical, although not as powerful in volume, as the Shama, and are often kept as cage birds by the natives of their country of origin. The alarm note is best depicted as a long drawn out hiss, repeated several times. They also give vent to a harsh chattering when they are annoyed,

They also are good songsters . . .

155

rather than alarmed. In the wild they build their nests in holes in trees, walls, house-tops, and even down in holes in banks at the side of paths, streams and pools. The pair in the Boehm aviaries selected an open fronted nest box and it was early in June that the female laid three eggs in the far corner of this box, completely clear of the coil of hay that had been placed in there when the box was put up. The eggs were pale green, mottled with reddish-brown, mostly at the thicker end, and they measured 22 by 17 mm. The female did not sit steadily, vacating the nest whenever anyone entered the aviary. Whether the incubation was shared or not we could never determine for, on the slightest sound of anyone approaching the area, both birds would be out chattering. The incubation period was assessed at thirteen days and must have begun with the laying of the first egg for the three chicks hatched on successive days. The nestlings were completely bare of all feathering and very dark skinned. Both parents shared with the rearing, live-food appearing to be the sole diet. The chicks remained in the far corner of the box and it was extremely difficult to follow their progress of feathering. However, at eight days it could be seen that they all had dark feathers

. . . the male bird escaped . . .

and, at that same time, the male bird escaped from the aviary due to a door having been left open. For six days he was around, coming for live food put out for him but avoiding the trap cage. At last he selected the wrong worm and click, the trap was closed. It was with some trepidation that we released him back into the aviary but, without any hesitation he flew to their own live food feeding stand, gathered up a beakful of mealworms, and straight up to the nest box as if he had never been absent. The female seemed to take it as a matter of course and there was no welcoming ceremony. Two days later the first chick left the nest and the others left the following day. When caught up for banding it was seen that the upper plumage was dark brown, white showing in the wings in such a pattern as to give a tortoiseshell effect. The throat and breast were pale buff, flecked with brown; the rest of the underparts white. Although we found the Dhyal Thrush to be peaceful with other birds, even at breeding time, the males are not too agreeable to their own kind and sex. For breeding purposes it is definitely recommended that it be restricted to one pair per enclosure.

I now come to an African species, the OLIVE-FLANKED ROBIN-CHAT, *Cossypha anomala,* which is to be found in the Malawai and Tanzania regions. The sexes are alike in colouring, the head and mantle brown with the upper tail-coverts and tail russet. The forehead, and a stripe over the eye, are grey, and the sides of the face are greyish. The throat is white, the chest and abdomen grey, and the lower flanks and under tail-coverts brown. They are a smallish robin-chat and possess very little song, their main call being a low croak, but the male does give forth with a chirruping whistle during the breeding season. Although we had what we thought to be a true pair for a few years, we were never fortunate enough to breed them. The reason we felt them to be a pair was because one would give the whistle, the other skulking in the bushes all the time. Since they were banded one could not be mistaken for the other. Once they did start to build a nest but it was soon torn apart by some other bird for we had nowhere we could put them on their own.

The CAPE ROBIN-CHAT, *Cossypha caffra,* can be found from Cape Province northward through Zambia, Mozambique, Tanzania and Kenya to the Sudan. The sexes are alike, the head grey with the sides of the face blackish. There is a broad white stripe over the eye, and the upper plumage is mainly olivaceous-brown. The lower rump, upper tail-coverts and the tail are a tawny chestnut, except the central pair of feathers which are the same colour as the upper plumage. The throat to chest is dark tawny with a black streak on each side of the chin. The breast and flanks are grey with the belly white, the lower belly and under tail-coverts are deep buff. They are very secretive birds, much at home in a densely planted aviary where they can hide in the bushes. The best time to view them we found was early in the morning at feeding time, or at dusk when they could be located by their lively, short, musical song. We had two of them for quite a while but they never showed any inclination to go to nest so, since their songs were identical, we concluded we had two of the same sex.

We also had the BLUE-SHOULDERED ROBIN-CHAT, *Cossypha cyanocampter,* that comes from tropical parts of Africa. This is another retiring species but it does have a more varied song than the Cape Robin-chat, and is a very good mimic, picking up the melody of a whistled phrase quite readily. The sexes are dissimilar but only to the extent that the female is more brown on the mantle than the male. One needs to be very familiar with the species to be able to sex an individual bird accurately. The adult male is black from the forehead to the nape and has black cheeks. A white stripe runs from the base of the bill, over the eye, and down the sides of the neck. The remainder of the upper plumage is slaty to olivaceous-brown, with

. . . the other skulking in the bushes . . .

the shoulders blue. The wings and central tail feathers are very dark, almost black, the rest of the tail tawny with black edges and tips. The pair we had went to nest but the eggs were clear. They measured 23 by 15 mm., and were a glossy greenish-blue with the thicker end more or less obscured with rufous and lilac-grey mottlings. The Blue-shouldered Robin-chat is about 7½ inches (19 cm) in total length.

The WHITE-THROATED ROBIN, *Cossypha gutturalis,* winters in eastern Africa but breeds in Turkey, Syria, Iran and Western Turkestan. The adult male is grey above with a black tail. There is a white stripe over the eye, and the sides of the face and neck are black. Chin, neck, lower belly and under tail-coverts are white, the rest of the underparts, including the wing-coverts, tawny. The female is more ashy-grey above with the sides of the face and neck the same colour. Further, the underparts are less tawny. We never found these birds an interesting aviary inmate as they were too self concealing and had a very mediocre call.

Another species we had of a comparative size to the Blue-shouldered was the WHITE-BROWED or HEUGLIN'S ROBIN-CHAT, *Cossypha heuglini,* but this has a much more extensive range being found right from above the equator in Ethiopia down the central and eastern parts of Africa to Tanzania. Again there is a slight difference in the sexes in the colouring of the mantle, that of the female being browner. In song it resembles the Blue-shouldered Robin-chat, but has a much wider range of notes, most of its singing done from concealment, as it also is a shy bird, liking the undergrowth. From the top of the head to the nape of the neck the adult male is black, as are the sides of the face, but there is a broad white stripe over the eye, dividing the black of the crown from the black of the face. The mantle is slaty-blue to olivaceous-brown with the wings pale slate. The lower rump, upper tail-coverts and tail are a tawny orange, except for the central pair of feathers which are olivaceous-brown. Although we had a pair for many years in a very commodious aviary they never made any attempt to go to nest.

The NATAL ROBIN, *Cossypha n. natalensis,* a most colourful bird with its rich cinnamon-rufous and slate-grey, can be seen over a wide area in Africa ranging from the Sudan to Ethiopia, the Congo and Angola, down to Tanzania, through the northern parts of Rhodesia to South Africa. Often, with a species of such a wide distribution, subspecies are designated from the various regions, but the only other one I am aware of is the race from Kenya, *Cossypha n. intensa*. However, it was a pair of the nominate race that we received from East Africa in September 1960. They are about $7\frac{1}{2}$ inches (19 cm) in total length and the sexes are very similar. The adult male has a cap of cinnamon-brown, hence another name for it is the Red-capped Robin, the mantle being the same colour except that it is finely marked with slate. The wings are slate-blue, and the sides of the face, the rump, and the entire underparts are rich cinnamon-rufous. The tail also, except for the central feathers, is cinnamon-rufous, those feathers and the edges of the outer tail feathers black. The female is slightly paler on the underparts, and often is smaller too, but the variations are so slight that to sex accurately an individual bird by colouration and size alone is very debatable. They both have a pleasing song, the male's stronger and more varied, and their powers of mimicry are amazing. They can pick up a tune of a human whistle and seem happy to partake in a call and response session. Further, they have a certain limited ventriloquial gift that can be very confusing when trying to locate them by sound alone. Although they were housed in an outdoor aviary almost from the time of their reception, it was not until the July of 1963 that the female was seen carrying nesting material. Although all the bushes and shrubs were examined carefully, no signs of any nest building could be found. It was not until July 11th, when the first egg was laid, that the female was seen to leave an old woodpecker's nest hole about 8 feet (2.5 metres) above ground level. It was only with the aid of a flashlight that the egg and nest could be seen, for the hole was about ten inches (25 cm) in depth. The nest appeared to be the open cup type, resting on the bottom of the hole and made up of dried grasses. Three eggs were laid in all, on successive days, and incubation apparently began on the completion of the clutch. In the light of the electric torch, the eggs looked coffee coloured but, when an empty shell was picked up later, it could be seen that they were blue, washed with olive-green, and heavily mottled in brown, the basic colour almost obscured. Allowing for the missing cap, it was assessed that they must have measured about 21 by 16 mm. Although it cannot be stated conclusively, it did appear that incubation was by the female only, since this was the only bird ever seen to enter or vacate the nest hole during this period. As she left the nest immediately anyone entered the aviary it was possible to make daily observations of the eggs and, on July 27th., three tiny chicks could be seen. They appeared to be covered with brown fluff and had bright yellow

. . . with the aid of a flashlight . . .

159

gapes, margined in orange. Both parents fed the young entirely on live food consisting of moths, other insects and mealworms, the male, if anything, doing the major portion although he never stayed to brood the chicks, this being done by the female all the time. Their eyes were open at six days and brown feathering, mottled with black, began to form on their backs but, owing to the fact that they were all huddled together at the bottom of the nest, it was not possible to get definite details of the feathering. At twelve days they left the nest and it could then be seen that they closely resembled fledgling European Robins, being yellowish-brown, heavily mottled with black. Their tails, however, small as they were, were bright rufous, the central pair of feathers black. By the time they were three weeks old the mottling has started to go from their underparts and their flight feathers had changed to slate-grey. They were independent at four weeks and full adult plumage was obtained at three months. There were two females and one male in this brood but, over the years they have bred since and the sexes have about equalised out.

The SNOWY-HEADED ROBIN-CHAT, *Cossypha niveicapilla*, is another African species with a wide range from West Africa across to Ethiopia, and down into the Kenya and Tanzania regions. It is a distinguished looking bird and a very fine songster. The only difference we were able to detect in the sexes was that the female is somewhat smaller and has not got such a varied song. The centre of the head, from the forehead to well behind the eye, is white, with the sides of the face black. There is a cinnamon-brown collar round the nape, and the wings, mantle and tail are dark brown, except for the central pair of tail feathers which are blackish-brown. The chin is chestnut, the remainder of the underparts tawny-orange. This is one of the few after-dark songsters of the genus and, like so many of these birds, is an excellent mimic. They are larger than the Natal Robin being about 8½ to 9 inches (21 to 23 cm) in total length.

. . . a very fine songster . . .

The final species of the genus *Cossypha* we had was the GREY-WINGED ROBIN-CHAT, *C. polioptera*. With a more restricted range, confined from Northern Angola to Kenya and Tanzania, again the sexes are alike. The top of the head is dark grey with a blackish streak through and beyond the eye. There also is a black and white spotted line above the eye. The rest of the upperparts, including the wings, are olivaceous-brown, but the wing-coverts are slaty-blue. The upper tail-coverts and tail are chestnut, the underparts orange-brown with a white patch in the centre of the belly.

The INDIAN BLUE CHAT or BLUE ROBIN, *Erithacus brunnea,* is an Asiatic species found from 6,000 to 11,000 feet (1900 to 3400 metres) in the Himalayas where it breeds, wintering in the hills of south-west India and Ceylon. There is a second race resident in Burma. It is a species where there is a marked difference in the sexes, the adult male having upper plumage, including the exposed portions of the wings and tail, of dark blue. The hidden parts of the wings and tail quills are brownish-black, the sides of the face and neck are black and there is a long, broad, white superciliary stripe. The throat, breast and sides of the body are bright chestnut, paler under the chin, and the thighs are ashy-grey. The remainder of the under plumage is white. With the female the entire upper plumage is olive-brown tinged with russet on the sides of the wings and above the tail. The sides of the face are russet with paler fleckings. The middle of the throat and chin, the abdomen and a patch under the tail are white, the remainder of the underparts warm fulvous or olive-brown. The bill of the female is dark brown, whereas that of the male is black. Normally shy, running on the ground under whatever cover they can find, we found that they became very tame in captivity, responding to a whistle and coming to eat out of one's hand. Care needs to be taken when placing a pair in an aviary for, by our experience, if the male does become too amorous for the female's mood, she does not hesitate to attack him viciously and, in a small area, this can be fatal. Although we did not breed this species we had a female who built a nest and laid eggs, all before a male was introduced to her. The nest was beautifully made of fine grasses and Spanish moss, and was well concealed in an azalea bush. The eggs were a uniform pale blue and measured 20 by 14 mm. Eventually a male was acquired and, so as to make the introductory period safer, he was placed in the aviary in a cage. After about four days she started coming to the cage whistling her very soft, dulcet song. On the sixth day it was noticed that something was wrong with the male; he had but one leg. Catching him up it could be seen where the leg had been taken off close to the body, some dried blood still being on the abdomen. Since he was a whole bird when put in the cage it could only be surmised that it was the work of a mouse, for we had experienced this sort of injury before with birds in cages. Needless to say this dispelled all thoughts of using them as a breeding pair, so he just became a house pet. By the time a second male was obtained her very tameness had led to her undoing for one of the men engaged in

. . . all before a male was introduced . . .

removing dead shrubbery accidentally trod on her, crippling her, leaving no alternative but to put her to sleep.

Another cheerful little inmate of an unheated aviary was a male ROBIN REDBREAST, *Erithacus rubecula.* We only ever had the one which had arrived with a shipment of birds from the continent. The sexes are practically alike, the upperparts being olive-brown, with the frontal band, lore, chin, throat and upper breast reddish-orange, bordered on the throat and breast with bluish-grey. The flanks are brown, the remainder of the underparts white. They are about $5\frac{3}{4}$ inches (15 cm) in total length. The male has a very cheerful song and also a peculiar shrill single note he utters whenever he is warning off an intruder, for they are very territorial. We kept this male in the open aviary the year round, severe weather not affecting him in any way. In fact he became very tame and was a cheering sight when the aviary was covered with snow and ice and there he was, singing away and flashing his colourful breast. Unfortunately, at the time the Dhyal Thrush escaped so did our Robin Redbreast and we never saw him again. It is an European species, resident in the United Kingdom, migrating from the Scandinavian and Baltic countries and from Iceland, in the winter months. Various subspecies of the British Robin are found throughout Europe, western Asia and north-west Africa.

. . . we never saw him again.

Now back to Africa with the genus *Erythropygia.* The BEARDED SCRUB-ROBIN, *E. barbata,* is to be found from Angola to Tanzania. The sexes are alike, the top of the head through the mantle earthy-brown. There is a blackish stripe, with a white bar below it, running from the forehead to over the eye. The ear-coverts are brown, the lores blackish. The wing-bar is tipped with white, and the base of the primaries also is white. The lower rump and the upper tail-coverts are chestnut. The tail feathers are brown with the ends of the three outermost white, the amount of white increasing outwards so that the extreme outer feathers are almost wholly white. The chin, neck and a cheek stripe are white, but there is a black moustachial streak running from the base of the lower mandible down the side of the neck. The remainder of the underparts are tawny-buff except for the centre of the breast to the belly which is white. They have a most pleasing song, heard best at the early morning or just before nightfall. The female did start to construct a nest in an ilex but a rat got her and we were never able to obtain a replacement. They are a little smaller than the Natal Robin, but have a slighter build and a longer tail than that species.

The BROWN-BACKED SCRUB-ROBIN, *E. hartlaubi,* is a West African species being found from Cameroon to Uganda, and from northern Angola to Tanzania. Here again the sexes are alike, the upperparts blackish-brown with a superciliary white stripe from the bill to the back of the eye. The wing-coverts bear white spots and the upper tail-coverts are chestnut. The tail also is chestnut at the base for about two-thirds of its length, the remainder black, all except the central feathers which are tipped with white. There are diffused grey streaks on the chest, the flanks and under tail-coverts are buff. These birds have a loud and cheerful song that they give vent to from the upper branches of shrubs, but most of their time is spent on the ground foraging for insects.

The RED-BACKED SCRUB-ROBIN, *E. leocophrys,* also known as the WHITE-BROWED SCRUB-ROBIN, is synonymous with the *E. zambesiana* which extends from the Congo to the Sudan, and down into Tanzania, Kenya and Mozambique. The sexes are alike being warm-brown above, darker on the head. There is a white stripe from the base of the bill to over the eye. The wing-coverts are tipped with white, the upper tail-coverts and tail russet and chestnut, with subterminal black bands. All except the central feathers are white tipped. The chin and throat are white and there is a blackish moustachial streak down the side of the throat. The chest is streaked with black, the flanks pale brown with the centre of the breast to the abdomen white. Their call, a series of descending notes, can be rather monotous, but the gestures of fanning the tail and raising it above the back at the end of each series of notes is fascinating and does tend to compensate for the wearying song.

. . . can be rather monotonous . . .

One of the favourites of this genus with us was the EASTERN BEARDED SCRUB-ROBIN, *E. quadrivirgata,* which primarily is a Mozambique and eastern Tanzania species. It is rather similar to the Bearded Scrub-robin described above except that it is browner above and the stripes on the head are blacker. Further, the white is more extensive on the breast and abdomen. Although very shy they have a delightful song and are very good mimics. We used to locate a pair of them every morning by just whistling and they would reply in almost the same identical notes. The male's song was stronger and more complete for the female did tend to skip a note or two.

Contributions from North America were represented with members of the genus Hylocichla. The first of these so far as we were concerned was the GREY-CHEEKED THRUSH, *H. minima,* which breeds from Newfoundland and Canada down to Massachusetts and the New York State. As it winters in South America it is included in both the Nearctic and Neotropical regional lists. The sexes are alike, and they are rather inconspicuous birds, a uniform greyish-olive above, the tail slightly browner. The sides of the head are mostly greyish-olive, and streaked with a darker shade. The underparts are white, passing on the sides and flanks into pale olive-grey. The chest varies from buffywhite to pale cream-buff, is marked with triangular spots of greyish-dusky, those on the lower part of the chest being more transverse, and there is a broad streak of dusky along each side of the throat. The breast is marked with transverse spots of light greyish-olive. Although we had a pair of these birds, no effort was made to breed them since their prime presence there was as live models for Mr. Boehm's porcelain creations.

The WOOD THRUSH, *H. mustelina,* was another species retained for modelling purposes rather than breeding. They are a little larger than the Grey-cheeked being some 7½ inches (19 cm) in total length as against 7 (18 cm) for the former. However, they are more colourful having a crown of fawny-brown passing into cinnamon-brown on the back and shoulders and then into greyish-olive on the rump, upper tail-coverts and tail. The wings are slightly less cinnamon than the back, and there is a distinct eye-ring of white. The sides of the head are dusky greyish-brown, narrowly streaked with white, and the cheeks are white flecked with dusky. The underparts are white, tinged with buff on the breast, and there is a broad streak of black or dusky along each side of the throat. The chest, sides and flanks are marked with large roundish or drop-shaped spots of brownish-black. They are very good songsters, particularly at dusk, and we have even heard them singing late at night. This also is an eastern North American bird, breeding from northern Florida to northern New York State and spending the winter in Central America, Texas and the West Indies.

The only other member of the genus we had was the OLIVE-BACKED THRUSH, *H. ustulata swainsoni.* We only ever had one, a male received with a shipment from Brazil but, since I had had the good fortune to breed the species in England we did not attempt to obtain a female. They are very similar in appearance to the Grey-cheeked except that it does have a very conspicuous eye-ring of buff, and lacks the cheek patches. Further, it is slightly smaller, being only some 7¼ inches (18 cm) in total length. Its song also is dissimilar in that it commences at the foot of the scale and gradually works up. They are constant songsters in the early morning, commencing just before dawn and carrying on until the sun is well up. They commence again in the evening and carry on until dark. Bright moonlit nights will often encourage them to start all over again. Although they breed over the greater portion of North America, even up to Alaska, they winter in South America, as far down as Argentina. It took me three years to breed them in England for, in the first two instances, although they hatched young, they failed to rear them beyond four days old. Observing them carefully it was noticed that the male pursued the female every time she left the nest for feed for the young. In consequence, although it was there for the taking, she never had the chance to give them enough. On the third year it was decided to remove the male the day before the eggs were due to hatch. The reason for this long deferment was that it had been seen that the male used to feed the female on the nest since she did all the incubating, only leaving the eggs when nature dictated. Although the male assisted in collecting material in the form of dried grasses, it was the female who did all the constructing. She built an open circular nest of about six inches (15 cm) across the top with the sides rising some three inches (7.5 cm). As it was a very dry summer, we supplied mud in the form of well soaked "John Innes Compost." With the combined use of natural dried grasses from the outside flight and the "super" quality mud, a beautiful nest was the result. The first egg was laid on June 11th, the full clutch of four completed by the 14th. The eggs were sky-blue in colour, heavily flecked in sepia at the broad end, and measured 16 by 22 mm. Having learned that they normally hatch on the fourteenth day after the laying of the first egg, indicating that incubation did not commence until the clutch was complete, I removed the male on the 24th. The first chick hatched in the afternoon of the 25th., and all four were there by dawn of the following day. As before, an abundance of live food was placed in the inside flight, but, we noticed her searching in the ground outside so some more was put there as well. This she immediately gathered up, about ten gentles at a time in her bill, and flew in to the babies with them. From then on the outside flight was stocked as well as that inside. During the brief periods we were able to observe her, it appeared that she fed the chicks about every twenty minutes or so, this period lengthening as they developed. By the time they were eleven days old she was doing all she

Bright moonlit nights will often encourage them . . .

could to entice them to leave the nest, flying in with a mealworm in her bill and taking up a position on a branch about nine inches (23 cm) from the nest. Here she would call to them, turn and fly out of the shelter, repeating this manoeuvre time after time. Her efforts were finally rewarded by one venturing forth and, by the following day all four were out on the branches in the flight. It was now possible to study them for, after the years' previous failures, we had never gone to inspect them in the nest. Their general colouring was dark brown above with a collar of dark fleckings and the underparts a clear buff. The rapid change that took place in their plumage was amazing for, within 48 hours, the collar of fleckings had extended until it covered completely the upper portion of their breasts and the underparts had changed from clear to mottled. In fact it was almost a counterpart of the adult birds general colour even to the "V" shaped clear patch running from the lower mandible down the throat, except that the underparts were a greyish buff as against the clear buff of the parent bird. The fifth day after fledging she began feeding them fruit and soft food as well as live food. She was now spending quite a time reconstructing her nest and, by the time they were independent, eight days after fledging, she had two more eggs in the nest. One of the youngsters spent a lot of time sitting on these eggs and, although its feathering was darker than the other three, and they finally proved to be three males and one female, this could well have been a sex indicator. However, since they were not rung and identification was not positive, I would not dare to suggest that it is a means of sexing them at that early age. Most thrushes are extremely territorially minded when it comes to the breeding season but we did find that some of the larger species could be kept in the same aviaries as Scrub Robins. Unfortunately the Scrub Robins did not go to nest so the experiment cannot be said to have been completed.

The RUBYTHROAT, *Luscinia calliope,* is an Asiatic species also known as the Chinese and Siberian Rubythroat. The latter name is more correct geographically although they breed in N.W. China as well as Siberia. It is a winter visitor to the Phillipines, Formosa and north-west India. The adult male has upper plumage of olive-brown with the wings and tail plain brown. A superciliary stripe runs from the base of the bill to behind the eye, and there is a broad white molar stripe. The chin and throat are adorned with a brilliant patch of ruby-scarlet edged with black. The breast is lightish grey, the abdomen and lower parts whitish. The female is similar except that the scarlet

Her efforts were finally rewarded . . .

throat patch is pinkish, almost white, and the white stripes are not as well defined. They are about six inches (15 cm) in total length. Young males resemble the females but, on moulting, have the significant white stripes of an adult, the red throat not showing until much later. This species has been bred in captivity.

The BLUETHROAT, *Luscinia svecica*, is widely distributed in the Palaearctic region and there are many races. It was the *L.s.pallidogularis*, an Indian migrant, that we had at the Boehm aviaries. They are about 5½ inches (14 cm) in total length and the sexes differ. The male has upper parts of warm brown, with a fulvous to white stripe running through the eye. The upper tail-coverts and base of tail are chestnut, the rest of the tail dark brown. Chin, throat and gorget are brilliant ultramarine succeeded by bands of black, white and chestnut, the rest of the underparts whitish. There are two closely related forms, distinguished from each other by the colour at the spot in the centre of the blue throat patch—the Red-spotted Bluethroat having a chestnut spot, and the White-spotted Bluethroat a white one. The blue and chestnut of the lower plumage vary according to the age, season and race, being almost absent in some specimens. In the female the whole of the underparts are whitish with a brownish band across the chest. We were never fortunate to have one of each sex at the same time so never obtained first hand information on their nesting and breeding habits. We were able to keep them in the same aviary as Rubythroats, but whether this closeness would have been acceptable if there had been breeding pairs is an unanswered question for us. They are lovely songsters, this quality leading to their being often called the Swedish Nightingales.

Also from the Oriental region we had two species of the genus *Monticola*. The first of these was the BLUE-HEADED ROCK THRUSH, *M. cinclorhynchus*, which breeds in the Himalayas but winters throughout the Indian peninsula, even extending to western Burma. They are very hardy and we have kept them outside throughout the year in temperatures dropping well below freezing level at times. The only thing to guard against is frost bitten feet, and this can be avoided by an adequate supply of hay-filled boxes for them to roost in at night. The sexes are dissimilar in colour, but both are about 7 inches (18 cm) in total length. The adult male has a head of cobalt-blue, divided by a broad black line from the base of the bill, through the eye, to the back and shoulders which also are black. The wings are black, washed with blue, and there is a conspicuous

. . . an Indian migrant . . .

167

white patch on the wing quills. The rump and under plumage are chestnut and the tail is black, again washed with blue. The upper plumage, wings and tail of the female are olive-brown tinged with ochraceous, the chin and throat are whitish, as is the lower plumage, but the breast is tinged with ochraceous and barred in black-brown. The male has a very pleasing song and they make good aviary birds. They have been bred in captivity.

The BLUE ROCK THRUSH, *M. solitarius,* is widely distributed in southern Europe, Africa and the greater part of Asia. There are several races but the pair we had came from the Himalayas, being recognised as *M. s. pandoo.* Here again the colouring of the sexes differs, for the entire plumage of the adult male is dull dark blue. It is brighter over the eye, on the sides of the head and throat. The feathers of the upper parts have brown fringes, those of the lower parts being more or less barred with blackish and fringed with white. The wings and tail are dark brown, washed with dark blue, most of the wing feathers being tipped with creamy white. These fringe markings are prominent in their winter plumage but wear off during the summer, giving the overall feathering a brighter, more uniform blue, with wings and tail in dark contrast. The upper plumage, wings and tail of the female are similar to those of the male except that they are duller, almost olive-brown. The chin, throat and upper breast are creamy buff, the feathers margined in sooty black. They are about 7 inches (18 cm) in total length. The male has a fine song, similar to that of the European Blackbird, but shorter. This species also has been bred in captivity.

The male has a fine song . . .

A North American Thrush that we always found attractive was the TOWNSEND'S SOLITAIRE, *Myadestes townsendi.* The appeal did not lie in the colouring for it is a uniform grey with a white eye-ring, white outer tail feathers, and a buff patch in the centre of the wing, but in its song. This is loud, clear and sweet. The manner in which it maintains its solitary status, never mixing with the other birds, but always ready to snatch at any flying insects, almost flycatcherlike in its movements, also attracts one. This species is about 9 inches (23 cm) in total length and ranges from Alaska to N.W. Mexico, being migratory to and from the northern regions. We had these birds several times but were never fortunate enough to get a pair to nest. This could well have been attributed to the fact that in all instances they were with mixed collections which perhaps did not meet up with their solitary inclinations despite the aviaries being very spacious.

The BLUE WHISTLING THRUSH, *Myiophoneus caeruleus*, is one of the larger thrushes being some 12 inches (30 cm) in total length. It is a bird that requires to be seen in the correct lighting to appreciate its colouring. The sexes are alike, the entire plumage deep blue-black, becoming brighter and bluer on the wings and tail, and duller and browner on the abdomen. There is a black velvety patch in front of the eye, and all the body feathers are more or less tipped with deep shining blue, some of the wing-coverts being tipped with white. The bill is yellow, the upper mandible sometimes blackish-yellow, which may be an indicator of age. The legs and feet are black. Their native range is throughout the Himalayas and it is widespread in the eastern parts of India throughout Burma and into China. An aggressive bird, it cannot be kept safely with any species smaller than itself. This fact we learned the hard way and, subsequently, they were put in an aviary with various jay thrushes and there were no breedings by any of them. Nests were made and eggs laid but each predated on the other. They have a harsh, screeching alarm note to which they give voice at the slightest provocation. I have, however, heard their song early in the morning, and at dusk, and it is a long, clear, melodious whistle, making it apparent how they acquired their common name.

This fact we learned the hard way . . .

I now come to the WHEATEAR, *Oenanthe oenanthe*, the species that is migratory to the British Isles and other countries. There are many species of wheatears stretching from Greenland, through the North Americas, to Europe, Asia and Africa, but the only one we ever had was that mentioned above. The sexes are dissimilar, the male being grey on the head, neck and back, and having black wings. There is a superciliary stripe of white, and the forehead and rump are white also, the lores and ear-coverts black. The tail feathers are white with broad black tips, except the central pair which is wholly black. The underparts are white-buffish at the throat and breast, and the under wing-coverts are mottled with dark grey and white. The female is brown on the back and ear-coverts, and the underparts are more buff. A pair of these birds that we had in England lived happily together in a three foot (1 metre) cage for almost two years; a little flighty, but never showing any animosity towards each other. Having prepared a planted aviary for them, we released them into it in the early summer and, within 30 minutes, the male killed the female. Since they have been bred in captivity this state of affairs cannot be the general rule, but just one of those misfortunes faced by aviculturists.

We now come to the various species of redstarts that are included in the genus *Phoenicurus* that Mr. Boehm had over the years. There is a bird with the common name of American Redstart but this is not a member of the Turdinae, but of the Parulidae and is dealt with in that section.

The DAURIAN REDSTART, *P. a. aurorea,* has an extensive range from south eastern Siberia through to Japan, and the sexes differ. The adult male has a head and nape of silvery-grey with the upper back, throat and upper breast of black. The lower back, rump, lower breast and abdomen are rufous-brown. The wings are black with a central white bar, and the tail is a deep rufous-brown, except for the central feathers which are black. The female is generally various shades of brown with small white patches on dark brown primaries. The tail is bright rufous-brown.

The BLUE-FRONTED REDSTART, *P. frontalis,* is a resident throughout the Himalayas at high elevations, and extends into Burma and western China. The sexes differ, the male being dull blue and chestnut, and the female brown and a paler chestnut. The blue on the male covers the forehead and brow streaks, and extends down both the breast and back, fading into slate-blue. The abdomen, rump and tail are russet, with a black terminal band on the latter. I have never heard them render a loud song, just a very quiet whistle, with small range of notes. Being shy, retiring birds, their alarm note is heard more frequently, this sounding like a small clockwork motor being wound.

The PLUMBEOUS REDSTART, *P. fuliginosa,* is found throughout the Himalayan region where it breeds from 4,000 to 9,000 feet (1250 to 2800 metres), and has been seen to elevations of 13,000 feet (4000 metres). It winters in the foothills and, apart from this seasonal altitude change, is a resident species. Purely a water-side bird it can always be found where there are streams and rivers, particularly in the vicinity of falls. The Plumbeous is smaller than the Blue-fronted, some 5 to 5½ inches (12 to 14 cm) in total length, and the sexes differ. The entire plumage of the adult male is dull plumbeous slate, except for the tail which is bright chestnut. In the female the upper plumage is dull bluish-brown, the tail is white with a large triangular patch at the end. The wings are brown, edged with pale rufous, and the lower plumage is ashy-brown flecked with light scale-like markings. They are bold birds, not skulking in the bushes, and the constant fanning and flicking of the tail, chestnut with the male and white with the female, is most fascinating. We had a pair build a nest in a hole by a waterfall but no eggs were laid. It was the open cup type, constructed of fine grasses and Spanish moss. A second pair built in a hanging flower basket and did produce three eggs. The ground colour a pale greenish-white, almost entirely obscured by mottling and flecking of dingy reddish-brown, particularly at the thicker end, they measured 19 by 15 mm., but were clear.

The WHITE-CAPPED REDSTART, *P. leucocephalus,* also is an Asiatic Species found throughout the Himalayan range from west to east, even extending into western China. Another stream and river lover, it descends to the foothills during the winter. The sexes are alike, the most distinguishing feature being the shining white cap that covers the entire crown. The remainder of the head, the back, breast and wings are black, the rump and lower plumage from the breast downwards of bright chestnut. The tail is chestnut also with a terminal band of black. It is not renowned for its song but, early in the morning and just before dusk, they do give voice to a long, drawn-out little whistle, more like a squeak than anything else. Although they have been bred in captivity we did not have any luck with them for, whenever we tried two of them in the same aviary, or even in adjacent aviaries, they spent their entire time fighting or pecking through the wiring. Anyway, as singletons we always found them a most attractive bird, never showing belligerency towards any other bird, even thrushes, but just to each other. Maybe we had all of one sex although this seems hardly possible with the ten specimens we had over the years.

. . . more like a squeak than anything else.

The BLACK REDSTART, *P. ochruros,* is a true Palaeartic species ranging from the southern parts of the British Isles to western China. It is a breeding species in the United Kingdom, as well as an autumn migrant, remaining well on into the winter when it goes south. The southern limit is north Africa where it is a resident as it is in Iran, Afghanistan and the central Himalayan range. There are several races in their wide distribution and we had two others as well as the nominate race. These, both known as Black-fronted Redstarts, come from India and bear the names of *P. o. phoenicuroides* and *P. o. rufiventris.* They differ from the nominate race in that the first mentioned has the lower part of the breast chestnut, and the second has a bright chestnut lower belly and vent. With the Black Redstart the adult male has body plumage of sooty-black, the lower parts of the rump and abdomen bright chestnut, as is the tail except for the central pair of feathers which are brown. The flight feathers and larger coverts are brown, edged with rufous. The plumage appears to be paler in the autumn but it is the effect produced by the grey edges to the black plumage, these gradually wearing off as the winter progresses. The female is brown tinged with fulvous, paler below and suffused with orange from the abdomen downwards. Rump and tail are chestnut, except for the central feathers which are brown. Further, there is a pale brown eye-ring.

The COMMON or EUROPEAN REDSTART, *P. phoenicurus,* common so far as Europe is concerned, is a migrant to England and Scotland, arriving in the spring and departing in the autumn as some of the Black Redstarts arrive. It is basically a central continental bird although a few venture into Ireland, Portugal and Greece. Sexes are dissimilar, the adult male having the crown, nape and mantle of dark slate, the rump and tail feathers being chestnut. Here again, as with most of the redstarts, the central pair of feathers differ, these being brown. The forehead is white, and the chin, throat and cheeks black. The underparts, including the wing-coverts, are chestnut. The female is brown on the whole of the upperparts except for the rump and tail, which, as with the male, are chestnut, but duller. The underparts are dull rufous. They are hole-nesting birds in so much as they will select any cranny in rocks, ancient masonry, rotten tree stumps etc., where they construct a loosely built nest of grasses, moss, fibres, rootlets and are not adverse to pieces of wool, the whole lined with hair and feathers. The average clutch is six, and, although they will use the same site year after year, it is seldom that they have more than one brood a season. The young are mottled brown above and below, but have the distinctive tail of a redstart. Our experience with them dictated that, under no circumstances, should two males be housed together; in fact I do not recommend that they be put with any member of the same genus.

The PIED STONECHAT, *Saxicola caprata,* is a mainly Oriental bird, found from Iran to Java. There are at least three races, one with the abdomen mainly white, another with it black, and a third with a much heavier bill. The species we had was the *S. c. caprata,* the sexes of which differ. The adult male is black all over except for a large patch at the base of the tail, a wing patch and the lower abdomen which are white. In fresh autumn plumage they appear to be a brownish-black for the feathers have rusty-brown edges, these wearing off as the winter ap-

. . . are not adverse to pieces of wool . . .

proaches. Upper plumage of the female is greyish-brown with a rufous patch at the base of the tail. The wings are dark brown, the feathers having paler edges. The lower plumage also is greyish-brown gradually darkening at the breast and becoming fulvous towards the tail. Similarly as with the male, the early autumn plumage has grey margins, making the general overall colour appear paler. They are about 5½ inches (14 cm) in total length. Although we had them build a nest in a hole in a tree and lay two eggs (bluish-white with freckles and blotches of reddish-brown concentrated round the thicker end), they were both clear.

The INDIAN ROBIN, *Saxicoloides fulicata,* is a larger bird of some 7 inches (18 cm) and is more or less confined to India and Pakistan where it ranges from the Himalayas southward to Ceylon. The sexes are unalike, the adult male is glossy black, with a blue sheen, and has a white shoulder patch. Flight feathers are brown and the centre of the chest deep chestnut, as is a conspicuous patch under the tail. The female has upper plumage of dark brown, the front and sides of the face paler. The tail is darker, almost black, and the centre of the abdomen and under-tail patch are dark chestnut. We had a pair of them housed in a planted aviary with a pair of Lesser Birds of Paradise and for some eight months everything went well. However, the female robin built herself a nest at the junction of two of the aviary's side beams. It was very neat, compact and constructed of very fine twigs, grasses and fibres. She laid four eggs, sea-green in basic colour with freckles and shadings of pale sienna-red mainly round the thicker end, and they measured 19 by 15 mm. Incubuation began on the completion of the clutch and then the male attempted to assert his territorial rights. The Birds of Paradise immediately killed both of them, ate the eggs, and tore the nest apart. Maybe it was foolish to think that, even in a 40 by 40 feet (12 by 12 metres) aviary, another species, also territorial at breeding time, would tolerate each other. We had accomplished breedings under similar conditions in other locations and the main purpose of the aviaries was for Mr. Boehm's research into the ways of birds.

. . . for some eight months everything went well.

The WHITE-STARRED BUSH ROBIN, *Tarsiger stellata,* from southern Sudan to Kenya, is one of the most beautiful bush robins, the sexes being alike. The head and neck are dark slate-blue, and there is a white spot above the front of the eye and another at the base of the neck. The mantle is dark olive-green, the upper tail-coverts and lower plumage are golden yellow. Wings are slate and the tail feathers golden yellow, the outer edges of the outermost and the tips of all of them being black. They have a variety of soft call notes but the alarm note is a grating squeak. We were never fortunate enough to breed them but did raise a young bird to full adult plumage. This bird was sent to Mr. Boehm by the late Cecil Webb. The colouring of the young, black above heavily spotted with pale golden yellow, is a similar pattern to that of the Natal Robins although of different shades. Full adult colouring was attained at about seven months of age. White-starred Bush Robins tend to be rather retiring and keep under cover as much as possible but, like most of the related birds, do gain confidence in captivity, and come out fearlessly at feeding time.

. . . tend to be rather retiring . . .

I now come to the genus *Turdus* of which six species were kept. The first of these is the Grey-winged Blackbird, *T. boulboul,* about 11 inches (28 cm) in total length and a common bird in the Himalayan region. The adult male is deep glossy black, paler and duller below. There is a wide silver-grey patch across the upper side of the wing. The female is olivaceous-ashy-brown, the wing patch pale rufous. The eye has an orange-yellow rim and the bill is coral red to deep orange, dusky at the tip. They are very similar to the European Blackbird, *T. merula,* except for the silver-grey wing patch and the fact that their song is not as extensive. In an aviary containing a very mixed collection, a pair of each of these species nested in adjacent trees, reared their young and all lived in perfect harmony. There was virtually no difference in the construction of the nests, the eggs were the same colour except that those of the Grey-winged were streaked and mottled a little more intensively, and they were the same size.

We had two further European species, the SONG THRUSH, *T. ericetorum*, and the MISTLE THRUSH, *T. viscivorus*. Since there was not sufficient aviary space to give them separate accomodation they were confined to the bird house and no breeding was attempted. The Song Thrush is about 9 inches (23 cm) in total length and the sexes are very much alike; the general colouring is olive-brown, with buff tips to the wing-coverts forming an obscure wing-bar. The underparts are whitish, tinged on the breast and flanks with fulvous to rufous, and spotted with brownish-black on the breast. The only difference we could detect in the sexes was that the throat of the female was less spotted than that of the male, but to sex an individual bird by this alone could be difficult. They are renowned for their liking for snails, breaking the shells by smashing them against stones.

The Mistle Thrush is larger, some 11 inches (28 cm), and again the sexes are much alike. The upperparts are a uniform ash-brown with the underparts buffish-white, heavily spotted with dark brown. Both of these species may be found throughout Europe right through to Siberia, breeding through this entire range, but migrating southward in the winter. However, the Mistle Thrush is only a partial migrant, many British birds leaving in the autumn to winter on the continent, while as many arrive to winter in Britain. They are one of the earliest nesters, March and April, and have been known to nest in February. They have a mild, clear song, rather like the European Blackbird, but not with the same beauty of tone. As their name implies, their main food is berries such as ivy, yew, hawthorn and mistletoe, but, like the Song Thrush, they also eat earthworms.

They are one of the earliest nesters . . .

The PALE-VENTED ROBIN, *T. fumigatus obsoletus*, is a South American species, and those we had were brought back from Ecuador by Mr. Boehm on one of his collecting trips. The sexes are alike, the upper plumage dark russet-brown, slightly darker on the lores and ear-coverts. Wings are brown with the covets and inner-most secondaries dark ochraceous-brown, fading to buffish-white on the centre of the belly. The chin and throat are a similar colour to the upper breast except that they bear faint streaks. The under tail-coverts are whitish with ochrous edges, while the flanks and thighs are pale brown. The under wing-coverts are rich chestnut, the inner edges of the quills paler. The bill, legs and feet are brown. Although a successful breeding took place with two pairs in the Boehm aviaries in 1961, it was not until two years later that we were able to obtain definite identification of the species. Another of the races is the SABIAN THRUSH, *T. f. fumigatus*, but *T. f. obsoletus* comes from the interior of tropical South America whereas the nominate race is confined to east of the Andes. The Pale-vented ranges to the Lower Antilles, Costa Rica and down the western side of the Andes. On receipt, they were released into outdoor aviaries in April. One pair was in a small aviary of 16 by 20 feet, (4 by 6 metres) and the other into one of 60 by 30 feet (18 by 9 metres). The first mentioned settled down immediately and, early in May, the female was observed constructing a nest in a hemlock tree. It was a typical thrush nest, the outer casing bound with mud, with an inner lining of soft, fine grasses. Three eggs were laid over the period 14th to 16th, two of which hatched on

June 2nd and 3rd, the other being clear. The eggs had a ground colour of pale blue, mottled, marked and streaked with pale brown, the markings evenly distributed with no greater concentration in any one place. They measured 29 by 21.5 mm. The incubation, which began on completion of the clutch, was shared, as was the rearing of the young. The young were pale skinned with pale yellow-brown fluff on the top of the head and down the middle on the back. Their gapes were pink, margined in bright yellow. The rearing food in the early days consisted entirely of live food in the form of mealworms, supplied hourly, and any insects the parents could forage for themselves. Development was steady, the eyes opening and quills showing in the wings at seven days. On June 20th, with one 17 and the other 18 days old, they both left the nest. Their plumage was dark brown on the upper parts, including the wings, the throat and upper chest brownish-white mottled with brown. The remainder of the underparts was clear brownish-white. Within two days of their leaving the nest the parents started feeding them fruit and raw ground beef in addition to live food, the fledglings finally attaining independence at thirty-two days old. Full adult plumage was not obtained until they were some six months of age. The pair placed in the larger aviary also reared two out of three eggs, these being hatched in July and independent by late August. Losing one of the adult males later in the winter, his female was transferred to the aviary where the other pair was. Everything went well and each female went to nest early in May. Again they each had three eggs, two hatching from each clutch. It was

. . . intriging to watch the bigamist . . .

intriguing to watch the bigamist male going from nest to nest with live food trying to satisfy both families. Apparently he did so for they were all reared to maturity. This was the first time we had met up with this mutual polygamy and we felt the need to identify the species was more paramount than ever. This was achieved finally when we presented the four birds from the first year's breedings to two different zoos, asking them to verify the species. They both came back with the same answer, the Pale-vented Robin, and the breeding was recognised as a first in captivity.

Another first in America was accomplished with the KUR-RICHANE THRUSH, *T. libonyanus,* a resident over an extensive area in Africa, ranging westward from Malawi and the Transvaal northward to the Sudan, and westward to Senegal. There are several recognised races through this region, the variations mainly in colouring and size, those of the east being generally richer in colour and larger than the western races. The nominate race comes from Kurrichane, West Transvaal, but it was an eastern race, *T. l. tropicalis*, from Mozambique, that we had. They are about eight inches (20 cm) in total length and the sexes are alike. The top of the head, through the back, wings and tail is brownish-grey, the throat and belly white. The chest is buffish-grey with black streaks on the sides of the throat and neck. The flanks and under-wing feathers are deep yellowish-buff, the legs and feet flesh to pale yellow. The bill is bright orange, and the eye is brown with a fine yellow line encircling it. There is a narrow pale buff superciliary eye-stripe running from the base of the upper mandible, over the eye, to the back of the head. We had four of them in the first instance, placed in an aviary in a mixed collection in February one year and it was noticed that, unlike other thrushes we had, these never became really tame, skulking in the bushes at feeding time, only coming out when the aviary was entirely free of humans. In the September of the same year we received another specimen from the same source so, after colour banding it, a standard procedure with us, it was released into the aviary with the others. Careful watch was maintained to ensure it was accepted, and everything was well. It was in March of the following year that the new arrival was seen carrying nesting material to a 2 inch (5 cm) ledge above the aviary door, so an open fronted box, 8 by 6 inches (20 by 15 cm) with a 2 inch (5 cm) front and 6 inch (15 cm) sides was affixed at that spot. The top was made with a 2 inch (5 cm) overhang to give protection from the moisture dripping from the plastic covering of the aviary, and as a deterrent to other birds. The box was accepted and a typical thrush nest constructed therein. A clutch of three eggs was produced, all clear and deserted. They were pale bluish-green in ground colour, finely speckled and spotted all over with pinky-brown, and measured 26 by 18.5 mm. A further clutch was produced and this time two did hatch out but the chicks died at two days old. In the meantime another pair had selected a similar ledge about half way along the side of the aviary, so here went another box. Again a clutch of clear eggs. However, in June three more eggs were laid and incubation, which was shared, began with the laying of the first egg and lasted fourteen days, the chicks hatching on successive days. The nestlings were covered with gingery coloured down and had bright orange gapes. Their eyes were open at six days by which time quills were showing in the wings. This trio never looked back, the parents being most assiduous with

. . . when the aviary was entirely free of humans.

their care and the first fledged at fourteen days, the other two at fifteen days old. Their upper plumage was greyish-brown, like the adults', but the breast was buff, heavily spotted in dark brown, the abdomen was white and the bill dark coloured. There was very little sign of the rich buff yellow on the flanks, these being flecked with brown. At fourteen days after leaving the nest they were feeding themselves and their bills were yellow. It was not until they were some thirteen weeks old that the spottings and fleckings had disappeared from the breast and flanks and they resembled their parents. Their food throughout the rearing period consisted of our own soft food mixture, ground raw beef, and an abundance of live food in the form of mealworms, gentles and crickets. Unlike the Pale-vented, the young Kurrichanes were reared on the above mixed diet from about four days old. The entire group of eight birds, five adults and three young, continued to live amicably together in that same aviary for several years, there being many more breedings, the results of which were dispersed throughout various zoos.

The AMERICAN ROBIN, *T. migratorius*, is purely a North American bird ranging from Canada to Louisiana. It is migratory up and down the country and even a vagrant to Europe. Despite the name Robin, it is a typical thrush, about 10 inches (25 cm) in total length, the title being ascribed to it by the early settlers, the bright chestnut underparts reminding them of the European Robin Red-breast. Sexes are very similar, the female just a paler edition of the male. The head and back are dark grey with bold white markings around the eye. The outer tail feathers bear white tips, clearly seen when the bird is in flight, and the chin is white streaked with black. Underparts, from the throat to the belly, are brick-red, paling to buffish-white under the vent. The bill is yellow, the legs and feet a dark horn colour. We kept a pair of them in the bird-house as living models for Mr. Boehm's porcelains. There was no need to confine them to an aviary to study their breeding habits for a pair nested regularly in a tree just outside the bird-house door. Some older males stay around the entire winter but, normally, in New Jersey, the males arrive early in the spring, the females two to three weeks later. They are very territorial, selecting their nesting sites in a tree, shrub, bush, or even in old buildings, taking over the immediate vicinity around. The nearest we ever found two pairs was at a distance of 25 feet (8 metres) and it was noticed that each pair 'hunted' in a circle away from each other. If one did happen to stray over the invisible boundary line, it was quickly

Fledgling American Robin porcelain sculpture by Edward Marshall Boehm

expelled by the other. Their nest is a thick but symmetrical open bowl made of mud reinforced with leaves and twigs, into which is woven paper, twine and rags. The whole is lined with soft grasses and the clutch varies from 4 to 6 plain greenish-blue eggs. They usually have two broods a season, even three sometimes. They are very insectivorous, a good 40% of their food being noxious garden pests, the remainder made up of small fruits and berries.

The final member of the genus Turdus we had was the CUBAN or RED-LEGGED THRUSH, *T. rubripes,* which has a wide range through the West Indies. It is a large bird, some 10 to 11 inches (25 to 28 cm) in total length, and there is a geographical variation in the colour of the underparts, but it is recognisable by the predominant slate-grey colour, red feet and black tail with broad, white terminal bands to the outer feathers. The chin and throat vary from black to white, according to the region they inhabit, and the bill is reddish. The underparts of the race from Cuba, the one we had, are ochraceous. We never found them a particularly good aviary bird for they are inclined to be bullies and lack any appreciable song. The Cuban Thrush had been bred in the United States and this, coupled with their unsociability, led to them being donated to a zoo.

. . . inclined to be bullies . . .

I now come to the last genus of the Turdinae with which we have been concerned, *Zoothera.* The ORANGE-HEADED GROUND THRUSH, *Z. citrina,* is to be found over a large area of southeastern Asia, there being several races. It is a largish bird, some nine inches (23 cm) in total length, and the sexes are dissimilar. The adult male has the head, neck and lower parts of bright orange-chestnut, rather darker on the crown and the nape. The rest of the upper parts are bluish-grey, wings and tail of brown, marked with bluish-grey. There is a conspicuous white spot on the shoulders and another on the underside of the flight feathers. The vent and under tail-coverts are white. The female is similar except that the orange-chestnut is paler, and the bluish-grey of the upper parts, wings and tail is replaced with brownish-olive-green. This species has been bred in England, but, never having one of each sex at the same time, all we could do was to observe them. As their name implies they spend a lot of their time on the ground, scratching and searching for insects, but they do become very tame and will come to be fed out of the hand.

The last one on our list is the ETHIOPIAN GROUND THRUSH, *Z. piaggiae.* The general range is Ethiopia, Uganda, Kenya, and the eastern parts of the Congo and northern Tanzania. There are some five races and that we had was reputed to be from north-eastern Tanzania, the *Z. p. kilimensis*. They are about the same size as the Orange-headed Ground Thrush and the adult male we had was russet brown above, with the forehead and crown orange-brown. It had large white tips to the wing-coverts, and the chin to throat and flanks were deep orange-brown. The centre of the belly and under tail-coverts were white, the under wing-coverts olive-brown. I understand that the sexes are very similar except that the female generally is paler on the underparts. They have a peculiar call, rather like a hissing trill. As I mentioned, we only ever had the one and accepted the suppliers word that it was a male. It spent most of the time on the ground, only coming up into the bushes at evening time when it would give its quaint call.

They have a peculiar call . . .

Subfamily Timaliinae

This subfamily is comprised of the babblers, wren-tits and rockfowl (Picathartes). It is with the babblers only that we are concerned, for none of the other birds were ever kept at the Boehm aviaries. Babblers belong to the Old World and are found abundantly throughout the Oriental Region, including China and the Phillipines, and even extend to New Guinea, Australia and Africa. In all we had ten species, successful breedings being attained with three of them.

The COMMON QUAKER BABBLER, *Alcippe poioicephala*, is widespread in the Oriental region and there are several subspecies. Those we had were the *A. p. fusca* from Burma where they may be found all through the forests of the foothills, and up to elevations of 5,000 feet (1500 metres). They are six inches (15 cm) in total length and the sexes are alike. The top of the head is ashy-grey, remainder of the upper plumage olive-brown, becoming ferruginous on the wings and tail. The sides of the head and neck ashy-brown, lower plumage creamy-fulvous, darker on the breast, flanks and under tail-coverts. The bill is horny-brown, legs and feet greyish-fleshy. They have a musical call note, a quick succession of alternating high and low notes. Most of their time is spent on the ground or in low shrubs searching for insects.

The GOLDEN-EYED BABBLER, *Chrysoma sinense*, also an Oriental species occurring throughout India, Burma, Thailand and parts of China, is about 7 inches (18 cm) in total length, 4 inches (10 cm) of which is accounted for by the tail.

The sexes are alike the entire upper plumage rufous-brown, changing to cinnamon on the exposed portions of the wings. A patch in front, below and above the eye, and the whole lower plumage are white, tinged with fulvous on the flanks, abdomen and under the tail which is long and graduated and faintly cross-rayed. The bill is black, merging into yellow behind the nostrils. The legs and feet orange-yellow. The iris is yellow with deep orange eyelids. They are not ground frequenters, preferring tall grasses, low scrub and bushes, avoiding forests. Gregarious by nature they keep up a soft chattering as they search through the vegetation for insects.

The BLACK-HEADED SIBIA, *Heterophasia capistrata*, is to be found throughout the Himalayan foothills in the wooded areas. Mainly an arboreal bird, seldom coming to the ground, they may be seen in roving parties. They have a rather clumsy, heavy flight, the wing beats being jerky and noisy. They are about 9 inches (23 cm) in total length and the sexes are alike in colour. The only difference we could ever see between them was that the bill of the female was a trifle shorter than that of the male. To tell them apart was extremely difficult. The top, sides of head and crest are black, the upper back grey-brown, the remainder of the body plumage bright chestnut. The wings are bluish-grey, variegated with rufous and black, and with a white bar across the coverts. The long graduated tail is rufous at the base with a broad black band three parts of the way along, the tips of the feathers sooty-grey. Their song can in no way be deemed musical for, in the non-breeding season it is confined to an incessant quiet chatter of "ty-te-te". In the breeding season they have a long, loud whistle, repeated over and over again. Their alarm note, however, never varies, is loud and best described as "tchar-tchar". We had four of them that had wintered out in temperatures dropping well below freezing level for days on end and, although there was a feeding shelter they could have come into at night, they roosted outside in a hemlock tree. It was in July that two of them were observed busy constructing a nest about ten feet (3 metres) up in the hemlock. Fortunately it was at the side of the aviary and it was possible to follow developments by climbing up by the outer wiring. Both birds worked on it producing an open cup nest of rootlets, grass and pine needles, lined with finer grasses and dog hair. The first egg was laid on July 24, with a second the following day. They were pale bluish-green with splashes and splotches of reddish-brown but it was not possible to measure one. By now the difference

. . . may be seen in roving parties . . .

in the size of the bills had been noted, this indicating that the other two were both males but, beyond avoiding the hemlock, the four carried on quite peacefully with the sixty or so other birds in the same enclosure. Incubation was shared, lasting for fourteen days and one chick hatched, the second egg disappearing two days later. The nestling was covered with long, hair-like light brown fluff and had a reddish-orange gape. The rearing, also shared, was effected with live-food in the form of insects they foraged, supplemented with hourly issues of mealworms and gentles. Despite their heavy flight, they were swift enough in their swoops on any passing insect for they knew they had to be alert so as to compete with other birds that had young in the nest, or on the wing, in the same aviary. At five days the nestling's eyes were open and feathering up had commenced. Fledging at sixteen days, the young bird had a black cap, brown back and rump and rufous underparts. The black and white markings in the wings followed the same pattern as in the adults, but its flying abilities were very poor. It was almost two weeks before it was able to join its parents in the upper branches of the trees but, once this had been accomplished, it quickly became independent. Further broods were reared in subsequent years and the slowness in development of the fledglings was noted each time.

The SILVER-EARED MESIA, *Leiothrix argentauris,* another Asiatic bird, has a normal range extending through the Himalayan foothills to Burma, Thailand and Malaysia. There are at least three subspecies but it is with the nominate race that we are concerned. About 7 inches (18 cm) in total length, the adult male has an orange forehead, chin, throat and breast, nape of neck is also orange but with a greyish suffusion. Top of head and face black except for the extensive ear-coverts which are silvery-white. The mantle, back and rump grey, wings grey streaked with orange, and a large crimson patch in the centre of the primaries. The upper and lower tail-coverts are crimson, the tail dark grey, all the feathers edged with yellow. Fine black whiskers adorn the base of the upper mandible, which, with the lower, is yellow as are the legs and feet. The female basically is the same colour except that the orange portions and the crimson wing patches are not as brilliant. Further, the upper and lower tail-coverts are a dusky reddish-green. In the wild they move around in flocks and their cheerful song, the male having a chorus of seven to eight notes, make them readily identifiable by ear. The alarm note of the male, just four notes, resembles

. . . they move around in flocks . . .

182

the normal call of the female but is much shriller. In the same aviary as the Black-headed Sibias was one male and three female Mesias. A pair selected a nesting site in an azalea bush, and, after about four days work by both of them, an open cup nest of fine grasses, pieces of wool, and dog hair was completed, the whole being suspended from the branches of the azalea by shredded string. The total clutch was three, incubation shared, and the first hatched on the fourteenth day. One egg, being clear, provided the following data: pale blue, lightly mottled with reddish-brown concentrated round the thicker end, and measuring 21 by 14.5 mm. The nestlings were light skinned, covered with pale buff fluff and had gapes of bright orange. As with the incubation, the rearing was shared and, by the time the chicks' quill feathers were showing, their backs and head were covered with dark feathering and their eyes were open. Fledging at twelve days it was noticed that one had bright red tail-coverts, the other's being rusty-green, thus indicating that they are sexable on leaving the nest. In addition to the other two female Mesias there was a solitary female Pekin Robin in the same aviary and, although none of these birds had paid any attention to the nesting pair and their activities in rearing, once the young left the nest, all three joined in feeding them. The parent birds evinced no objections and, within two weeks, had another nest built, this containing four eggs which all duly hatched. By now the female Pekin Robin had taken over complete charge of the young male, the female Mesias looking after the other two. In the second nest there were three females and one male and again the foster parents took over the feeding of the fledglings thus permitting the pair to go to nest yet once more and to produce another male and a female.

. . . there was a solitary female . . .

The PEKIN ROBIN, *Leiothrix lutea,* is another Himalayan species extending right through to China. There are several geographical races, those we had coming from India, the *L. l. callipyga.* They are smaller than the Mesia being some 6 inches (15 cm) in length. The adult male has upper plumage of dull olive-green, throat and breast bright orange-yellow, the remainder of the lower plumage olive-green with a yellowish suffusion. A ring round the eye extending to the bill is dull yellow. The edges of the wing feathers are brightly variegated with yellow, orange, crimson and black. The tail is olive-brown, blackish at the tip which curves outward, the upper tail-coverts extending two-thirds of the length of the tail and terminating in a thin white line. The bill is orange-red in the breeding season, the base turning blackish during the winter. The female is duller in plumage, has no crimson on the wing, and the bill is not as colourful. It is sometimes referred to as the Japanese Nightingale on account of both its song and its eastern origin. They make excellent aviary birds, as easy to cater for as the Mesias, being fruit, ground raw beef and insect eaters, and are very hardy. Further, they are sociable as may have been gathered from the account of the Mesia breeding.

The BLUE-WINGED SIVA, *Minla cyanouroptera,* also from the Himalayas ranging from the eastern parts, through Burma and into northern Malaysia, geographical races being recognised in the various locations. The nominate race, the one we had, being from Nepal. They are six inches (15 cm) in total length, nearly half of this accounted for by the tail, and the sexes are alike. The top of the head, nape, wings and tail are sky-blue striped with black and white, the remainder of the upperparts reddish-olive. The underparts are whitish with grey thighs, brownish-flesh coloured legs and feet, and a yellowish bill. In the wild they move around in small parties and have no characteristic call note. They are very hardy, and have wintered out in New Jersey. Although they did breed in the Boehm aviaries no detailed report can be given for, until such time as four came into the winter feeding shelter one day, we were not even aware that their numbers had doubled somehow during the summer months. This does tend to indicate that they are very secretive about their nesting sites for the aviary was under constant scrutiny with its forty or so different species. We did know that five species were breeding in there at that time and these are all covered in this work.

. . . they are very secretive . . .

The RUSTY-CHEEKED SCIMITAR BABBLER, *Pomatorhinus erythrogenys,* has a wide range through the entire length of the Himalayas into China. They are 11 inches (28 cm) in total length, and the sexes are similar. The forehead, sides of head and neck, thighs and under tail-coverts are chestnut, the chin, throat and abdomen white, the chin and throat striped with pale grey. The upper plumage, wings and long, graduated tail are olive-brown, the bill, long and curved over and downward light horny. The small roundish wings give an ungainly appearance, and these babblers spend most of their time on the ground and, when disturbed seldom fly but make off in long bounding hops. However, when they do fly they are very strong on the wing and fly in a direct line. The male has a two-note call, the first high and the second low, but we never heard the

female utter but one, about midway in tone between those of the
male. It was only heard early in the morning or just before dusk,
the harsh, scolding alarm note being the normal greeting during
the day.

The RED-CAPPED BABBLER, *Timalia pileata,* is a common resident throughout Burma and parts of India. They are
7 inches (18 cm) in length, sexes are alike, the deep crimson
crown with a white streak over each eye being most distinctive.
The remainder of the upperparts are olive-brown with a deeply
graduated tail. The throat and breast white, finely streaked
with black, the abdomen a pale rufous with olive-grey vent and
under tail-coverts. They do not make good aviary birds since
they spend most of the time hidden in the shrubberies. The
only time we could ever see them was at the early morning feeding when they might dart out to seize a mealworm, and then back
under cover.

The YELLOW-NAPED IXULUS, *Yuhina flavicollis,*
another Himalayan species, is 5 inches (13 cm) in total length
and the sexes are alike. Dark brown head and bushy crest, grey
ear-coverts, buffy-rufous nape and back of neck and a white
eye-ring. The cheeks and throat are white with a long, black
moustachial streak. The remainder of the upperparts olive-
brown, the underparts white with a buffish tinge. They make
delightful cage or aviary birds being very tit-like in their movements, raising and lowering their fluffy crest at the slightest
provocation.

The last member of the babbler group we had, and the smallest being but $4\frac{1}{2}$ inches (11 cm) in total length, was the BLACK-CHINNED YUHINA, *Yuhina nigrimentum intermedia*. This was the smallest insectivorous bird we ever had the pleasure to breed and rear to maturity. Native to the northern parts of India and Pakistan, they can be found throughout the Himalayan foothills through to China. The sexes are alike but there are three main features that distinguish this species from all other Yuhinas. A red lower mandible, a white throat, a black spot on the chin and a salmon-pink gape. The crest, at repose lying flat but erected with every movement the bird makes, is black and the nape grey. The remainder of the upperparts are dark brown with light brown flight feathers. Except for the throat, the underparts are pale buff with flesh coloured legs and feet. The upper mandible is dark grey, contrasting sharply with the red of the lower. Yuhinas are very tit-like in all their movements and, to most of their own size, very pugnacious. This fact was borne out with us when four of them in a large planted aviary very quickly reduced their numbers to the pair that bred.

. . . and we were able to rescue them.

They also attacked some Yellow-naped Ixulus but this was detected and we were able to rescue them. It was only a matter of days after this episode that they began carrying nesting materials up to the upper timbers of the aviary. As they did not appear to be having much success in attaching the fine grasses, an open grass nest was made by us and suspended just below the roof. This they took to immediately, the first egg of four being laid on July 11. Although not removed for measuring, they appeared to be about 10 by 6 mm and were pale blue, heavily spotted with brown. It was difficult to observe if the incubation was shared for they were so quick in all their movements that to attempt to compare the size of the crest, the only distinguishing sexual feature, with that of the sitting bird was fairly hopeless. Similarly, owing to the location of the nest, it is not definite as to when the eggs hatched but, on July 24, early in the morning, it was seen that both birds were catching flies and carrying them up to the nest. Immediately the morning issue of mealworms was produced they both seized on one each, beat it to a pulp and then took it up to the nest. From then on mealworms and gentles were supplied at frequent intervals throughout the day and it was interesting to note how they went for the larger ones first. Actually this preference for the bigger mealworms had been noticed even before they started to nest, and this prevailed throughout the rearing period and became the habit of the young bird on attaining independence. Only one was reared to maturity although it is known that three hatched, the two bodies being found. Fledging on August 4, the upper plumage was dark brown, flanks buff, underparts pale buff, black spot on the chin but the white throat did not evolve for a further eight days. The bill completely black, the red of the lower mandible showing at seven weeks and, by the end of the eighth week, both upper and lower mandibles had changed colour. It attained independence at twenty days and, after our previous experience, was separated from its parents without delay.

. . . was
separated
from its
parents
without
delay.

Subfamily Paradoxornithinae

We only ever had one species of this subfamily and that was the EASTERN BEARDED REEDLING, *Panurus biarmicus russicus,* also known as the Bearded Tit-mouse, or Reed Pheasant. It is a subspecies that comes from the Far East and our pair were a gift to Mr. Boehm by Dr. K. C. Searle of Hong Kong.

The sexes are unalike in appearance, even as fledglings as will be explained later, the adult male having a blue-grey head, the remainder of the upperparts tawny-orange. From the lores, and partly encircling the eyes, is a black patch that runs down the neck in a conspicuous moustachial streak, ending in pointed feathers. The scapulars are buffish-white, the secondaries steaked with buff, black and tawny. The primaries and outer tail feathers are margined with white. The chin, throat and breast greyish-white, the breast having a pinkish suffusion. Flanks tawny, under tail-coverts black, bill orange-yellow, legs and feet black and the irides yellow. The female has no moustache, the top of the head dark brown and the under tail-coverts buff. They were about 6½ inches (16 cms) in total length.

In the wild their normal habitat is reed-beds where they spend most of their time down amongst the roots searching out insects and small molluscs. Their unmistakable "ping, ping" call note, invariable answered by others in the area, discloses their presence. There being no reed-beds in the aviary they were allocated to, our pair selected a nesting site in a privet, the upper branches of which had grown through a taxus bush. The female did most of the building, the male collecting Spanish moss, dog hair, shredded string and fine grasses. With these she constructed a deep woven nest, securely binding the two shrubs together. The entrance was at the top, slightly off centre, and, in all, some seven days were spent on the constructing.

*Far Eastern
Bearded Reedling
nestling*

The first egg was laid on June 28, with a second and third on the next two days, incubation commencing with the laying of the last, and two hatched on July 11th. The third egg was clear, measured 19 by 15 mm, was creamy-white with a pinkish suffusion in ground colour, thinly speckled with pale brown spots and marked with wavy lines of the same colour. The nestlings had most intriguing gapes of red, the roof of the upper mandible being a deeper shade and bearing conspicuous white spots, the whole margined in deep orange. Both parents tended to the rearing, the female doing most of the brooding. To provide sufficient small insects, leafmould and rotting bark was gathered from the neighbouring woods four times daily and spread near to the nest. In addition the smallest mealworms it was possible to sort out were given at hourly intervals. At six days the nestlings' eyes were open and they were feathering up in tawny-orange with black stripes. By now the parents were feeding them larger mealworms, larvae and moths caught in the night traps. Fledging at twelve days, their colouring favoured that of the adult female except that their heads were streaked with dark chocolate and there was a broad, dark coloured band running down the centre of the back. Both had dark coloured under tail-coverts, one being much darker than the other's, and the darker one also had a black spot below each eye. These are the sex indicators referred to earlier, the one with the darker under tail-coverts and the spot under the eye being a male. This statement is not just based on this one breeding, for subsequent young proved its validity. Independence was attained at 23 days and full adult plumage acquired at the early age of ten weeks.

. . . peaceful and easy . . . They make excellent aviary birds, peaceful and easy to cater for as adults for they will take a little seed, soft food mixture, ground raw beef and whatever live food they can forage. Spending most of their time on the ground, their flight is weak and of a short, undulating nature. As mentioned earlier, their "ping, ping" always discloses their whereabouts.

Subfamily Sylviinae

This subfamily is made up of the Old World warblers, kinglets, tit-warblers and fern-bird. We only had three species, one from Africa, one from Asia and the other from Europe.

The RED-WINGED WARBLER, *Cisticola erythroptera rhodoptera,* is an African subspecies ranging from Kenya to

Zambia and Mozambique. The sexes are said to be alike and, since we had but one specimen, we did not know if it was a male or a female. The top and sides of the head are grey, the mantle olivaceous-brown, wings chestnut, the flanks, belly and under tail-coverts pale tawny, the throat and breast creamy-white. The tail is russet with subterminal dusky bands and white tips. About 5½ inches (14 cm) in total length, they have a very penetrating twittering call and are very insectivorous.

The YELLOW-BELLIED WREN-WARBLER, *Prinia flaviventris,* is widespread throughout south-east Asia and also is about 5½ inches (14 cm) in length. The forehead and crown are dark grey, the mantle and tail olive, the tail feathers having white tips. Throat and breast white, the remainder of the under-parts faintly washed with yellow, more prominent on the flanks, and the bill and feet are black. It has a weak flight and, whilst flying, makes a curious clicking or snapping sound, whether by the wings or the bill we could never determine. It had a cheery little song, sometimes very quiet and at others a clear, loud treble repeated frequently. As with most of the singleton specimens Mr. Boehm received from time to time, both the Red-winged Warbler and the Yellow-bellied Wren-warbler were passed on to a zoo where a breeding programme was not the main objective.

The final member of this subfamily we were concerned with was a pair of BLACKCAP WARBLERS, *Sylvia atricapilla,* that I brought over from England. Actually they preceded my wife and me by two days and the male Blackcap caused quite a stir for he escaped whilst they were unpacking some twenty or so boxes of birds we had sent over. The following morning Mr. Boehm had a call from the local garage telling him that a strange grey bird with a black head and a silver band on its leg was walking around the gas pumps and taking pieces of bread from the attendants. It took no time to get down there and reunite him with his mate for we had trained him to come and feed out of our hands. It is a common European bird found wherever there are woodland glades with undergrowth. About 5½ inches (14 cm) in total length, the sexes are unalike. The adult male has a glossy black crown, down to eye level, with the sides of the head and the underparts ashy-grey. The mantle and tail are greyish-brown. The female has a red-brown crown, and a browner back and underparts than the male. The male has a rich, warbling song, very varied and building up in strength towards the end. Their song has often been compared to that of the European Nightingale. Unfortunately we were not to breed

. . . they preceded my wife and me by two days . . .

them in America for a weasel got into their aviary and, amongst some twenty birds it slaughtered, both the Blackcaps were included.

Subfamily Malurinae

This subfamily consists of the Australian wrens, wren-warblers and warblers. There are some 80 species to be found in Australia, New Guinea and New Zealand, but it does not include the three species of New Zealand wrens for these are grouped in the suborder Tyranni in the family Xenicidae. Although we had none of the latter, two species of Malurinae were kept, with breeding results from one of them.

The CRIMSON CHAT, *Epthianura tricolor,* can be found throughout Australia with the exception of the Cape York Peninsula. The sexes are dissimilar, the male having a crimson crown, base of tail, breast and abdomen. The face, back of head, mantle and wings are dark brown as is the tip of the tail which also is spotted with white. The throat and vent are white. The female lacks the crimson crown, breast and abdomen, and the base of the tail is a duller shade. The throat is white and the abdomen is a pinkish colour. They are just over 4 inches (10 cm) in total length and their main food is insects. They are best kept in an aviary as they do not settle well to cage life.

They are best kept in an aviary . . .

The FAIRY BLUE WREN, *Malurus cyaneus,* is native to south-east Australia and Tasmania. In these areas they are also referred to as the Superb Wren, Blue Bonnet, Cocktail and, on account of their song, the Superb Warbler. They are some five inches (13 cm) in total length but, since half of this is accounted for by their tail, they appear to be much smaller. The adult male in full colour has enamel-blue ear-coverts, crown, nape and lower back. The throat is dark blue, the upper chest, face and upper back black, the lower abdomen and under tail-coverts whitish-grey. The tail is blue and the flight feathers are dark brown, as is the bill. The adult female is greyish-brown with a dark brown tail, lighter underparts and a reddish-brown bill. She also has reddish-brown lines over and below the eye, joining at the back of the head in the form of an horizontal V. For the first three years of age the males have an eclipse plumage in which they lose all their enamel-blue colouring and much of the black. However, they do retain the blue tail and the dark bill and, normally, there are scattered patches of black on the upper back.

We received four pairs in July 1961, three males being in full colour. Only one pair was placed in an aviary, the others being retained in the birdhouse. Within ten days of being out there the female was observed building a nest. All the construction, even down to collecting material in the form of fine grasses, rootlets, dog hair etc., was undertaken by her, the male just flitting around singing his head off. When the nest was almost complete she began to pull it apart and started on another one a little further into the aviary. This also was discarded and a third, and last, was completed in an azalea bush. The final structure was dome shaped, with an entrance near to the top and protected by a form of overhang. It was deep and completely concealed the hen when she began to sit on the first egg produced on August 19. The final clutch was three and all incubating was carried out by the female. Over two weeks elapsed but, finally on September 6 she left the nest unattended for the entire morning. Examination revealed that all the eggs had been damaged but they were all fertile. They were pinkish-white, lightly spotted with reddish-brown, and measured 10 by 17 mm. Another nest was made in the same bush, of much better construction this time, and the first egg of three was laid on September 14. This time all went well, the first chick hatching on the 27th, followed by two more by the evening of the following day. All that could be seen of them was just three bright pink gapes for they were too far back in the nest for any other details to be discernible. By the time they were seven days old they advanced to the entrance hole and then one could see six dark little eyes set in heads covered with greyish-brown feathering. As soon as the first hatched the male took up his responsibilities and began seeking out live food. For the first three days he fed everything direct to the female as she sat on the nest but, after that, he took the food to the nestlings themselves. In addition to the many flies and insects they foraged for themselves, hourly issues of small mealworms and gentles were made throughout the day. Further, each evening an illuminated insect trap was set up, the contents being released into the aviary at intervals the following day. The catch consisted of all manner of flying insects ranging from large moths to minute midges, all caught alive. The female preferred the bigger moths which she would carry to the nest, strip off the wings, and then cram the fat bodies down the tiny throats. The male was never seen to do this, he confining his collecting to the smaller insects and bugs. They fledged at ten days and, although very tiny, were very strong on

. . . singing his head off.

191

the wing, following their parents all round the aviary asking to be fed. Their colouring closely resembled that of the adult female but was of a lighter shade and the V-shape marking round the head was missing. They roosted with their parents, the entire five of them not taking up much more than two inches (6 cm) of perching space. Although picking up for themselves at three weeks, it was not for another week that the parents gave up feeding them entirely. At four months of age blue feathers began to show in the tail of one of them and the final sexing was one male and three females. Several more breedings took place over the ensuing years, both by the pair written on above, other pairs and even by the birds bred in the aviaries for they come into breeding condition at their first year. Although gregarious in the nonbreeding season they are very territorially minded when it comes to selecting their nesting site, and it is strongly recommended that not more than one breeding pair be kept in a single enclosure.

Subfamily Muscicapinae

This subfamily, comprised of the Old World flycatchers, is distributed over the entire eastern hemisphere and some species have even been colonised in New Zealand and the Hawaiian Islands. Their ecological niche in the New World is filled by the subfamily Tyrannidae, dealt with earlier. The largest group of Muscicapinae is in the Australasian region where some 350 species are recognised, most of them being migratory. The Ethiopian region has over 150 species within its bounds, only 4 being resident. The Palearctic region has but 14 species, all migratory.

Flycatchers are insect eaters primarily, taking only a modicum of other varieties of food. In consequence they are one of the more difficult groups of birds to keep in confinement, particularly when housed just in cages. However, with judicious feeding they can be "meated off" on to an insectile soft food mixture and ground raw beef, but it does require time and *. . . time and* patience to induce them to take sufficient of these foods to sustain *patience . . .* them. Many flycatchers we had at the Boehm aviaries lived by taking insects on the wing and, with such species, we used to toss mealworms to them, release flies into their rooms, together with any other insects we could procure, for several days before we could induce them to come down and help themselves to moving live food in their feeding dishes. We might have had to do this every half hour or so for the first day gradually lengthening the period until, by about the fifth day, they would begin to look round for themselves. Once this stage was accomplished then was the time to introduce the insectile mixture with the live food on top of it. Needless to say much of the live food buried itself in the other food necessitating the birds having to dig for it, thus getting a taste of the soft food.

Mr. Boehm's principle was to allow about one month before he felt more or less confident that the birds were fully converted to domestic feeding. However, if a suitably planted outdoor aviary was available before that time, we used to release them there after only about fourteen days of acclimatisation. Great care had to be exercised in the selection of species for an aviary because flycatchers do not agree with each other. In all, over the years, we had twenty different species, but very few breeding successes.

. . . do not agree with each other.

The GREY FLYCATCHER, *Bradornis microrhynchus*, an African species, ranges through much of eastern and north-eastern Africa, and it is considered synonymous with *B. griseus ukamba* which is quite common in Kenya. Sexes are alike, plain coloured ash-grey above with dusky streaks on the head. The underparts are paler, the throat and centre of the belly whitish. This species is not common in confinement and we had but one pair which became readily adapted to cage life. They appeared to have very little song; the only sound we ever heard being a low, mellow tweet, tweet. They were one of the easiest we ever had to "meat off", readily taking to the soft food and the ground meat with but a small amount of live food. We kept them for about eighteen months, in a cage, and then donated them to a zoo.

The BLACK-NAPED MONARCH FLYCATCHER, *Hypothymis azurea*, is common in south-east Asia. About $6\frac{1}{2}$ inches (16 cm) in total length, the male is azure blue with a black skull cap and narrow black bands on the forehead and upper breast. The flanks and abdomen are white. The female is duller, lacking the black markings, and the back, wings and tail are dull olive-brown. There are several subspecies, the pair we had, from Burma, being *H. a. styani*. They are very docile in all their habits but do require a plentiful supply of live food to keep them in good condition. Except for a quiet little call note, tweet, tweet, tweet, and an alarm note like a prolonged hiss, we heard no other sound from them.

Of the genus *Muscicapa* we had ten different species, the

first the JAPANESE BLUE FLYCATCHER, *M. cyanomelana*. This, as the name implies, is a Far Eastern bird breeding in China and Japan but migrating to Malaysia, Thailand and the neighbouring countries, even going as far afield as Borneo, during the winter. Seven inches (18 cm) in total length, the sexes are dissimilar. The adult male has a crown of glittering blue, the rest of the upperparts dark blue, except for the base of the tail which is white. The female is brown with a lighter throat patch, whitish belly, and has a buff eye-ring. Although insect eaters in the wild, they also consume a great amount of berries and, in confinement, we found them very partial to dried currants and the smaller raisins, seeming to prefer them dry as against being soaked, the manner in which we normally served them to other berry-eaters.

The WHITE-EYED SLATY FLYCATCHER, *M. fischeri*, of which there are three subspecies, is African, ranging over a large area of East Africa. About 7 inches (18 cm) in total length, the sexes are alike. Above is slate-grey, the breast, abdomen and under tail-coverts being white with a buffish wash. Not only do they hawk insects on the wing, they also search assiduously through the foliage for them. Tiny nestlings also are taken. This fact we found out the hard way after the mysterious disappearance of some newly hatched tanagers. The flycatchers were caught in the act. This variation in their diet makes them fairly easy to acclimatise. Despite their rather plain colouring, they are attractive for their entire posture and movements are emblematic of vitality. They can hardly be credited with a song as such for their call is more of a chattering trill on a descending scale. We had two housed together for several years but, although there was a slight difference in the intensity of the eye-ring, and one's head was slimmer than the other's, they never made any attempt to go to nest or indulge in amorous overtures towards each other.

. . . they are attractive . . .

The PIED FLYCATCHER, *M. hypoleuca*, is a summer breeding visitor to Great Britain, frequenting Wales through to north-east England, and is a passage migrant, very restricted in distribution in the British Isles. It breeds throughout Europe, temperate Asia and West Africa, wintering in tropical Africa. In summer dress the adult male is markedly pied, black above and white below. The forehead is white and there is a broad white wing-bar. The female is brown and white, lacks the white forehead and her wing-bar is smaller. In the autumn both sexes are alike except for the difference in size of the wing-bar.

They are both about 5 inches (13 cm) in total length and, although they hawk insects in the air, they also descend to the ground in search of food. They are hole-nesters, any aperture in a wall, tree or building sufficing, old woodpecker's nests often being utilised. The male has a very pleasing song, not unlike that of the European Redstart. Like the majority of flycatchers, when they are resting on a perch they normally drop their wings down to the sides of the body. A pair my wife exhibited in England many years ago were faulted for this typical posture, much to everyone's surprise. By way of consolation, the late Percy Bufton presented a very handsome water-colour of the pair to my wife, and it is still one of our treasured possessions. Actually this was the pair that was in the Boehm aviaries for we took them with us when I took up the appointment of curator there.

The LESSER NILTAVA, *M. macgrigoriae*, is an Asiatic species from the higher hills of Burma, and extending westward through East Pakistan to the Simla Hills in India. It is a small bird, about 5 inches (13 cm) in length, and the sexes are unalike. The adult male is brilliant blue above, the underparts ashy-grey. There is black round the eyes and bill, and the throat, ear-coverts, cheeks and breast are purplish. There are small blue patches on the side of the neck, a characteristic with niltavas. The female is olive-brown above and buff below, but also bears the two blue neck-tabs. The male has a soft, four-note song, rising in pitch at the end of the second note and then falling. Although not as secretive as some, this species tends to frequent shrubberies, darting out on any unwary insect. They are most swift in all their movements and, when kept in aviaries, the necessity to have an adequate safety door cannot be overemphasized as they will fly down to ground level to catch any insect disturbed by the opening of a door and, before you know it, they are through your legs and away. We found them very congenial in a mixed collection and highly recommend them as aviary birds.

The BLACK and YELLOW FLYCATCHER, also known as the NARCISSUS, *M. narcissima*, is an eastern Asian species that migrates southward as far as Burma during the winter. This also is about 5 inches (13 cm) in total length, and the sexes are dissimilar. The adult male has upperparts of black except for a bright yellow eye-stripe and rump, and a white shoulder patch. Underparts from the chin downwards are orange, paling towards the vent. The female is olive-green above with a fine white eye-ring and two whitish wing-bars. Her underparts are buffish with a yellowish wash. We only ever housed them as cage birds but their confident manner, and habit of flicking their wings and tail, is most appealing, and they do make excellent exhibition birds. Their need for live food did not appear to be as great as that of the Lesser Niltava for they did very well on our soft food mixture and small berries, with but a modicum of mealworms or gentles to supplement their daily diet.

The RED-BREASTED FLYCATCHER, *M. parva,* is a rare British visitor for its main breeding area is in eastern Central Europe and Asia, spreading through to Burma. Again the sexes differ in that the male has the throat and breast pale red, the remainder of the plumage brown above and white below. The head is greyish-brown and there are two conspicuous white patches at the base of the blackish tail. The female is similar except that the red is much paler, and the head is the same colour as the rest of the upperparts. Slightly smaller than the Pied Flycatcher, it is much more secretive in its habits, hiding in the foliage, sallying forth to catch up an insect, and back to hiding again. It too has a pleasing song, seldom heard owing to the bird's seclusive nature, but uttered usually from a high position in a tree. The alarm note, however, is harsh and jarring, like a toy wooden rattle rotated at speed, and it is usually this that advises one of their presence. They are definitely non-gregarious, and should never be housed with more of their own species.

. . . like a toy wooden rattle . . .

The BLUE-THROATED FLYCATCHER, *M. rubeculoides,* is another Asiatic species, most of those trapped for export coming from the Himalayan foothills. They are about 6 inches (15 cm) in total length, and the sexes are unalike. The entire upperparts of the adult male are dark blue, paler on the rump and shoulders, and the forehead is even a paler blue. The sides of the throat and breast are ferruginous, this colour continuing through the underparts, paling towards the vent to almost white. The female, lacking all the blue colouring, is darkish brown above with a buff chin and throat, ferruginous breast, the rest of the underparts white. The Blue-throated is sometimes confused with the TICKELL'S FLYCATCHER, *M. tickelliae,* another Indian species we kept. However, in the case of the latter, the ferruginous of the breast extends up through the throat to the chin, leaving only a tiny patch of blue at the base of the bill. Both species are most at home in a thickly planted aviary for, in their natural habitats, they are forest dwellers, being fully at home in the undergrowth and on the banks of wooded streams. They are two of the gentler dispositioned flycatchers and we have housed them quite safely together but, as insects are their main food, it is essential to ensure there is an adequate supply the year round. Both species are shy, and observing and studying them requires patience and quietude. The Tickell's has quite a pleasant song of five or six notes, usually heralded by a couple of sharp clicks, the song following being repeated over and over again. The Blue-throated's song is similar but, to my ear, not as sweet.

The ORANGE-GORGETTED FLYCATCHER, *M. strophiata,* is another peaceful species and we kept them with the Tickell's and Blue-throated. The sexes are very similar in colouration, the adult male olive-brown above with black cheeks and throat, and an orange-red spot under the throat. The forehead and brow are white, the sides of the neck and breast slate-grey, the remainder of the underparts paling to greyish-white. There are two distinct white patches at the base of the tail. The female lacks the black cheeks and throat, this colour being replaced with grey. Further, the orange-red throat patch is much paler. We had several of them over the years and, although we never got them to go to nest, they became very tame, readily coming to be hand-fed.

. . . they became very tame . . .

One of the most beautiful flycatchers is the RUFOUS-BELLIED NILTAVA, *M. sundara.* Its range is throughout the Himalayan foothills, being found from the Murree Hills right through to Assam and the northern parts of Burma where it follows the hilly country down both the eastern and western sides. Further, it extends into Laos, Vietnam and the Yunnan district of western China. It may be found at elevation of 5,000 to 8,000 feet (1500 to 2400 metres) and I have spent many happy hours watching them in both the Murree and Simla Hills. Three races are listed, *M. s. fastuosa, M. s. sundara* and *M. s. denotata.* They are about 6½ inches (17 cm) in total length and the sexes are dissimilar. The adult male has a black forehead, lores, sides of head and throat, the crown, nape, rump, greater wing-coverts and upper tail-coverts of brilliant blue, the remainder of the upperparts deep blue. The underparts from the throat downwards are rich rufous. On the sides of the neck are two tabs of brilliant cobalt-blue. The bill is thin with black rictal bristles, so regularly found in flycatchers. Colouring of the female is confined to varying shades of soft browns and, in addition to the neck tabs, there is a white throat patch. Both sexes have pleasing songs, that of the male being varied and quite distinct. The

Young Asiatic Niltava

female's by comparison, however, is very faint, but very tuneful. Peaceful towards most other birds, except flycatchers, they make admirable aviary inmates, their diet being mainly live food, ground raw beef and a little fruit. Males, however, can be very quarrelsome amongst themselves and two should never be housed in the same quarters. As the breeding season approaches a pair need to be watched carefully for the males tend to come into breeding condition ahead of the females, at least this was our experience with them, and, in confined quarters, this can lead to fatal results. We bred them at the Boehm aviaries despite the fact that it took us two females to achieve it. The first one was nearly killed by the amorous male, but the second was more than a match for him and everything went well. Their first nest was built in the top of a trumpet vine, a most untidy cup nest, in which she laid four eggs. These disappeared four days later. She then chose a hole in the masonry of the wall of the main bird-house, which backed on to their aviary. This was in such a position that it was possible to watch the entire sequence of events. Again it was an untidy open cup nest and four more eggs were laid. Incubation, by the female only, began with the laying of the last egg and two hatched at the end of thirteen days, the others being clear. The eggs measured 20 by 16 mm., and were basically white, speckled very finely all over with pinkish-brown, giving, at first sight, an impression that they were an uniform pinkish-white. The following day the two chicks and the eggs had vanished. This was attributed either to a pair of Hoopoes that had young in the nest, or to the Masked Wood Swallows that had young on the wing. A test case was set up by placing a clear egg from a Black-headed Sugarbird in the nest and watching. Within five minutes of my leaving the aviary the male Wood Swallow entered the nest, took the egg in his bill, flew over to his young and fed the contents to them. Immediately the Wood Swallow's entire family was caught up and transferred to another aviary. Whilst the female Niltava had been sitting, she had busied herself tidying up the loose ends of grass and, by the time incubation was completed, it was very neat and tidy. Fortunately the setback had not deterred her for she laid another round of four and this time three hatched. The nestlings were minute, covered with dark fuzz and had pinkish-orange gapes. Their eyes were open at eight days by which time they were well feathered in dark brown. Fledging at thirteen days they could be sexed immediately, the young male having bright blue tips to his little

. . . was more than a match for him . . .

tail, and was much darker than the other two who had white throat patches. Independent at eleven days of vacating the nest, they had to be removed as the father began to persecute them. By four weeks of age the young male's tail was fully grown and as bright blue as that of his father's. Although not visible at this time, they all had the blue neck tabs for these could be seen by parting the feathers with one's fingers. The blue on the crown and wings of the male did not begin to show until he was about two months old, but, at six months, he had acquired full adult colouring, except that the blue neck tabs did not become visible until he was ten months of age, the same applying to the females.

The WHITE-BROWED FLYCATCHER, *M. superciliaris*, breeding in the Himalayan regions and wintering in the southern parts of the Indian peninsula, is a small bird, 4½ inches (11 cm) in total length, and the sexes differ in colour. The male has the entire upperparts blue, the lower parts white, and there is a conspicuous white line above the eye. The female has the upperparts brown, except for blue on the rump and tail, and she lacks the eye-stripe. It is very much like the Tickell's in its habits and feeding pattern, and we never found them quarrelsome in mixed collections.

The final member of this genus we had was the VERDITER FLYCATCHER, *M. thalassima*. This species breeds throughout the Himalayas from India through to Burma, even as far as western China, and can be found at elevations of four to ten thousand feet (1200 to 3300 metres) during this season. For the winter they migrate to southern India, as far south as the State of Travancore. The sexes are unalike, the male bright blue with a black patch in front of the eye. The under tail-coverts are broadly fringed with white, and the concealed portions of the wings and tail are blackish-brown. The bill, which is black, is flatish and fringed with bristly hair-like feather. Legs and feet also are black. The female is duller throughout, the chin and sides of the throat mottled with white. The Verditer is about 6 inches (15 cm) in total length and they are very good aviary birds, being peaceful and selecting open, conspicuous spots to perch from where they hawk their prey on the wing. Unlike many flycatchers, they do not necessarily return to the same perch after each sortie, but prefer to vary their locations, gradually working up and down the aviary.

. . . they hawk their prey on the wing.

The SCARLET ROBIN, *Petroica multicolor,* so called but in fact a flycatcher, comes from Australia and is widely distributed throughout the southern parts of that continent, from southern Queensland right through to southern Western Australia, and is also in Tasmania and Suffolk Island. It is about 5 inches (13 cm) in total length and the sexes are dissimilar. The adult male has the head, throat and underparts black, adorned with a white cap and white bars on the wings. The breast is scarlet, the lower abdomen dullish white. The female is brown throughout, the breast tinged with red, and with smaller wing-bars. The first pair we ever had, direct from Australia, obviously were a pair from captivity for they both wore leg bands, and the male was light orange in the parts normally scarlet. However, after a year in a planted aviary, being fed on Mr. Boehm's special soft food, and going through a complete moult, it was back to its natural colouring and looked magnificent with its black and red being set off by the white cap. The female did build an open cup-nest of dried grasses and dogs' hair and laid two eggs. These were brownish-white, thickly mottled and spotted with shades of brown and purplish-grey. However, neither the male nor female looked after them and the nest, and eggs, were destroyed by some other inmate of the communal aviary. Soon after this the female died but, although a new breeding had been thwarted, at least we had had the opportunity of seeing what proper care and feeding could do in the way of restoring and retaining the natural colour in birds.

*Australian
Scarlet
Robin*

The WHITE-THROATED FANTAIL FLYCATCHER, *Rhipidura albicollis,* is common from the eastern Himalayas through to Burma and Malaysia. I have seen them both in the

Murree Hills in India and in northern Malaysia and, although subspecies are recognised, I was unable to detect any significant difference in the birds. Admittedly, I only got fleeting glimpses of them in the field and there was a lapse of ten years between the sightings. They are about 7½ inches (19 cm) in total length, of which the tail accounts for nearly half. They are basically dark grey with a black head adorned with a fine white superciliary stripe. The wings are dark brown; the tail dark grey edged with white. With a conspicuous white throat, the remainder of the underparts are sooty-brown. The continual pirouetting through the branches, fanning the tail incessantly, and giving vent to a low squeeky note cannot but attract one to them, be they in an aviary or the wild. We only ever had a male but I understand that the females are very similar in colouring, just a little browner on the upperparts.

The PARADISE FLYCATCHER, *Tersiphone paradisi*, of which there are ten or so races, all have one characteristic in that the males are dimorphic, there being both a red and a white phase, the proportion per race varying according to the regional habitat. They can be found from Turkestan through to India, across Pakistan, Burma, the Far East and even into China and down into Ceylon. The adult male in the red phase has a head, chin and throat of glossy violet-blue-black, the rest of the upperparts, including the tail and upper wing-coverts chestnut. The flight feathers are dusky edged with tawny, now and again with white, and the chest to the belly is grey. The lower belly, under tail-coverts and under wing-coverts are white. The two central tail feathers are very long, up to fifteen inches (38 cm) I have collected, but, excluding these, the body length is about 9 inches (23 cm). The female has the top of the head only violet-blue-black, the remainder of the upper plumage chestnut, as is the chin and throat. They are voracious insect eaters, catching most of their food on the wing. They are purely arboreal, the legs and feet being too small and fragile for easy progress on the ground. On account of this feeding habit they are not the easiest of birds to "meat-off" for retention in confinement. The method we adopted at the Boehm aviaries was, with new arrivals, to toss mealworms, flies, crickets and gentles to them about every hour during the daytime. After about three days of this it would be cut down to once every two hours and feeding cups containing live food, plus soft food and ground meat in other cups would be placed in their rooms. After another three days the tossing of live food would only be done about once every four hours or so

. . . catching most of their food on the wing.

. . . dawn to dusk supervision . . .

for, by this time, they had begun to come down to feed themselves. Out of a dozen or more we had over the years we lost but two new arrivals, one Asiatic and one of the African species, but it does require patience and dawn to dusk supervision.

In the white phase the adult male has a head, neck and crest of glossy blue-black, the remainder of the plumage basically white. The upperparts are faintly lined in black, the wings and outer tail feathers heavily streaked. The central pair of tail feathers are very elongated and are pure white. Of this species we gathered some moulted tail feathers of nineteen inches (48 cm) in length.

The RED-WINGED PARADISE FLYCATCHER, *T. s. swahelica*, is from eastern Africa. They are very similar in colouration to the red phase of the Asiatic species described above, except that the chestnut is more tawny. They have to be treated in an identical manner as their Asiatic cousins. We only ever had a male of this species although we did have, for many years, a pair of the white phase of the Asiatic bird but were never fortunate enough to breed them or even have them make any attempt to go to nest.

The last member of the subfamily Muscicapinae to be dealt with here is the CRESTED or BLUE-MANTLED FLY-CATCHER, *Trochocerchus cyanomelas*, which is to be found from Somalia down the east coast of Africa to the island formerly known as Zanzibar, across Tanzania into the southern Congo. There are several races, the pair we had coming from Kenya, the *T. c. bivattatus*. They are about 7 inches (19 cm) in total length, the adult male having a head, crest and chin of glossy blue-black, the rest of the upperparts bluish-slate with a white bar and patch on the wing. From the breast to the lower abdomen they are white. The females are duller and lack the white wing-patch, and from the chin to the chest are mottled. Like so many of the flycatchers they are not very musical, having a high pitched song, normally concluding it with three or four loud clicks. We had a pair for but a short time since we had no spare accommodation and they were passed on to a zoo.

Subfamily Pachycephalinae

This subfamily, Thickhead or Whistler, is restricted to the Australo-Papuan area, the Great Sundas, the Malay Peninsula, the Philippines and some oceanic islands. They are basically flycatchers and it is considered by some that they could well be included in the subfamily Muscicapinae. They all have robust bodies, thick heads, imposing not much flattened bills like a shrike, and vary in size from that of a sparrow to a jay.

The only one we ever had was the GOLDEN WHISTLER, *Pachycephala pectoralis,* which comes from Australia where it may be found in north-western Queensland, New South Wales, Victoria, Tasmania and South and Western Australia. The adult male is so striking that it was selected for depiction on an Australian air-mail stamp. It has a white throat, black head, and a black band across the chest, the remainder of the underparts a rich golden yellow, with the upperparts olive-green. The female is brown, paler on the underparts with a whitish throat, faintly streaked with dusky. They are about 7 inches (18 cm) in total length, the male being a very fine songster with many varied melodious calls, usually ending with a staccato note. They are very insectivorous but also partake of seeding grasses and berries. We found them very easy to cater for, but a pair of Magnificent Birds of Paradise with which they were housed for almost a year decided to go to nest, claimed all the territory, and killed the pair of them.

Family Paridae

This family of small, active, woodland birds is widely distributed, although not represented in South America, Malagasy or Australasia. They fall into three distinct subfamilies, the typical tits (Parinae), the long-tailed tits (Aegithalinae), and the penduline tits (Remizinae). We only ever had specimens of the first two named.

Subfamily Parinae

The typical tits, comprised of some 40 species, are distributed throughout North America and parts of Mexico, Europe, much of Asia and Africa, wherever there is suitable woodland. They feed mainly on insects, some species also largely on seeds. They are well able to deal with hard shelled seeds or nuts, holding them down with the foot and hammering woodpecker style to extract the contents. Some of the northern species even store food in the fall for use during the winter.

. . . hammering woodpecker style . . .

The GREY-BACKED or GREAT TIT, *Parus major,* has a wide distribution throughout Europe, north-west Africa, and across Asia to China and Japan, there being slight variations in their colouring according to the district they are from. About 5½ inches (14 cm) in length, the sexes are alike. The whole of the head, chin, throat and a median line running down the breast through the abdomen, glossy blue-black; cheeks white; mantle yellowish-olive; pale white spot on nape; wing-coverts and tail bluish-grey, outer tail feathers broadly edged white; narrow white wing-bar; underparts greenish-yellow.

The SOUTHERN BLACK TIT, *Parus niger,* from the southern parts of Africa, ranging clear across from the west coast to Mozambique and down into eastern Cape Province, is about 6½ inches (16 cm) in length, and the sexes differ. The general colour of the adult male is glossy blue-black; edges of wing-coverts, flight feathers, outer web of outer tail feathers and tips of tail feathers, white. The female is duller above and dull slaty-grey below but retains the white edges to the wing-coverts, flight feathers and tail.

. . . a hole in a tree stump . . .

The female of the pair we had selected a hole in a tree stump as her nesting site, and it was not until she was missing at feeding time that we detected it. The hole was just deep enough for her to be completely concealed and, when she did vacate the nest it could be seen that she had three eggs. It had been noted that the male had been more consistent with his trill-like call, but no mating was observed. She finally deserted the eggs 18 days later and it was then found that they were all clear. They measured 18 by 14 mm., and were creamy-white, heavily spotted with bright rufous. They made no further attempts to go to nest that season and were disposed of the following year.

The VARIEGATED TIT, *Parus varius,* from Japan, is about 5 inches (13 cm) in length and the sexes are alike. It is also known as the Bucket-bird in Japan where it is trained to pull up a little wooden bucket every time a sunflower seed is put into it. The forehead, cheeks, lores, ear-coverts and sides of the neck, cream coloured; crown of head to nape black with a white streak from the base of the nape up the back of the head; shoulders and flanks russet; mantle, wings and tail slate-grey; chin, throat and upper breast blackish; abdomen chestnut. They are easily tamed and will come readily to hand to be fed, be it a mealworm or a sunflower seed they are offered. We had three of them at one time and, although they all lived sociably together in the same aviary, no nesting efforts were made so they could well have been all of the same sex.

The YELLOW-CHEEKED TIT, *Parus xanthogenys,* is another Asiatic species, confined to the Indian Peninsular. It is about 5 inches (13 cm) in length, and the sexes are alike. Crown, a long pointed crest and a line through the eye, glossy black; superciliary line to a patch on hind neck and cheeks, canary-yellow; upperparts yellowish-green; wings black, small coverts spotted pale yellowish-white; flight feathers edged and variegated with blue, grey and white; tail black, washed blue-grey, tips of all feathers and the outer edges of the outer feathers, white. From chin to under tail-coverts canary-yellow except for a broad band of glossy black down the centre of the underparts from the chin to the vent. This was the longest lived species we ever kept, one specimen living for a known period of twelve years. Like the Variegated Tit they are very sociable and easy to tame to come to hand. Grey hair was the great attraction for the old-timer mentioned above for, if anyone who had grey hair entered the aviary they had to be prepared for this bird to settle on their head and tweak at the hairs. He definitely was not selective of persons, just colour.

. . . longest lived species we ever kept . . .

Subfamily Aegithalinae

This subfamily is comprised of the long-tailed tits and consists of some 8 species. Their feeding habits are the same as those in the subfamily Parinae, except that they do not tackle such hard-shelled food as nuts. Their vegetable matter intake is more or less confined to seeds and small buds. We only ever had one species, the RED-HEADED TIT, *Aegithalos concinnus,* an Asiatic species found in the Himalayan foothills clear across to Burma and into China. A small bird, about 4 inches (10 cm) in length of which almost half is accounted for by the tail, and the sexes are alike. Entire top of head chestnut; sides of head and a large circular patch on the throat, black; eyebrow, broad moustachial streak and chin, white; upper plumage, wings and tail bluish-grey, the tail long and graduated, the outer feathers tipped white; underparts ferruginous.

These birds can be very delicate on first receipt from their native habitat, many even arriving dead. Our practice was to put them on grated cheese immediately, plus a few very small mealworms and blow-fly cocoons. Most of them were ready within a week to start on the soft-food mixture and ground raw beef but, with others, it took up to four weeks before we considered them 'meated-off'. As soon as they were taking all the food they were released into planted aviaries where they could forage for themselves and supplement their diet. We found them to be very sociable birds although keeping very much to themselves. One pair did commence to build a nest of shredded string, wool, dogs' hair and fine grasses in a privet bush. It was a very deep affair and was almost complete when a pair of Verreaux's Twinspots selected the same bush, and killed both the tits.

All the species of tits we kept did very well on our soft-food mixture and ground raw beef, sunflower seed also being supplied to those of the subfamily Parinae. Live-food was an essential, this requirement being satisfied with mealworms and gentles, plus whatever they could forage for themselves.

Family Sittidae

This family is predominantly Palaearctic and Nearctic in distribution, most species being found in Europe and Asia. However, there are 4 species in North America and scattered species in other parts of the world with the exception of South America and New Zealand. There are some 30 species in all, ranging from $3\frac{3}{4}$ to $7\frac{1}{2}$ inches (10 to 20 cm) in length, but most of them average $4\frac{1}{2}$ inches (11 cm). They are all climbing birds, seeking their food consisting mostly of insects, spiders and other small creatures on trees and rocks. We only ever had one pair, the CHESTNUT-BELLIED NUTHATCH, *Sitta castanea*, of southern Asia. They are about $5\frac{1}{2}$ inches (14 cm) in length and the sexes differ. The general colour of the upper plumage of the adult male is slaty-blue, the lower plumage a uniform rich chestnut. A black streak runs from the nostril, right through the eye to the shoulder; a white patch from the chin to ear-coverts; central tail feathers ashy-blue, next two black with ashy-blue tips and edges, remainder black with white markings; under tail-coverts mixed chestnut and ashy; under wing surface black with a white patch. The face markings on the female are less clearly defined and the underparts are a paler chestnut.

. . . acts as an anchor . . . The hind toe is greatly developed and this more or less acts as an anchor when they are climbing up and down trees for they do not use their tail as a support in the manner of woodpeckers. We never supplied them with any special diet beyond our normal feeding pattern, but they also enjoyed getting the seeds out of pine cones which we gave them occasionally. Very peaceful in an aviary, keeping much to themselves, they did take over a boxed-in nest box with an opening at the front but, beyond laying eggs, three or four in a clutch at a time, no further progress in breeding them was accomplished. The eggs were white,

heavily spotted and freckled with brick-red and they averaged
17 by 14 mm., in size.

Family Dicaeidae

This is a family of small birds of Oriental and Australasian
distribution. Although there are some 55 species, we only ever
had but one. The SCARLET-BACKED FLOWERPECKER,
Dicaeum cruentatum, of south-east Asia. They are about 3¾
inches (9 cm) in total length and the sexes differ. The adult
male is red above and buffish-white below, the tail and wings
glossy black. The face, neck and breast black, flanks dark grey.
The female is greyish-brown above and buffish-white below, tail
and wings black and the upper tail-coverts red. They are noisy
birds with a stream of clicking, staccato notes and a constant
twittering at feeding time. Their habits are very similar to those
of sunbirds, being nectar, insect and fruit eaters, but are much
messier as cage birds, getting their plumage and perches con-
stantly stuck up with fruit juice and nectar. They make far better   *. . . far better*
aviary birds. Like so many of the nectar-feeders they are of im-   *aviary birds.*
portance as pollinators of tree and shrub flowers. Further, many
species of flower peckers feed almost exclusively on insects and
mistletoe berries and they are by far the most effective distribu-
tors of the mistletoe seeds.

Family Nectariniidae

For many years the name sunbird has been applied to this
family of Old World (mostly) brightly plumaged birds. They
are the ecological counterparts of the hummingbirds of the New
World, and are mainly small birds, ranging in length from 3½
to 10 inches (9 to 25 cm), the larger species having elongated
tails which account in many cases for almost half of their size.
The largest concentration occurs in Africa, but they also are to
be found in considerable numbers in southern Asia and in
Australasia.

With the majority the bill is slender and decurved, and the
tongue, highly protractile, is tubular in its anterior two-thirds
and split near the end. They are not truly sociable, although
birds of several species may gather, just for feeding, in flowering
trees and shrubs. The males are extremely pugnacious particularly in the breeding season.

Sunbirds feed on insects and nectar, extracting the nectar

both on the wing and from a perch, more often by the latter method. In their search for flowering shrubs and trees some species move from area to area but, except for this movement for food, they are not obviously migratory. Over the years we cared for more than twenty different species.

The YELLOW-BACKED SUNBIRD, *Aethopyga siparaja,* is to be found in southeastern Asia, with subspecies in Sumatra, Borneo and India, ranging in summer to the Himalayas. There is another species commonly referred to as the Yellow-backed also, *A. nipalensis australis,* from Malaysia, but it was the former we had. The name is rather a misnomer for the rump only is yellow, the back, chin, throat and breast being crimson. Front of crown of the adult male metallic green; nape brownish-green; sides of head and neck, back and lesser wing-coverts dull crimson; larger wing-coverts dark brown, edged brownish-olive. Tail violet-black, the elongated central feathers metallic green, as are the edges of the other feathers. A moustachial streak of metallic violet; abdomen dull greyish-olive. The female is dull olive-green above; wings and tail dark brown, feathers edged golden-olive and outer tail feathers tipped whitish. The entire underparts dull olive-yellow with a pale yellow patch under the wing. Averaging $5\frac{1}{2}$ inches (14 cm) in length, the elongated tail feathers accounting for over an inch (2.5 cm) of that. We were never able to do anything with the females for they either arrived dead or in such a poor state that they survived only a matter of hours.

. . . they survived only a matter of hours . . .

The COLLARED SUNBIRD, *Anthreptes collaris,* is an African species, the nominate race being confined to the island of Fernando Po. There are subspecies ranging through Cameroon, northern Angola, northern Burundi and the Sudan to south-eastern Africa. We had *A. c. zambesiana,* from East Africa. A small bird, about 4 inches (10 cm) in total length, the adult male's head, upperparts, chin, throat and lesser wing-coverts metallic green with a golden wash; wings black with green edges; tail blue-black with metallic green edges; a band of metallic violet across the chest; remainder of underparts yellow. The female lacks the violet band; chin and neck dusky-yellow; underparts duller than those of the male.

The VIOLET-BACKED SUNBIRD, *A. longuemarii,* is another African species, those we had being the subspecies *A. l. orientalis,* from Kenya. About 5 inches (13 cm) in length, the adult male is metallic violet above, the colour extending right through to the tail. Flight feathers and face black; wing-butts metallic violet with yellow pectoral tufts; throat metallic violet; remainder of underparts white. The female, sooty-grey above with a violet suffusion, and a distinct white eye-streak. Chin and breast white; flanks and abdomen yellowish; tail metallic violet. This was one of the many species we tried in a mixed collection of sunbirds but found them too aggressive to be accommodated in such a manner.

. . . *too aggressive* . . .

The RUBY-CHEEKED SUNBIRD, *A. singalensis*, is a Far Eastern species, those we had coming from Malaysia. About 4 inches (10 cm) in length, it may be found in the foothills, seldom above 3,000 feet (900 metres), descending to the lowlands as the cooler weather sets in. The sexes differ, the adult male a dark metallic green above, this colour only being recognisable in the sunlight, otherwise appearing as black. Cheek patches and ear-coverts metallic coppery-red; chin, throat and breast rufous-buff; remainder of underparts olive-yellow. The female is olive-green above, lacking the coloured cheeks and ear-coverts. Chin, throat and breast pastel buff; remainder of underparts greenish-yellow. Like the other members of the genus *Anthreptes* we had they were very insectivorous and readily took to small mealworms when flies were not available.

The AMETHYST SUNBIRD, *Chalcomitra amethystina*, from Africa is about 6 inches (15 cm) in length, and the sexes differ. We had three subspecies, *C. a. kirkii* from Mozambique where the male is mostly velvety purplish-black above with forehead to crown a metallic green with a golden sheen. Chin and throat reddish-purple; wings and tail purplish-black, tinged with bronze; shoulder-butts metallic violet and some have yellow pectoral tufts. Female ashy-green above with blackish flight feathers with a gloss of bronze; tail black with a bronzy tinge, all feathers tipped white; underparts olive-yellow with dusky brown streaks throughout.

The *C. a. kalckreuthi* from Somalia to Tanzania is identical in colouring but the wings are shorter. The Sudan subspecies, *C. a. doggetti*, has wings the same length as the first mentioned subspecies but the adult male has a metallic bluish-green forehead to crown. We were never able to discern any difference between the females of the three subspecies. We had one pair, received from Mozambique, build a hanging nest in a bamboo and two eggs were laid. Unfortunately it was destroyed by a Ribbon-tailed Bird of Paradise and, although we transferred the sunbirds to another aviary, they made no further attempt to go to nest.

The SCARLET-BREASTED SUNBIRD, *C. senegalensis,* is another African species, there being subspecies ranging from Ethiopia to South Africa and across to Cameroon. We had *C. s. gutturalis* from Kenya. About 5½ inches (14 cm) in length, the adult male's forehead and crown metallic green; shoulders metallic violet; remainder of upperparts velvety black. Flight feathers and tail brownish-black with a blush of old-gold; chin and upper neck metallic green; lower chin and chest crimson with blue markings just below the tips of each feather. When the feathers of the chest are puffed up these blue markings show up as blue flecks on an otherwise scarlet chest. The female is dusky-olive above, with the flight and tail feathers having a bronzy tinge; primaries are white edged. Underparts olivaceous-yellow steaked dusky-brown, the throat darker than the remainder. We did have one of the north Ethiopian sub-species, *C. s. cruentata,* arrive dead, the male being similar in appearance to that described above except that the chin and upper throat are black, and the metallic shoulder colouring is confined to the wing-butts.

The PURPLE SUNBIRD, *Cinnyris asiatica,* is an Asiatic species and many races are to be found from Iran on the west to Indo-China on the east. The nominate race we had from Burma is about 4 inches (10 cm) in total length, the sexes differ, and the male has an eclipse plumage. The adult male in breeding dress has head, neck, upper plumage, throat and breast of metallic black with a greenish-purple sheen; flight feathers dull brownish-black; tail bluish-black. A narrow band across the chest coppery-brown; remainder of underparts dull purplish-black. There is a brilliant tuft of crimson and yellow feathers under each wing which is clearly visible when in flight, but may only be glimpsed when in repose. The upper plumage, wings, sides of head and neck of the female are greenish-brown; tail dark brown, the outer feathers narrowly tipped with white; underparts bright yellow. In non-breeding dress the male is brownish above with dark yellow underparts, rather like the female, but retains the dark wings and a bright metallic violet stripe from chin to abdomen. Once acclimatised they are quite *. . . they are* hardy but inclined to be very quarrelsome, and are best kept on *quite* their own.

hardy . . .

THE PURPLE-BANDED SUNBIRD, *C. bifasciatus,* is about 4 inches (10 cm) in length and is confined to an area from Uganda to Kenya, southern Burundi, eastern Rhodesia, eastern Transvaal and Swaziland. The adult male's head, neck, mantle and lesser wing-coverts metallic green with a golden wash; wings and tail black with a blue-black gloss; wing feathers edged lightly metallic green. A metallic violet band across the chest followed by a band across the breast of maroon with some metallic violet tips to the feathers; abdomen black. The female is olivaceous-ash above; tail black with a slight blue-black gloss, outer feathers white edged and, except the central pair of feathers, all are white tipped. The male in non-breeding dress resembles the female except that the black wings and tail are retained, as is the metallic colouring of the wing-coverts and upper tail-coverts. The female also has a non-breeding dress where the upperparts are brighter olivaceous.

The COPPERY SUNBIRD, *C. c. cupreus,* is a little larger than the Purple-banded and has a wide distribution in Africa from Senegal clear across to Ethiopia, ranging down to the equator on the western side, and as far down as Mozambique on the eastern. The upper mantle of the adult male in breeding dress is metallic golden-copper, this colour covering the head and neck completely round to the upper chest; lower mantle, rump, upper tail-coverts and lower wing-coverts metallic purple; flight and tail feathers blue-black, the tail being markedly square with no elongations; underparts black. The female is olive-green above; tail blue-black with light edges and tips of the outer feathers; underparts yellow with a lighter patch at the throat. The male in non-breeding dress resembles the female except that the black flight feathers, and the metallic wing and upper tail-coverts are retained.

LOTEN'S SUNBIRD, *C. lotenia,* an Asiatic species from southern India and Ceylon, is about 4 inches (10 cm) in length and has a fairly long bill, curved downwards more than is customary in the general range of sunbirds. The adult male is metallic blue on the head, neck and upperparts; throat and breast purple; wings sooty-brown almost black; upper tail-coverts metallic blue; tail bluish-black; underparts sooty-brown. There is some doubt as to whether they do have a definite non-breeding plumage or not, but, with all those we had, at the commencement of the moult they did lose most of their brilliance, regaining it when fully refeathered. The female is olive-grey above; pale olive below; tail black, the feathers tipped yellow.

The MARICO SUNBIRD, *C. mariquensis,* is about 5½ inches (14 cm) in length and has a wide range in East Africa from Somalia southwards to South Africa. There is no eclipse

. . . curved downwards more than is customary . . .

dress. The adult male's head, neck, mantle to rump, and lesser wing-coverts vivid metallic green with a golden sheen; wings and tail blue-black; underparts smoky-black except for a metallic violet band across the upper breast, with a maroon band above. The female is ashy coloured above; underparts yellow except for the throat which is smoky, the feathers having white tips giving a flecked appearance; tail blue-black, outer feathers white edged and, except for the central pair, all are white tipped.

The EASTERN DOUBLE-COLLARED SUNBIRD, *C. mediocris*, from Kenya, is about 4 inches (10 cm) in length. The adult male's head, neck all round, lesser wing-coverts, mantle and rump, metallic golden-green with a bluish wash; upper tail-coverts metallic blue; wings blackish with olive edges to flight feathers; tail blue-black, outer feathers whitish on outer edges and tips. A narrow metallic blue band across the chest; broad scarlet band on breast; pectoral tufts yellow; abdomen to under tail-coverts yellowish-olive. The female is olivaceous moss-green above; wings duller black than the male's, and the olive edges to the flight feathers more distinct. Tail similar to the male; underparts olive-yellow; flanks and throat more olivaceous moss-green. There is no non-breeding dress.

. . . one of the smallest sunbirds . . .

The WHITE-BELLIED SUNBIRD, *C. talatala*, is one of the smallest sunbirds from the northern parts of South Africa being no more than 4 inches (10 cm) in length. The head and upperparts of the adult male metallic greenish-blue with old-gold reflections; upper tail-coverts more blue than green; wings dull black; tail blue-black with metallic green edges to the outer feathers. Chin sooty; throat metallic green; violet band across chest with a narrow black band below; remainder of underparts white. The female is ashy-grey above; tail bluish-black, feathers edged metallic green; upper tail-coverts metallic green; underparts dingy white. The male has a non-breeding dress in which he resembles the female except that the blue-black tail, metallic wings and upper tail-coverts are retained.

The YELLOW-BELLIED VARIABLE or FALKEN-STEIN'S SUNBIRD, *C. venustus falkensteini*, is from Kenya and is one of four subspecies, the others being *C. v. albiventris*, the White-bellied Variable from Somalia and Ethiopia; *C. v. fazoqlensis*, the northern Yellow-bellied Variable from the Sudan, and *C. v. igneiventris*, the Orange-bellied Variable from the Congo and Tanzania. They are all very similar in appearance, the main difference being in the colour of the underparts. The adult male *C. v. falkensteini,* the race we had, is a metallic bluish-green over the top and back of the head and the upperparts, with a sheen of old-gold. Forehead violet; upper tail-coverts darker bluish-green; tail blue-black with metallic green edges to the outer feathers, all feathers having lightish tips. Wings sooty-black; pectoral tufts yellow; throat steel-blue washed with violet; upper chest metallic blue; remainder of underparts bright yellow. The female is ashy-brown above, white below, and with no metallic edges to the upper tail-coverts, and only faint green edging to the tail feathers. In non-breeding dress the male resembles the female except that the metallic wing and upper tail-coverts are retained, and there are often a number of metallic tips to the body feathers.

The YELLOW-BELLIED SUNBIRD, *Cyanomitra jugularis,* from the lower regions of Burma, with subspecies in north-eastern Australia and the Phillipine Islands, is about $4\frac{1}{2}$ inches (12 cm) in length. The adult male's head, metallic green; remaining upperparts dark brown; throat metallic purple; maroon band across the chest; remainder of underparts bright yellow. The female is identical in colouring with the Purple Sunbird but a trifle larger in size. In non-breeding dress the male resembles the female except that it retains part of the throat patch.

The OLIVE SUNBIRD, *C. olivacea,* of which there are some nine subspecies throughout East Africa, only one above the Equator, is a sombre coloured bird. The subspecies *C. o. neglecta,* from Kenya, is about $5\frac{1}{2}$ inches (14 cm) in length, and, except for a shorter tail for the female, the sexes are very alike. Olive-green above; wings and tail dusky with olive-green edges; underparts pale olivaceous-green. Both sexes have yellow pectoral tufts, the only bright colouring in their make-up.

. . . the only bright colouring . . .

The MOUSE-COLOURED SUNBIRD, *C. veroxii,* about 9 inches (23 cm) in length, is even duller coloured. The subspecies *C. v. fischeri,* from Mozambique, is grey above with a greenish gloss; tail dull black with greenish edges to the inner webs; underparts greyish-white; pectoral tufts red, streaked with yellow. The female is similar in colour but lacks the pectoral tufts, and is slightly smaller.

The GREEN-HEADED SUNBIRD, *C. verticalis,* with races from West Africa clear across to Kenya is about 5 inches (13 cm) in length, and the sexes differ. The adult male's head, neck and sides of face, metallic green; remainder of upperparts moss-green; chin to chest metallic greenish-blue; pectoral tufts cream coloured; remainder of underparts dusky-grey. The female has the green head and neck of the male but it is not of such a bright shade; remainder of upperparts as with the male; chin to chest dusky-grey, merging into smoky-grey through the rest of the underparts; no pectoral tufts.

We found the four species of the genus *Cyanomitra* very peaceful and capable of being kept in the same aviary. However, we did not have any attempt to go to nest so no opinion can be voiced as to their behaviour in such conditions. None of them had any eclipse plumage.

The MALACHITE SUNBIRD, *Nectarinia famosa,* is about 10 inches (25 cm) in length and may be found over a wide range in East Africa from just north of the equator to as far south as the northern parts of South Africa. In breeding dress the head, neck and upper plumage of the adult male is metallic green with a golden wash; upper tail-coverts metallic emerald green; flight feathers and tail black, edged green, and central pair of tail feathers elongated. Chest to under tail-coverts metallic deep blue with a golden sheen; pectoral tufts bright yellow. The female is smaller than the male, about 6 inches (15 cm) in length, the difference mainly due to lack of the elongated tail feathers. Above olivaceous-grey; underparts yellowish-green, mottled dark green. A distinct yellow eye-stripe which, together with the downward curve of the bill, is one of the best aids of identification. The male in non-breeding dress resembles the female except that the black flight feathers and elongated tail feathers are retained. We found that the older the males became, the less metallic green colouring of the body is lost, one bird at eight years of age hardly having any difference in its colouring through the year. We did have one pair build a nest in the extreme upper branches of a tree but, unfortunately, a pair of birds of paradise in the same aviary made short work of it and it was

. . . to safer quarters.

necessary to move the sunbirds to safer quarters. They did not go to nest again.

The SCARLET-TUFTED MALACHITE SUNBIRD, *N. johnstoni,* is slightly larger than the preceding species and is more or less confined to the Nyasa alpine region of Tanzania. We only ever had one male, the general colouring metallic moss-green on chest, flanks and upper abdomen, all with a bluish wash; flight and tail feathers bluish-black; pectoral tufts bright red. In non-breeding dress the top and sides of the head, the mantle, and chin to chest turned dusky olivaceous, the flanks and abdomen olivaceous.

Both species of Malachite Sunbird have a shrill, harsh call, but, in the breeding season, the males have quite a pleasant song of high notes repeated rapidly after each other.

THE BRONZY SUNBIRD, *N. kilimensis*, from Kenya, is about 9 inches (23 cm) in length, the male having an elongated tail and no non-breeding dress. The general colouring of the adult male is dull metallic green with old-gold reflections. There is no green in the mantle, wing-coverts, rump and chest, these being purely metallic old-gold; remainder of underparts, wings and tail purplish-black; the elongated central tail feathers edged metallic-bronze; a fairly long, decurved bill. The upperparts of the female, including the wings, olive-brown; narrow yellow eye-stripe; tail blackish washed with purple, central pair of feathers slightly elongated; chin whitish; underparts yellow streaked brown; downward curved bill as with the male.

A pair of these birds built a nest of fine grasses, wool, dogs' hair and spanish moss in a crab apple tree, the female doing all the constructing. It was built in the form of an elongated ball, with the entrance way up at the top on one side. One egg was laid and, after 17 days of incubating by the female only, it hatched. The female tended the nestling although the male used to bring her insects he had caught. In addition to an increase in the amount of nectar the birds consumed, a plentiful supply of insects was maintained at all times by giving them most of those caught in the night traps. It was amazing how even quite large moths were taken and mashed up until suitable to be fed to the youngster. Vacating the nest at 15 days, it was seen that the young bird was fully feathered and had a fairly long bill at that early age. The upperparts dark green; underparts yellow-green; tail edged white. Unfortunately it died three days later. It was felt that this could only have been due to lack of sufficient food for, just as the baby sunbird fledged, a pair of Natal Robins in the same aviary had three young hatch out. Although the supply was stepped up to issues every thirty minutes throughout the day, the Natal Robin male kept the sunbirds penned down to just one part of the aviary, thus restricting their ability to forage far and wide. Further nests were made and eggs laid but, in each instance, they were destroyed. This is one of the drawbacks when there are two pairs of insect-eaters breeding in the same aviary.

The BEAUTIFUL SUNBIRD, *N. pulchella melanogastra*, from Kenya, is about 6½ inches (16 cm) in length, the sexes differ, and the male has an eclipse plumage. In breeding dress the adult male's general colour is metallic golden-green; flight

. . . in the form of an elongated ball . . .

215

feathers and tail blue-black, central pair of feathers elongated and edged metallic green; red patch in centre of chest; sides of chest mixed yellow and metallic green; abdomen black. The female is ashy-olive above, tinged with pale yellow, which colouring extends to the sides of the head; chin and throat yellowish-white; remainder of underparts yellow; tail blackish with narrow metallic green tips except for the outer feathers which have white edges and tips. Although it has been recorded that this species does not have a non-breeding dress, experience with keeping them over the years proved to us that it does. In its eclipse plumage the male resembles the female except that it retains the elongated tail feathers, and the metallic wing and upper tail-coverts.

. . . proved to us that it does.

The GOLDEN-WINGED SUNBIRD, *N. reichenowii,* from Kenya is about 9 inches (23 cm) in total length and the sexes differ, a characteristic feature being the accentuated downward curve of the bill, that of the male longer and more curved than the female's. The breeding dress of the male is a metallic old-gold with greenish reflections over the head right through to the upper tail-coverts. Wing-butts the same colour, remainder of wings and the tail, black with bright golden outer webs; central pair of tail feathers extremely elongated, representing one-third of the total length of the bird. Chin to chest metallic coppery-red; remainder of underparts black. In non-breeding dress the entire upperparts, and from the chin to chest, are black; the wings retain the metallic butts, and there is no change in the tail. The female is olive-green above; yellow mottled olive below; flight and tail feathers edged golden-yellow; no elongated tail feathers.

The TACAZZE SUNBIRD, *N. tacazze,* an East African species extending from the southern Sudan and Ethiopia southward to Kenya and north-eastern Tanzania, is about 10 inches (25 cm) in length and the male has an eclipse plumage. The head and neck of the male, in breeding dress, metallic bronzy-green; mantle to upper tail-coverts, wing-coverts, chest and breast, metallic reddish-violet; wings, tail and remainder of underparts black. Central pair of tail feathers elongated; outer feathers being broad giving a squared-off effect. Female olive-brown above with an eye-stripe the same colour; dusky-yellow below; central tail feathers slightly elongated. In non-breeding dress the male resembles the female except that he retains the black flights and the elongated central pair of tail feathers. From experience with this species, one male of which we had for over ten years, it was noticed that after seven years in our possession, it was an adult when we got it, it no longer went into an eclipse plumage.

The PURPLE-RUMPED SUNBIRD, *N. zeylonica,* is a purely Indian Peninsular species from the central and southern parts and Ceylon, those from the mainland a trifle larger than those from Ceylon. About 4 inches (10 cm) in length, the top of the head of the male, metallic lilac; rump metallic purple; wings brown edged rufous, metallic lilac and dull crimson on the smaller coverts; tail black with pale tips to the outer feathers; sides of head coppery-brown; remainder of upper plumage dull crimson. Chin and throat metallic purple; collar below throat of maroon; remainder of underparts bright yellow with white under the wings. The female is ashy-brown above; wings brown margined rufous; tail black with pale tips to the outer feathers; a faint white line above the eye, with a dark line below it running through the eye. Cheeks, chin and throat pale ashy-white; remainder of lower plumage yellow with white under the wings.

With the exception of those in the genus *Cyanomitra* we found that it was not practicable to house more than one pair of a species in one aviary, no matter how spacious or well planted, for any length of time without fatal consequences. We made experiment after experiment, increasing the feeding places, concentrating on those aviaries with the most luxuriant flowering trees, shrubs and plants, but always with the same results after only a matter of days in some instances, and even hours in others.

. . . one pair of a species in one aviary . . .

Family Zosteropidae

This family of Old World birds generally referred to as white-eyes, is to be found over the whole Ethiopian, Oriental and Australasian regions. They have been introduced to the Hawaiian Islands where they now flourish. There are some 85 species in all—over 170 forms if all subspecies are included—and, with one exception, they all have a ring of white feathers round the eye. The exception is the YELLOW-SPECTACLED WHITE-EYE, *Zosterops wallacei,* of the Lesser Sunda Islands in Indonesia. The sexes are always alike, and there are no seasonal changes in plumage. They are birds of trees and shrubs, only coming to the ground to bathe or snatch up an insect, and their main diet is insects, nectar and fruit, but all the various species we had over the years also took our soft-food mixture and the ground raw beef. Very sociable and gregarious, we never experienced any conflict amongst them, but we did take care to house each species separately from the others although in mixed collections otherwise. We were never fortunate enough to have any of them go to nest. Basically they are all very similar in appearance, slender, decurved and pointed bills, cobby in structure, varying from 3 to 5 inches (8 to 13 cm) in length, and of various shades of greenish-yellow to greenish-grey. However, each species does have its own variation from this general colouring, their overall distinguishing feature being the white eye-ring.

Very sociable . . .

The ORIENTAL or INDIAN WHITE-EYE, *Zosterops palpebrosa,* has the whole upper plumage greenish golden-yellow, the concealed portions of the wings and tail, dark brown; chin and throat bright yellow; remainder of underparts greyish-white, except the under tail-coverts which are yellow. About 4 inches (10 cm) in length, there are several races throughout India and Burma and even down into Ceylon. We also had a pair of the CEYLON HILL WHITE-EYE, *Z. ceylonensis,* about the same size as the Oriental White-eye but with much darker green plumage.

The CHESTNUT-FLANKED WHITE-EYE, *Z. erythropleura,* is a Manchurian species migrating to Burma for the winter. With these the chestnut flanks are a distinguishing feature, the remainder of the colouring being slightly paler than that of the *Z. palpebrosa.*

The YELLOW-BELLIED WHITE-EYE, *Z. siamensis,* from Thailand, is distinguishable by the entire underparts being bright yellow.

The BLACK-CAPPED WHITE-EYE, *Z. atricapilla,* from Malaysia, is one of the smaller species and is distinguished by its black forehead and general darker yellow-green mantle and upper breast.

We also had the EVERETT'S WHITE-EYE, *Z. everetti,* from Malaysia, this being a pale golden-yellow about 3¾ inches (9 cm) in length, with the entire underparts a pale clear yellow, fading towards the vent.

The YELLOW WHITE-EYE, *Z. senegalensis,* from Africa, has a distribution clear across Africa from the Senegal to the Sudan. Greenish canary-yellow above with a powdered mealy appearance, the forehead clear yellow, as are the underparts.

The KENYA GOLDEN-FRONTED WHITE-EYE, *Z.*

kikuyuensis, was one of the most attractive we ever had, the white "spectacles" being much larger than on any of the other species. Upperparts moss green; lower parts olive-yellow with more yellow on the throat and the centre of the belly. They also have a distinct yellow forehead and are about 4½ inches (11 cm) in length.

The CAPE WHITE-EYE, *Z. pallidus*, is one of the larger species, about 5 inches (13 cm) in length. They have a greenish-yellow back with grey-green to whitish underparts, except for the throat which is yellow. They have a wide range from South Africa up to Ethiopia, the pair we had coming from Lesotho.

I have always found white-eyes to be delightful birds to keep, be it in cages or aviaries. Comparatively easy to cater for, always alert and on the move, their bright little eyes constantly on the look-out for any errant insect, and ceaselessly twittering in a high-pitched note. For anyone contemplating taking up the care of nectar feeders, any of the white-eyes will make excellent training material.

. . . delightful birds to keep . . .

Family Meliphagidae

This is a group of arboreal, mainly nectar-feeding and fruit-eating birds of Australasian distribution with one genus in South Africa. The most striking feature is their brush-tongue with a structure notably different from the other groups of birds with similar feeding habits. It is long and protusible, the basal part curled up on each side, the distal part deeply cleft into four parts with the edges delicately frayed, thus forming the brush.

The YELLOW-FACED HONEYEATER, *Meliphaga chrysops*, is native to the eastern and south-eastern parts of Australia. About 6½ inches (17 cm) in length, the sexes are alike. The main colouring ashy-brown; two black lines along sides of face with a bright yellow band between. White spot behind eye; throat greyish-white; rest of underparts ashy-brown, lightening towards the vent. They have a lively little song consisting of but two notes repeated in quick succession.

The WHITE-BEARDED HONEYEATER, *M. novae-hollandiae*, also referred to as the Yellow-winged, is from southern and south-western Australia and Tasmania. They are about 7¼ inches (18 cm) in length and the sexes are alike, mainly blackish-brown with white markings. The cheeks, patch behind the eye and a line on side of nape, white; much yellow marking in the wings; tail, black, margined yellow and tipped white.

They are very secretive, hiding in the shrubberies, and are extremely difficult to see in a well-planted aviary. We had as many as six at one time and could never detect any difference amongst them. A very sharp and shrill call note we only ever heard from outside the aviary for, on anyone approaching, they gave vent to a harsh chattering and it was by this that one was able to locate them.

The WHITE-NAPED HONEYEATER, *Melithreptus lunatus,* has a much greater range, from Queensland and Victoria right across to Western Australia by the coastal regions and inland forest areas. About 5½ inches (14 cm) in length, the sexes are alike. Upperparts, yellowish-olive; wings brown; head and back of neck black, with narrow white band on nape; naked orange-scarlet eye-ring; underparts white. Completely unlike the preceding species they became very tame and we had them coming to hand to be fed.

. . . coming to hand to be fed.

The CRESCENT HONEYEATER, *Phylidonyris pyrrhoptera,* is an eastern Australian species and is also in Tasmania. Just over 6 inches (15 cm) in length, the sexes are unalike. The adult male dusky-black above with a black bar on each side of the breast; wings and tail marked golden-yellow; flanks dusky; underparts white. The outer tail feathers spotted white. The female is an overall dusky-brown with faint yellow markings on wings and tail. It is felt that they must have derived their common name from their call which is loud and varied in range but can readily be interpreted as "egypt", the land of the crescent. The female built a deep, open cup-nest of strips of reed and bark and small twigs, the whole lined with fine grasses and dogs' hair, in an azalea bush about 18 inches (46 cm) above ground level. She built it on her own, the male not even being seen carrying materials. Two eggs, pale flesh coloured, darker at the thicker end, spotted and speckled reddish-chestnut, and with a few faint markings of dull purplish-grey around the larger end were laid, and she began sitting with the first egg. Unfortunately the male Honeyeater was killed a few days later by a male Fairy-blue Wren and, although we had never seen him pay the slightest attention to his mate either whilst she was building the nest or sitting the eggs, it was considered at the time that he must have done so for, four days after his death she deserted the nest. The eggs were not removed from the nest for a further week, and when measured were found to be 18 by 13.5 mm., and, the hard part, were fertile.

The CAPE SUGARBIRD, *Promerops cafer,* from South

Africa, was, with another species, *P. gurneyi,* formerly classified on their own in the family Promeropidae but, due to their anatomical similarities and feeding habits, they have been regrouped in the main family of honeyeaters in the subfamily Promeropinae. The adult male *P. cafer,* the species kept by Mr. Boehm, varies in length from $14\frac{1}{2}$ to $17\frac{1}{2}$ inches (37 to 44 cm), the female some 5 inches (13 cm) smaller, mainly accounted for by the shorter tail. Dusky brown above with pale underparts; speckled on the flanks and sides of neck with russet-brown; centre of breast and lower abdomen paling off to dusky white. Under tail-coverts yellow; tail elongated and heavily feathered. They have a long curved bill, are avid insect eaters, great drinkers of nectar and very fond of soft fruits. Rather uninteresting in an aviary we found them, and the only sound we ever heard from the male was a series of noises like a badly-working mixing machine.

. . . like a badly-working mixing machine.

Although the whole family were insect-eaters with us, preferring the contents of the insect-traps to mealworms, they also partook of the raw ground beef and ate heavily of the fruit mixture.

Family Emberizidae

This family includes the following subfamilies;

Emberizinae	Buntings
Pyrrhuloxiinae (= Richmondeninae)	Cardinal-grosbeaks
Thraupinae (= Tanagrinae)	Tanagers
Tersininae	Swallow-tanager
Coerebinae	Honeycreepers

Subfamily Emberizinae

This is a group of Old World Buntings but also embraces some birds commonly known as "sparrows" and "finches" in North American and it is with one of these that we are concerned here.

The EASTERN TOWHEE, *Pipilo e. erythrophthalmus,* also known as the Chewink, Swamp or Marsh Robin, is an eastern North American bird breeding from near the Gulf coast north to Manitoba, migrating southward to southern Florida, Gulf coast in general and eastern Texas. Although primarily seedeaters, they also eat fruit and are insectivorous, rearing their young practically entirely on live-food such as beetles and their larvae, ants, moths, caterpillars and earthworms. The sexes are dissimilar, the adult male's head, neck, chest and upperparts black; sides of flanks uniform cinnamon rufous; under tail-coverts cinnamon buffy; abdomen and breast white. The wings are black with broad patches of white, and the tail has black central feathers, the outer feathers white with broad black bases. The female has all the black portions replaced by brown, dull above and more cinnamon-umber on throat and chest. White markings as with the male in the wings and tail. They are 8 inches (20 cm) in total length.

We had but one pair that were kept in the bird-house as models for Mr. Boehm's porcelain works. However, since there were plenty in the gardens it was possible to study them in the wild. They have a peculiar habit of scratching on the ground, using their feet alternately, like a domestic-hen. In fact they get most of their food by ground-foraging making a noise amongst the dried leaves that suggests a much larger bird or even a rodent. Ground nesters, under a clump of grass or bushes, their nests are always exceptionally well concealed. Nevertheless the Cowbird females seem to be able to find them for Cowbird eggs often are found in a Towhee's nest. We had one such occurrence on the grounds for, although we never found the Towhee nest, we did witness a female Towhee engaged feeding two of her own young and one young Cowbird.

. . . and one young Cowbird.

Subfamily Pyrrhuloxiinae

This group of a dozen genera is confined to the New World and is predominantly tropical in distribution with five of them extending up into North America, some of which are highly migratory.

The CARDINAL, *Pyrrhuloxia cardinalis,* often referred to as the Virginia Cardinal, is the best known species and is common to temperate North America and south into Central America. This is another species we kept solely for modelling purposes, releasing them as soon as the project was completed. About 8¾ inches (22 cm) in total length, the adult male is primarily vermillion-red with the front portion of the forehead, front part of cheek, the chin and throat black, forming a conspicuous area entirely surrounding the bill which is orange-red; rest of head vermillion-red, duller on the upstanding, conspicuous crest and the crown. The wings and tail dull red. The female's wings and tail are a duller red than the male's and the red of the head and body is replaced above by pale greyish-olive or buffy-greyish. The underparts are pale rufous, nearly white on the abdomen, and the chest is often tinged with red. They are common garden birds consuming noxious garden pests and the seeds of injurious weeds, and often nest in the gardens in the city suburbs. In the State of New Jersey they are year-round birds. These attributes, together with their brilliant colour and spirited song cannot fail but to make them a general attraction.

. . . and spirited song . . .

The GREEN CARDINAL, *Gubernatrix cristatella,* is a South American bird ranging through southern Brazil, Argentina and Bolivia. These also are omnivorous, although when with young in the nest, live-food is the main rearing food. The adult male is yellowish-green, with golden-yellow and blackish-green wing-coverts and tail. The centre of the crown, a superciliary eye-stripe, lores and throat black, the same colour as the erectile crest. Cheeks, breast and abdomen golden-yellow. A black stripe runs from the base of the bill, through the eye, to the back of the head. Under tail-coverts yellow; upper mandible sooty-black; lower mandible, legs and feet slate coloured. The female is duller throughout, the golden-yellow being replaced with yellowish-olive. The crest is smaller, as is the dull, blackish-olive throat patch. They are about 9 inches (23 cm) in total length.

We found them very hardy, wintering outdoors in an unheated but covered aviary. Very little song mostly consisting of a constant chatter. After having been out all winter, the female built an open-cup nest high up in a conifer. Mostly comprised of rootlets and coarse grasses, and lined with finer grasses, wool clippings and dogs' hair, about one week was spent on its construction by the female alone. Two eggs, whitish-grey lightly spotted with sepia mainly concentrated round the thicker end, were laid, and incubation, which was shared, began with the laying of the second egg. The incubation period was fourteen days, this being assessed by the day they began to take live-food up to the nest. Due to its location it was not possible to follow the progress of the chicks but two vacated the nest on the fourteenth day. The plumage of the young birds was dull olive-green and they had smart, small crests. One was a male, the golden-yellow beginning to show at about twelve weeks of age, full adult colouring acquired at ten months. Generally peaceful in mixed collections we did find that they aggressively objected to any bird of a similar colouring to themselves.

The BLACK-CRESTED FINCH, *Lophospingus pusillus*, often referred to as the Pigmy Cardinal, comes from the temperate parts of Argentina and Paraguay where they may be found on the eastern slopes of the Andes. They also are omnivorous partaking readily of seed, soft-food mixture, fruit and whatever life-food they can get. About 5½ inches (14 cm) in total length, the sexes are unalike. The adult male has a black, erectile crest, that colour extending through the centre of the crown to the nape. A black stripe runs from the base of the bill, through the eye to the back of the head, above and below this greyish-white. Throat black, extending as a black bib over the upper chest; back and underparts grey; flight and tail feathers black with grey outer edges. The female is similar in pattern except that she lacks the black bib and all the other black markings are of a sooty shade. The male has a cheerful song which he seems to prefer to advertise from the highest point he can find in the aviary.

I was fortunate enough to breed this species in England, the female imitating the male by selecting the highest point in a small conifer. In fact it was necessary to put a cover over that portion of the aviary to keep the rain out of the nest. This was a regular cup-shape about 10 cm across the top with a depression of about 5 cm. Fortunately it could be observed from outside the aviary so it was possible to follow daily developments. Two eggs, bluish-green heavily speckled with dark brown, were laid and incubation, by the female only, began with the first egg. It is estimated that the eggs were about 13 by 18 mm in size. At twelve days the first hatched, with the second the following day. The chicks were dark skinned, covered with long, grey down and their gapes were bright orange. The rearing was shared, the male for the first five days bringing everything to the female to pass on to the nestlings, after that he fed them direct. The first time he tried to give one of them a mealworm he held it across his bill and tried to force it down its throat that way. The female snatched it from him, held it lengthways and popped it in. From then on he did it the right way. Vacating the nest at twelve days of age, although they were minute, they were very strong on the wing and followed their parents everywhere begging for food. Eight days later the female left them to the male entirely whilst she began rebuilding her nest and producing two more eggs. The first round was independent just as the second round hatched. In all there were three rounds, two chicks from each.

From then on he did it the right way.

We thought we could sex them at an early age but found out that the males do not acquire their full colour until the second year. There are some slight changes in the plumage as they get older but these cannot be fully relied upon for, of four that became darker at their first moult, only two turned out to be males, these subsequently being joined by one that had retained its dull colouring the whole first year. I brought some of them to the States with me and we found them to be long livers, ten years or more, most peaceful aviary birds and good breeders.

Subfamily Thraupinae

This subfamily is comprised of tanagers, 9 primaried song-birds, confined to the New World, very largely to the tropical portion. There are some 200 species in all, ranging in size from under four inches (10 cm) to over fourteen inches (35 cm) in length, and the majority are very colourful with little difference between the sexes. They are tree and bush dwellers although seldom found in the interior of heavy forests, preferring the lightly forested and shrub areas. Mainly frugivorous, they also partake of insects, some to a much greater extent than others.

Over the years we had some 46 different species with successful breedings from four and near misses with others. Due to their preference for fruit, they are best housed in aviaries for, in cages, it is a case of continual cleaning as they are messy eaters, throwing the fruit about until they find just that morsel they want at that moment. If the cages are not kept scrupulously clean the fruit tends to mould, the greedy birds eat it when all else has gone and then become victims of a fungus disease of the throat. It is curable if discovered early enough, but is responsible for the death of many birds kept in unclean conditions.

The SCARLET-BELLIED TANAGER, *Anisognathus igniventris*, is about 7½ inches (19 cm) in total length and there are two subspecies, *A. i. erythrotus* from the Central Andes, and the *A. i. lunulatus* from the Eastern Andes. They are mostly glossy black with ear-tufts, lower breast and abdomen scarlet; lower back and wing-coverts intense blue. The difference in the subspecies is seen in the under tail-coverts, those of *A. i. erythrotus* being all black, or with mere traces of red, whereas *A. i. lunulatus* has under tail-coverts of distinct black and red.

The LACHRYMOSE or BLUE-SHOULDERED MOUN-

TAIN TANAGER, *A. lacrymosus,* of which there are several subspecies through northern South America is about 8 inches (20 cm) in length. Those we had were from Ecuador, *A. l. palpebrosus.* Above dark slaty-blue with bright blue on the rump and upper wing-coverts. Sides of head and neck black; patch behind the eye and spot below the eye yellow. Wings and tail blackish, the feathers edged greenish-blue. The entire underparts dull yellow. We found them to be rather aggressive with smaller birds, particularly at feeding times, so made a point of always housing them with birds of a comparative size.

. . . rather aggressive . . .

The BLUE-NAPED CHLOROPHONIA, *Chlorophonia cyanea,* is about 5 inches (13 cm) and found from Northern South America as far southward as Northern Argentina. The sexes differ. The adult male's head, throat and upper breast bright yellowish-green with an eye-ring of blue. Back bright blue; primary wing feathers and tail black, edged green; secondaries grass-green. The female is very like the male but duller with the back green, lower breast and abdomen olive-yellow.

The GREEN and YELLOW CHLOROPHONIA, *C. flavirostris,* is from Ecuador and those we had were personally collected by Mr. Boehm whilst in that country. Actually they were the first to be seen in the States for many years and Mr. Boehm presented some to the Bronx Zoo. They are about 4 inches (10 cm) in total length, the adult male mainly bright grass-green, the centre of the breast, abdomen and under tail-coverts bright yellow. Bill reddish-brown, legs and feet reddish-yellow. The female's upperparts are bright green, the upper back crossed by a broad yellow collar. Lower breast and abdomen yellow, divided from the green of the upper breast by a narrow chestnut band. Bill yellow, legs and feet salmon-coloured. They are mainly berry eaters, preferring mistletoe to all others, and we found them very hard to cater for since it was not possible to get such berries, or any comparable, in our area.

. . . preferring mistletoe . . .

The MAGPIE TANAGER, *Cissopsis leveriana,* is confined to the northern regions of South America but there is a similar species, *C. major,* to be found in the southern parts of the same area. It is with the former that we were concerned. About 11 inches (28 cm) in total length, the sexes are almost identical. Head, neck, upper breast, wings and upper tail-coverts glossy black with the remainder of the plumage, including the lower tail-coverts, white, as are some of the under wing feathers. These under feathers tend to become exposed in part giving the appearance of scattered white spots and barrings. They have shrike-like bills, black, the same colour as the legs and feet. A striking feature is the bright yellow eye-ring which, as will be seen, is an age indicator. They can be sexed by slight differences in the length of the tail, the shape of the head, that of the male being bolder and the white wing fleckings more prominent. We originally had three, two males and one female, and they were housed together with several other birds for seven months. One morning one of the males was seen dancing up and down with pieces of twig in his bill, but there was no sign of the other male. A search revealed it had been killed. The pair were caught up and transferred to an aviary by themselves. About three weeks later they built a nest of fine twigs, rootlets and coarse grasses in a hemlock. The nest was lined with dried leaves but, since it seemed rather fragile and insecure in the fork of the branch they had selected, a wicker basket was fixed just below. As it turned out this precautionary measure was justified for the nest did sink down until it rested in the basket. The clutch consisted of two eggs, laid on consecutive days. They had a creamy-buff basic colour, heavily streaked with rich brown. They measured 19.5 by 14.5 mm. The incubation appeared to be shared for at no time were the eggs exposed from the time of laying of the second one. Twelve days later, two chicks, dark skinned and covered with light brown fluff hatched. They had gapes of bright orange. Rearing was shared from the outset, the primary diet live-food in the form of mealworms and whatever else they could forage for themselves. One of the chicks was thrown out of the nest but the other flourished, quill feathers were showing at five days and its eyes were open. Vacating the nest at fifteen days, the head, mantle, chest and wings were black, remaining parts white. The bill was entirely dissimilar to that of the adults, being flat, and it was almost a week before it began to assume the shrike-like shape of the parent birds. The eyes lacked the yellow eye-ring, this feature not becoming manifest until the bird was nine months old. Except for this feature, at two months the young bird was a replica of its parents. Although this first breeding was a male, subsequent breedings revealed that the age at which the eye-ring shows is the same for both sexes.

. . . there was no sign of the other male.

The BLUE-WINGED MOUNTAIN TANAGER, *Compsocoma flavinucha*, from the northern parts of South America is about 7½ inches (19 cm) in total length. There are some four subspecies and it was *C. f. cyanoptera* that we had. The sexes are alike, the forecrown, sides of head and neck and the back black. Centre of crown to nape and entire underparts golden-yellow; rump mixed olive and black; wings and tail black, wing-coverts glistening violet-blue, flight feathers edged violet-blue.

The BLACK-CHINNED MOUNTAIN TANAGER, *C. notabilis,* from the northern part of Ecuador is larger, some 9 inches (23 cm) in length. Again the sexes are alike, head and sides of neck black, with a yellow patch on the nape. Back glistening olive-yellow; wings and tail black; wing-coverts and flights edged glistening violet-blue. The underparts are orange-yellow, this colour coming to a point at the throat.

. . . very greedy eaters . . .

We found that Mountain Tanagers are best kept with birds of a comparable size for they are very greedy eaters and can become most aggressive around the feeding places.

The HEPATIC TANAGER, *Piranga flava,* is to be found in the south-western United States, breeding in Arizona, New Mexico and Texas, migrating southward in the winter through Central America to Brazil and Argentina. There are several subspecies, some being purely resident to South America. I do not know which subspecies was shipped to us from Ecuador but the adult male was entirely a dark crimson-red with greyish lores and a dark bill. The female was greenish above with bright yellow underparts. They are about $7\frac{1}{4}$ inches (18 cm) in length.

The SUMMER TANAGER, *P. r. rubra,* also breeds in the United States, wintering from Mexico southward to the northern parts of South America. About the same size as the preceding species which they resemble in colouring except that the male has a pale bill and the entire plumage is a rosy-scarlet, darker above. The upperparts, wings and tail of the female are yellowish-olive, underparts dull yellow. We found both species to be good mixers but had no breeding success with either.

The genus *Ramphocelus,* of which there are several species all having the same characteristics, strong powerful bills, the base of the lower mandible of the male generally silvery or greyish white, this also occurring in some of the females. They range from 6 to 8 inches (15 to 20 cm) in length and can be very aggressive. It is recommended that they not be housed with smaller birds, this being of particular importance when they are breeding. They are to be found throughout the northern parts of South America and in Central America.

The SILVER-BEAKED TANAGER, *R. carbo,* is about 7 inches (18 cm) and the sexes differ. They are to be found in northern South America and Trinidad. Head and breast of the adult male dark crimson; back and upper tail-coverts velvety maroon; wings and tail brownish-black. The male is recognisable by the base of the lower mandible which is bluish-white. The female is duller, head, wings and tail brownish; back reddish-brown; rump and upper tail-coverts dull crimson; underparts dull red and the bill is black.

The CRIMSON-BACKED TANAGER, *R. dimidiatus*, is the same size as the preceding species and generally from the same area, northern Southern America, except that they also frequent Panama and are not in Trinidad. The adult male's whole head, upper breast and mantle deep maroon crimson; rest of plumage crimson scarlet. Wings, tail, thighs and centre of abdomen black and base of lower mandible silvery. The female is reddish-brown above, clearer red on the rump and upper tail-coverts; throat and chest dark brownish-red; remainder of underparts a lighter shade; bill black.

The FLAME-RUMPED or VARIABLE TANAGER, *R. flammigerus*, is a larger bird, some 8½ inches (22 cm), and is more confined to the northern parts of Ecuador and Colombia. The adult male is mainly glossy black with a bright orange rump and lower back. The female is duller, black on the upperparts with underparts of pale lemon and duller rump feathering. Their clutch, based on three nestings, appears to consist of but two eggs, sky-blue with irregular black spots mainly concentrated around the thicker end. Although they were not measured, it was estimated they were about 23 by 17 mm. The male assisted in the building of the nest, mainly by taking material to the female, but took no part in the incubation. The nest was a deep, open cup with a total width of 11 cm., 6 of which was comprised of the cup-like depression which was 4 cm deep. Rootlets, pine-needles, fine fibres and grasses formed the basic components of the nest.

. . . took no part in the incubation.

Incubation began with the laying of the first egg and, in twelve days it hatched with a second chick the following day. They were very dark skinned, covered with a grey down, gapes orange streaked with red. Both parents attended to the rearing which was with live-food only for a few days, fruit being added after about five days by which time the chicks had their eyes open and quill feathers showing. Vacating the nest at fourteen days, they closely resembled the adult female in colouring with a pale orange rump and buffish underparts. Their bills were thick and black, the silver of the lower mandible not showing until they were nine weeks old. They were sexable at sixteen weeks. It was when the young birds left the nest that the aggression of the male became apparent. In all he killed eight smaller tanagers plus the young of a Black Tanager but left the other species of *Ramphocelus* entirely alone. Placed in an aviary on their own they had two further nests that year all following the general pattern of the first.

The LEMON-RUMPED TANAGER, *R. icteronotus,* from Panama and western Venezuela is the same size as the Flame-rumped, and has the same glossy black plumage but the lower back, rump and upper tail-coverts are brilliant lemon-yellow. The upperparts of the female are greyish-brown, tinged olive; lower back, rump, upper tail-coverts and underparts lemon-yellow; throat and sides of head whitish.

The VELVET or SCARLET-RUMPED TANAGER, *R. passerini,* is the smallest of the genus we had being about $6\frac{1}{2}$ inches (16 cm) in length. Their range is Mexico to Panama. The adult male is rich velvety black except for the brilliant orange-scarlet rump and upper tail-coverts. Head and neck of the female grey, brightening to dull orange on chest and orange-olive on back. Lower back, rump and upper tail-coverts dull orange; wings and tail grey-brown, the feathers edged olive-orange; abdomen and under tail-coverts olive-grey.

The WHITE-CAPPED TANAGER, *Sericossypha albocristata,* from northern South America is one of the larger tanagers, some 11 inches (28 cm) in total length. The sexes are very similar, the adult male mostly black with the crown and region before the eye white. Throat and breast carmine-red flowing into purplish on the lower border; wings and tail glossy blue-black. With the female the throat and breast are dusky red, the remainder of the colouring as in the male.

PRETRE'S TANAGER, *Spindalis pretrei,* is one of a small group confined to the West Indies. This species is from Cuba and is about 6 inches (15 cm) in length. The male's back olive; collar, rump and breast orange; wings and tail black, margined white. The head is black with a white bar above and below the eye; throat and underparts yellow. The female is mainly plain olive-grey, darker on the upperparts and tinged yellowish below; wing feathers margined in white.

There are several tanagers known basically as black tanagers, the actual species being identified by addition of a superlative such as white-shouldered, red-crowned etc. All in the genus *Tachyphonus,* they are to be found from Central America to the northern parts of South America.

The RED-CROWNED TANAGER, *T. coronatus,* is about 9 inches (23 cm) in length and, as adults, can be sexed at sight. The male is glossy black, this colour relieved by a red stripe running through the crown of the head. The feathers making up this marking lie flat on the head at normal times and are hardly visible. However, when the bird is agitated, the side feathers part and the red line is raised slightly but not to such a degree to be able to classify it as a crest. The underparts of the shoulders white, bill and legs dark. The female is rich russet brown above, underparts duller; bill black, legs and feet slate. They are hardy, peaceful, good mixers and fairly ready breeders. The nest, an open cup some 90 mm across the top with a depression of some 75 mm., is comprised of rootlets, fibres and coarse grasses, lined with finer grasses. In our breeding of the species three eggs were laid on successive days and they averaged 20 by14 mm., rather small for the size of the bird. Pinkish-cream in ground colour with golden-brown fleckings, mainly around the thicker end. Incubation by the female only apparently began with the laying of the last egg for all three hatched at the same time, twelve days after completion of the clutch. The chicks were dark skinned, covered with black downy fluff and had gapes of orange streaked with red. Live-food was the sole diet to begin with and it was not until their eyes were open at the fifth day that fruit and ground meat was added. At nine days they were completely feathered up and vacated the nest the following day. Unfortunately it is not possible to give any further information on their development since, at twenty days old they were killed by the male Variable Tanager, the breeding and aggressiveness of which has been covered earlier.

. . . fairly ready breeders.

The WHITE-SHOULDERED TANAGER, *T. rufus,* is slightly smaller than the Red-crowned. The adult male is a lustrous blue-black, inner upper wing-coverts and under wing-coverts white. The female is bright rufous above, paler below. They are to be found in the same areas as the Red-crowned and are good mixers.

The genus *Tanagra* contains a number of small and colourful species generally known as euphonias. They should not be confused with the genus *Tangara* which is dealt with later. The male euphonias are mostly black glossed with violet, blue or green on the upperparts and yellowish below. They range from Central America southward to northern Argentina and feed mainly on small berries such as mistletoe, which is their favourite.

The LESSON'S EUPHONIA, *T. affinis*, is commonly found in Mexico through to Costa Rica in company with the Bonaparte's. They are about 4 inches (10 cm) in length, the adult male having yellow on the forehead, breast, abdomen and under tail-coverts, the remainder of the plumage glossy purplish-black except for white at the base of the outer tail feathers. The female is olive, brightening into yellow on the flanks and under tail-coverts, and into grey with a faint blue gloss on the crown, hind-neck and upper back.

The BLUE-CROWNED EUPHONIA, *T. elegantissima,* another Central American species is about 4½ inches (11 cm) in length. The adult male's forehead orange-brown, followed by a narrow black line, then by light blue through the whole crown and hind-neck. Back, wings and tail rich glossy purple; chin and throat purplish-black; rest of underparts deep tawny-orange. The female is olive-green above except for blue on the crown and a forehead of orange-brown. Brownish-yellow throat, rest of underparts yellowish-olive.

The BONAPARTE'S EUPHONIA, *T. lauta,* just over 4½ inches (11 cm) in length is, as mentioned earlier, to be found in company with the Lesson's. The male is golden-yellow through the underparts and on the forehead, rest of the plumage glossy blue-black except for white on the inner webs of the outer tail feathers. The female, olive above, greyish-white on the throat, breast and abdomen, with yellow on sides, flanks and under tail-coverts, is a fraction smaller than the male. We had a pair in a planted room in the main birdhouse and the female built a dome-shaped nest, entrance at the side, in a hanging basket of house ivy. Two eggs were laid but, except that they were very small and light coloured no further data was obtained as they were at the bottom of the nest and the entrance hole was only just big enough to allow the female in and out. As far as we could tell the female only incubated and, after a period of fourteen days discarded the eggs from the nest. We found them on the ground all broken and muddied up. She made two further nests in other hanging baskets but did not produce any more eggs.

. . . in a hanging basket of house ivy.

The RUFOUS-BELLIED EUPHONIA, *T. rufiventris,* from Venezuela southward to Bolivia, is about 5 inches (13 cm) in length. The upperparts, throat, centre of upper breast of the adult male steel-blue; wings and tail black, edged steel-blue; underparts tawny-rufous with yellow at sides of breast. The female is olive above, including the wings and tail; chin pale yellowish; sides of head and breast olive-yellow; throat, centre of breast and abdomen ashy-grey; under tail-coverts tawny-ochraceous.

The ORANGE-CROWNED EUPHONIA, *T. saturata,* is smaller, about 4 inches (10 cm) in length, and is to be found in Ecuador and Peru. The male's crown orange-yellow; remainder of upperparts glossy purple becoming steel-blue on the rump, wings and tail. Throat glossy purple, remainder of underparts deep tawny-orange, yellower on the sides of the breast. The upperparts of the female bright olive; throat, breast and sides of body olive-yellow, and yellow in the centre of the abdomen.

The last of the euphonias we had is the VIOLET, *T. violacea,* from the northern parts of South America, Trinidad and down to south-east Brazil. This also is just over 4 inches (10 cm) in length. The male's forehead orange-yellow; crown, sides of face, back, rump, wings and tail steel-blue. Throat and underparts orange-yellow, becoming paler on the abdomen and under tail-coverts. The female is yellowish-bronze-green above; throat and underparts greenish-yellow, paler on the abdomen and under tail-coverts.

We found that all euphonias had melodious little songs, hence the name, that of the Violet being particularly flute-like. They are most peaceful birds and, provided they are not subjected to draughts or chills, make very good cage or aviary birds. Their diet is a thing that has to be watched for they take a negligible amount of live-food being mainly fruit-eaters which they prefer chopped up into small berry-like pieces.

Their diet is a thing that has to be watched . . .

The genus *Tangara* contains some of the most colourful species in the entire Tanager family. They have a wide range from Central America through to South America, mainly confined within the latitudes 20 degrees North and 20 degrees South. Principally fruit-eaters, they also partake of a little live-food, this intake increased at breeding times. Many of this genus used to be referred to as callistes but this term is no longer in use. We had some 19 different species over the years but, although several went to nest only one reared young to maturity, the remainder being subject to predation by other birds. With the majority, the sexes are alike or very similar.

The GOLDEN TANAGER, *T. arthus,* is about 5½ inches (14 cm) in length and is mostly golden-yellow with the mantle streaked black. The lores, ear-coverts, wings and tail black; inner primaries and wing-coverts edged greenish-gold to orange-yellow. There are several subspecies to be found in Venezuela, Ecuador, Peru and Bolivia, the difference being in the colour of the underparts. We had three, *T. a. occidentalis* with rich dark yellow underparts; *T. a. sclateri* where the underparts are a rich amber brown and *T. a. aurulenta* with golden-yellow underparts.

The RUFOUS-CROWNED TANAGER, *T. cayana,* from Venezuela, the Guianas, Brazil, Paraguay and Northern Bolivia, is larger, some 6½ inches (16 cm) in length. The crown rufous; lores and sides of head black; wings and tail verditer blue; the remainder of the upperparts shining golden straw colour. Lower breast and abdomen golden-buff merging into buff on under tail-coverts. The females are similar but much duller with more buff underparts.

The PARADISE TANAGER, *T. chilensis,* about the same size as the preceding species is undoubtedly the most colourful of all the tanagers and is from southern Venezuela, the Guianas, northern and western Brazil, Ecuador, Peru and Bolivia. Above velvety black with the lower back and rump scarlet. Forehead and eye-ring black; top and sides of head shining golden-green; throat, upper breast, outer wing-coverts and primaries violet-blue; inner wing-coverts and entire underparts shining turquoise blue; centre of abdomen, wings, tail and under tail-coverts black. This description is of the nominate race of which we had several but we also received the subspecies, *T. c. coeli-color,* with which the lower back is orange-scarlet and the rump golden-yellow.

The SPECKLED TANAGER, *T. chrysophrys,* about 5½ inches (14 cm) in length, has the feathers of the upperparts black, edged broadly in green giving a scale-like effect. Eye-ring and a streak around the lores yellowish; underparts white, the feathers having black centres giving a spotted appearance; flanks and under tail-coverts green. Wings black, edged verditer blue; tail black, edged green. They are to be found from Costa Rica southward to Venezuela.

The BLUE-NECKED TANAGER, *T. cyanicollis,* the same size as the Speckled, is the one that did manage to rear its young. They are to be found in the same areas as the Golden Tanager, and in Brazil. We had a pair of the subspecies *T. c. caeruleo-cephala* that Mr. Boehm brought back from Ecuador. The whole head turquoise-blue; purplish-blue in the middle of the throat; back and breast black. Abdomen shining purplish-blue; wing-coverts, lower back, rump, upper tail-coverts and margins to inner flights glistening silvery green. Tail black, edged greenish-blue. The pair selected a hanging basket of asparagus fern as their nesting site making a small, open, cup-shaped nest down

. . . brought back from Ecuador.

234

in the roots of the plant. Two eggs were laid and incubated by the female. We knew it was the female for, like all birds in the aviaries, they wore coloured leg-bands and it was the one with the blue band that laid the second egg and sat on them. Hatching at 13 days, one died at five days but the other left the nest at 17 days and was independent in a further 12 days. They had another round of two, one only living to be reared but, at their third effort, the two chicks were taken by a White-eyed Slaty Flycatcher that had been hanging around their nest from the very start. Up to then one had always been on duty to protect the nestlings but this time they both went off to feed. We actually witnessed the flycatcher grab first one chick and gulp it down immediately, flying off with the other as we moved towards it.

. . . one had always been on duty . . .

The DESMAREST'S TANAGER, *T. desmaresti,* from Venezuela is entirely green except for a copper-red head and thighs. We had only one and this survived but a few hours after receipt.

The SUPERB TANAGER, *T. fastuosa,* is almost as colourful as the Paradise. The upper surface of the head glistening emerald green; upper back velvety black; lower back and rump brilliant orange-red. Wings and tail black edged above purple. Outer secondaries brilliant orange; lesser wing-coverts emerald green. Chin and throat black, divided from each other by a greenish-blue line; breast silvery-blue passing into deep purplish-blue on the rest of the underparts. They are about $5\frac{1}{2}$ inches (14 cm) in length and come from Brazil.

The FESTIVE TANAGER, *T. festiva,* from south-eastern Brazil, is only about 5 inches (13 cm) in length and the main colouring is grass-green. Black around the bill and on the back and shoulders, the tail and wings are green and black. Top of head and throat blue; cheeks and back of neck red. They are not as robust as the Superb and require careful acclimatisation and attention. Far better as aviary birds than caged.

The YELLOW TANAGER, *T. flava,* also from south-eastern Brazil, is about the same size as the Superb and the adult male is basically tawny-yellow, wings and tail black, edged green. Around the bill, throat, breast and middle of abdomen black. The female has a pale green back and the cheeks and breast are grey.

The SPOTTED TANAGER, *T. guttata,* is green above; yellowish-green on the head; underparts white tinged bluish-green. With the exception of the wings, lower back and tail, the entire plumage is spotted with black. This species may be found throughout northeastern South America.

The SILVER-THROATED TANAGER, *T. icterno-cephala,* is one of the larger species, some 5¾ inches (14 cm) in length and has a range from Costa Rica to Panama and northwestern Ecuador. The top and sides of the head of the adult male are golden-yellow; throat and sides of neck silvery-green; a black line from the bill extending backwards separating the yellow from the green. Remainder of underparts golden-yellow tinged green. The female is of similar colouring but duller and the crown is dull greenish-yellow; back streaked yellow and black; rump golden-yellow. We had pairs build very neat, cup-shaped nests but none of them produced any eggs as far as we are aware.

The TURQUOISE TANAGER, *T. mexicana,* is about the same size as the preceding species and the sexes are alike. Lores, chin, centre of crown, nape, back, wings and tail black, the primaries edged turquoise-blue. The remainder of the plumage is mainly purplish-black, the lower throat and sides of head spotted black. Centre of abdomen, under tail-coverts and tufts on the sides of the breast golden-yellow. They are to found in Venezuela, the Guianas, Trinidad, Brazil, Peru and Bolivia.

The MASKED TANAGER, *T. nigro-cincta,* is about 5 inches (13 cm) in length and, except for the female being generally duller in colour, the sexes are alike. Lores, chin and ocular region black; cheeks and ear-coverts pale green; rest of head pale lavender. Breast, upper back, wings and tail black; lower back, rump and upper tail-coverts cornflower-blue; lesser wing-coverts blue; medium wing-coverts silvery-green; centre of abdomen white; sides bright blue. They have an extensive range from southern Mexico through to northern South America to western Brazil.

The FLAME-FACED TANAGER, *T. parzudakii,* about 6½ inches (16 cm) in length, has the forehead and a patch behind and below the eye scarlet. The ocular area, throat and posterior ear-coverts black; crown and nape to behind ear-coverts golden-yellow. Mantle, wings and tail black; lower back, rump, upper tail-coverts, inner wing-coverts, breast and sides of body glistening opalescent blue; greater wing-coverts edged blue; centre of underparts cinnamon buff. They have a limited range in northwestern Venezuela, Ecuador and Peru.

The RUFOUS-THROATED TANAGER, *T. rufigula,* is just over 5 inches (13 cm) in length and the upperparts are black, the feathers narrowly edged with copper-green giving a scaled effect. Wings and tail black, feathers edged silvery-green; lower back and rump silvery-green. Chin and throat rufous-chestnut, the centre of the throat paler; rest of underparts whitish except under tail-coverts which are buff. The feathers of breast and flanks centred black and fringed silver-green. They are more or less limited to Colombia and northwestern Ecuador.

The YELLOW-CROWNED TANAGER, *T. xanthocephala*, is slightly larger than the previous species and, in addition to the areas where that one is to be found, these are also in Peru and Bolivia. The crown, cheeks and ear-coverts golden-yellow; forehead, lores, throat and extreme upper back black; remainder of back streaked blue and black; rump and upper tail-coverts shining blue. Lower throat, breast, and flanks opalescent greenish-blue; centre of abdomen and under tail-coverts fawn; wings and tail black, edged blue.

To complete our tanager collection we now come to the genus *Thraupis*, all species of which average 6½ to 7¾ inches (16 to 20 cm) in length and, in our experience, are all good mixers and hardy.

The SILVER-BLUE TANAGER, *T. cana*, is about 7¼ inches (18 cm) and is generally pale blue, brighter on rump, paler and greener below. This species is from Central America, Colombia, Venezuela, Ecuador and Peru and the shoulders are violet-blue. A male paired up with a female BLUE-GREY TANAGER, *T. episcopus*, from the Guianas that is very similar in colouring except that the shoulders are bluish-white. One day it was noticed that the male bird was carrying nesting material into a hole in an old dead tree trunk about eight feet (2.5 metres) up. Two days later the female was missing but later was seen to emerge from this same hole. The nest was in such a location that it could not be examined closely so no knowledge is available as to the number of eggs, their colour or their size. The male was never seen to actually enter the nest-hole although he did take food up to the female who appeared to be sitting steadily. From these observations it was estimated that the incubation period was about thirteen days. Seventeen days later two fledglings emerged, very strong on the wing and resembling the adult female in general colour. Independency was acquired fourteen days later and the pair went to nest again producing one more young. The five birds lived amicably together and the only way to tell the young from the adults, other than by the leg-bands, was the colouring of the shoulders, those of the young birds being between a bluish-white and a bluish-purple.

. . . very strong on the wing . . .

237

The PALM TANAGER, *T. palmarum*, is slightly larger than the preceding species and is not very colourful. Crown pale green; rest of plumage shining greyish olive-green, heavily glossed with violet on breast and mantle. Wing-coverts and base of primaries pale greyish-green; wings and tail brownish-black. The female is very similar except that the colour is duller and greener with less gloss both above and below.

The *Thraupis* are among the easier tanagers to cater for. They are fairly hardy, not quarrelsome amongst themselves or with other birds but, when nesting we learned that the male maintains a vigilant watch and keeps all comers away from the nesting site just by adopting a threatening posture.

Subfamily Tersininae

There is but one member of this subfamily, the SWALLOW-TANAGER, *Tersina viridis*, which is to be found in the northern parts of South America, up to the Panama, and in Trinidad. They are partially migratory, breeding in wooded country with clearings in the mountains, but spending the non-breeding season in the humid lowlands. They are about 6 inches (15 cm) in total length, the male mainly a brilliant turquoise blue, with a black face and throat, and black bars on the flanks. Centre of abdomen and under tail-coverts white; wings and tail black, feathers broadly margined in blue. The female is mainly grass-green, black facial area replaced with grey. Wings and tail black, broadly margined in green. The centre of abdomen and bars on flanks pale yellow. They are both fruit and insect eaters, the latter being taken on the wing. When eating fruit with seeds, they hold the whole fruit in their wide-open bill turning it around and around until they have extracted all the pulp and flesh, and then discard the seed. As they have a distensible throat-sac in which they store fruit after swallowing it, each feeding often appears to be excessive for the size of the bird. We found them good mixers, peaceful, and a colourful addition to any aviary.

. . . a distensible throat-sac . . .

Subfamily Coerebinae

This is a purely neotropical group commonly known as honeycreepers or sugarbirds. They are generally small birds with thin, decurved bills and the females usually are much duller coloured than the brilliantly coloured males. Fruit and nectar feeders, they also are very insectivorous.

The GREEN HONEYCREEPER, *Chlorophanes spiza*, also known as the Black-headed Sugarbird, is from Central America and the northern parts of South America. About six inches (15 cm) in total length, the adult male with his jet-black head and shining emerald-green body is most striking. The female is grass-green, lacks the black head, but has greyish-green cheek patches. The upper mandible of the male is black, the lower bright yellow whereas with the female, the upper is duller black and the lower is yellow at the base, shading to the same tone as the upper about half way along. Their one failing is their aggressiveness towards each other and it is never advisable to house two males in the same aviary or cage. At times they also can be troublesome to other small birds and, in a mixed collection, careful watch should be kept at all times.

At breeding time the male becomes particularly offensive, permitting the presence of no other bird near the nesting site. Nest building is by the female only, the male sitting by singing loudly. It is not a very melodious song being comprised of a short range of high notes but, by virtue of its pitch and strength, can be heard for a considerable distance. The open, cup nest is of the suspended type, a shrub, creeper or bushy tree usually being selected. It measures about 9 cm across the top and 6 cm in depth, the female almost completely concealed when she is sitting. The clutch varies from two to three eggs of a pinkish-brown colour, heavily flecked with umber, the thicker end almost obscured. They average 21 by 16 mm in size. Incubation is by the female only, starting with the laying of the first egg, and lasts twelve days. The newly hatched chicks are very dark skinned, bare of all body covering and have bright pink gapes. There are two red spots at the outer base of the lower mandible, presumably "targets" for the parents when feeding. In all our breedings of this species, every year for five years, it was noticed that only the female fed the young for the first five days, the diet being regurgitated nectar and live-food in the form of flies, other insects, and mealworm pupae. At the outset small mealworms were collected for them but these were ignored for the pupae so, from then on it was only the latter that was ever provided for them until they attained independence. By the end of the five day period their eyes were open and quill feathers showing. Now the male assisted in the rearing but the bulk of the feeding was still done by the female. Nest sanitation was effected by the female only, she waiting for the young birds to excrete, then taking the sac and swallowing it. This pro-

It is not a very melodious song . . .

Black-headed Sugarbird female on nest

cedure continued right up to the time they vacated the nest at twelve days of age. The fledglings' upper plumage was dark bottle-green, the underparts grey. However, in every instance their heads were completely bare giving them a bizarre appearance. At three weeks their heads had feathered up and the upper plumage had taken on a lighter shade of green, the underparts also changing to that colour. Prior to this, however, the female had laid again and the male took over entire responsibility for the first brood. The initial five days of the female's attendance on the nestlings now became significant for it was not until the second round chicks were five days old that the first were independent. As the male began to harass them at this stage they were removed from the aviary. The second round followed the exact pattern of progress as the first and there was no difference in the behaviour by either of the other two pairs that were breeding in other aviaries at the same time. They were all sexable at ten weeks of age, the first year producing five males and four females. Subsequent breedings revealed that they breed in their first year. We did have one case of a female who had reared chicks changing her colour pattern the following year to that of a male. We never heard "it" sing and unfortunately it was killed before we could pair it with a female to see if a complete sex change had taken place. In another instance, a paired female on eggs was killed two days before they were due to hatch. As there was a solitary female in an adjoining aviary that had built a nest and laid eggs just over six days prior to this, the clear eggs were removed and the fertile ones substituted. Two days later the first egg hatched, the second the following day and the foster female reared both the chicks to full independence.

. . . the fertile ones substituted.

The BANAQUIT, *Coereba flaveola*, ranges from Mexico southward to Ecuador and Venezuela, and from the Guianas southward to Argentina. Further, they are prevalent throughout most of the West Indian islands. They are about 4 inches (10 cm) in total length, the sexes being similar. The crown sooty-grey, bordered at each side by a clear white superciliary stripe; the rest of the head, including the chin and throat, light grey. The upperparts greyish-olive except for yellowish-olive on the rump and a white patch at the base of the primaries. The breast lemon-yellow, the flanks olive, and the abdomen and under tail-coverts white. All the tail feathers except the central pair are tipped with white on the inner webs. We had a presumed pair that built a nest in which they slept at night but they never attempted to build their normal breeding nest the whole time they were with us.

The PURPLE HONEYCREEPER, *Cyanerpes caeruleus*, is about 4½ inches (12 cm) in length, just over half an inch accounted for by the conspicuously curved bill. They are to be found in the northern parts of South America and on the island of Trinidad. The adult male has a body colour of uniform purple-blue with the crown and sides of head a brighter and purer blue. The forehead, lores, chin, throat, wings and tail black, as is a stripe running through the eye. The legs and feet bright lemon yellow. The female's upperparts, wings and tail grass-green, the forecrown narrowly streaked with buff. The forehead, lores and ocular regions tawny buff, throat buff with a blue malar streak, the rest of the underparts green streaked with yellow, the centre of the abdomen and under tail-coverts plain yellow.

The YELLOW-WINGED or RED-LEGGED HONEY-CREEPER, *C. cyaneus,* is to be found in the same regions as the preceding species. About 5½ inches (14 cm) in total length, the bill is about ¾ inch (2 cm) and only slightly curved. The adult male is black on the forehead, ocular region, mantle, wings, tail and under tail-coverts. The feathers of the crown are a brilliant turquoise with an enamel-like finish. The sides of the head, nape, lower back, scapulars, upper tail-coverts and underparts are purple-blue, as is a narrow line surrounding the crown patch. The inner margins of the flight feathers are a canary yellow, only visible when in flight. Legs and feet bright red. The entire upper plumage of the female is dull grass-green except for the eyebrow which is yellowish-white, the same colour as the throat. The breast and flanks dull grass-green, the breast streaked with yellow, and the centre of the abdomen plain pale yellow. The wings and tail dusky, the wing-coverts and flights margined olive-green.

Legs and feet bright red.

The BLUE HONEYCREEEPER, *Dacnis cayana,* ranges from Nicaragua to Ecuador and Venezuela, and from the Guianas to Argentina and Bolivia. Like the Purple and Yellow-winged it is also to be found in Trinidad. The sexes are dissimilar, the adult male mainly turquoise varying to light or dark purple-blue according to their native habitat. The forehead, lores, throat, centre of back, wings and tail black, flight feathers margined in turquoise. The female is mainly grass-green with the top and sides of head blue and throat grey. They are about the same size as the Yellow-winged.

It was our experience with the Blue that the females are far more delicate than the males for, even after full acclimatisation, the slightest change in temperature, routine or surroundings, appeared to affect them adversely. With the exception of the Purple we found it was safer to only keep one pair of Honeycreepers in the same aviary for they can be very quarrelsome at times.

Family Icteridae

This family is comprised of New World orioles of which there are some 80 species ranging from 6½ to 21 inches (16 to 53 cm) in total length. This heterogenous New World family includes such diverse natural groups as the oropondolas, caciques, grackles, American blackbirds, troupials, cowbirds and meadowlarks. The name oriole was no doubt assigned to the troupials by the early settlers from the Old World by virtue of the colouring of the birds, mainly yellow. They are mainly confined to the tropical regions at lower altitudes, but several species are to be found in the temperate regions, one even venturing into the Arctic Circle. They are omnivorous in the temperate areas, but most of those found in the tropics are fruit and nectar feeders together with insect life. We found them to be good mixers although any with yellow in their plumage were inclined to be antagonistic towards birds of a similar colouring.

. . . good mixers . . .

The YELLOW-HOODED BLACKBIRD, *Agelaius icterocephalus*, from the northern parts of South America is about 7 inches (18 cm) in length, the adult male having a yellow head with black lores; throat and upper breast also yellow. Remainder of plumage glossy black. The upperparts of the female are brownish-black margined with yellow; sides of face and throat citron-yellow; remainder of underparts greyish-brown tinged yellow.

The YELLOW-RUMPED CACIQUE, *Cacicus cela*, is much larger, the males being up to 11½ inches (29 cm) and the female up to 10 inches (25 cm) in length. They are to be found in Central America and the northern parts of South America, including Trinidad. The general plumage is glossy black; the lower back, rump, upper and under tail-coverts, basal half of tail and a large patch on the inner wing-coverts bright golden-yellow. The female is duller on underparts, the lower breast and abdomen dusky olivaceous. The bill is greenish or yellowish-white.

The BALTIMORE ORIOLE, *Icterus galbula,* is about 8 inches (20 cm) in length. This species breeds from southern Canada southward to Mexico and winters through Central America to the northern parts of South America. The sexes differ, the whole head, throat, mantle, wings, central tail feathers of the male black; wing feathers margined white; outer tail feathers yellow, basally black. Underparts, wing-coverts, lower back, rump and upper tail-coverts orange-yellow. The female is greyish-olive above, crown and rump tinged yellow. Throat, breast and under tail-coverts yellow; abdomen whitish; wings blackish with two white wing-bars. Tail dull yellowish-brown.

We only kept this species for modelling purposes then releasing them, but, they did breed in the grounds building a long, hanging nest attached to the very end of a branch high up in a tulip tree. It was fascinating watching it swaying in the breeze, this in no way deterring the parent birds going in and out.

. . . watching it swaying in the breeze . . .

The BLACK-THROATED ORIOLE, *I. gularis,* about 10 inches (25 cm) in length is a Central American species very much like the Baltimore Oriole except that the black is restricted to the wings, tail, back, narrow facial mask and a throat patch. There is only one white wing-bar and the innermost secondaries are white-edged. The female is a little duller than the male.

The SPOTTED-BREASTED ORIOLE, *I. pectoralis,* also a Central American species is only about 9 inches (23 cm) in length and the sexes are alike. A rich orange except for black of the lores, chin, throat, back, wings and tail; sides of chest boldly spotted with black; secondaries edged white and a small patch of white at the base of the primaries.

The YELLOW-HEADED BLACKBIRD, *Xanthocephalus xanthocephalus,* is another species kept only just as long as required for modelling from. They have a wide range in central and western North America, going southward to breed and wintering in Central America. About 10 inches (25 cm) in length, the sexes differ. The male's head, neck and chest orange-yellow; lores, eye region, forward portion of cheeks and chin black; rest of plumage black relieved by a white patch on the wing; ventral area yellow or orange. The female is generally dusky greyish-brown or sooty; cheeks, chin, throat and a stripe over the eye dull whitish, tinged with yellow passing into light yellow on the chest. Breast broadly streaked with white; no white on the wings; ventral area yellowish.

Family Ploceidae

This is an Old World family of birds generally referred to as weavers, and is mostly confined to Africa south of the Sahara, with a few species in Asia. The family has been divided into three subfamilies, Bubalornithinae, the buffalo weavers; Ploceinae, the 'true' weavers; and Passerinae, the sparrows. Although not regarded as softbills, some of the species of weavers Mr. Boehm had are included in this book for, by their omnivorous feeding habits, they did follow the feeding pattern of softbills far more than that of plain seedeaters. Soft-food mixture, ground raw beef, fruit-mix, live-food and millet sprays was the only feed we ever put out for them, their other vegetable requirements being obtained direct from the seeding grasses and shrubs in their aviaries.

Subfamily Bubalornithinae

. . . no special affinity for buffaloes . . .

This subfamily is comprised of just 3 species, all in Africa, and they are heavily built birds, about 10 inches (25 cm) in total length. Actually they have no special affinity for buffalos, but were so named by the early settlers who first saw them in the vicinity of those animals.

The only species we had was the WHITE-HEADED BUF-FALO WEAVER, *Dinemellia dinemelli,* of which there are two subspecies, our pair being the *D. d. boehmi* from Kenya. Top of head pale greyish-white; remainder of head, neck all round and underparts white; mantle, wings and tail black; basal half of primaries white; spot on bend of wing, lower rump, upper and under tail-coverts orange-red. The sexes are alike. They have a twittering call note but also frequently give vent to a harsh trumpet-like cry. Although freely partaking of all the food supplied, they spent most of their time on the ground foraging for insects.

Subfamily Ploceinae

This is the family of the 'true' weavers of which there are some 90 species. Mostly confined to Africa, but with 5 species in India and Malaysia. They fall into two groups, one bearing the common name of weavers, the other referred to as whydahs or widow-birds, this name being originated by the resemblance of the males' long, black tail feathers to widows' weeds.

The JACKSON'S WHYDAH, *Euplectes jacksoni*, is from Kenya and the sexes differ. The general colour of the adult male in breeding dress is black; wing shoulder light brown with black centres to the feathers; rest of wing feathers edged pale brown; under wing-coverts deep buff; the tail feathers are long, broad and curved upwards towards the ends. The female is smaller, and is broadly streaked above black and brown; wing shoulder feathers edged dull yellow; underparts buffish brown with brown streaks on chest and flanks; under wing-coverts buff. The male in non-breeding dress loses the black of the body and the long tail feathers, is very much like the female but browner, and retains the wing colouring as in breeding dress. They are believed to be polygamous but, since we only had but one pair, I have no observations on this. Our male did, however, indulge in a display. He selected an area under a pine tree where he wore a veritable circle in the grass by his dancing up and down, literally springing up in the air with his head thrown back and the tail curved up to touch the nape, always moving in a circular direction. Despite all his efforts, the female paid no attention to him at all, normally being in some distant part of the aviary searching out insects in the grasses.

. . . by his dancing up and down . . .

The GIANT WHYDAH, *Euplectes progne*, is larger than the preceding species and has a wider distribution being found in Angola, Kenya and eastern South Africa. The male in non-breeding dress is about $9\frac{1}{2}$ inches (24 cm) in length and the female about 7 inches (18 cm). The general colour of the adult male in breeding dress is black; wing-shoulder red; median wing-coverts white; tail long, the central pair of feathers about 18 inches (45 cm) in total length. The general colour of the female is brownish, streaked above with buff, tawny and black; underparts streaked pale buff on chest, breast and flanks; under wing-coverts black; tail feathers narrow and pointed. The male in nonbreeding dress resembles the female but is more broadly streaked above and below, and retains the wing and shoulder colouring of his breeding dress. The long tail feathers are dropped, the tail then becoming similar to that of the female. We never witnessed this species partaking in any definite display, but the male did make an attractive picture as he flew up and down the 60 feet (18 metres) aviary with his tail streaming out behind him.

Both the Jackson's and the Giant Whydahs were very partial to seeding grasses and fresh bunches were hung up for them daily whilst available, millet sprays being utilised during the winter months. They also consumed a considerable amount of fruit, ground raw beef and soft-food mixture and were always ready for their daily ration of live-food.

The BLACK MOUNTAIN-WEAVER, *Heterhyphantes melanogaster,* has races in Cameroon, the Congo, southern Sudan and Kenya. The subspecies we had, *H. m. stephano-phorus,* from Kenya, is about 5 inches (13 cm) in length and the sexes differ. The forehead, crown and sides of face of the adult male are yellow with a black streak through the eye; remainder of plumage black, as is the bill. The female has the chin, sides of face, forehead and front of neck yellow; remainder of plumage black. They were good mixers and mainly fed on the fruit-mix and ground raw beef, live-food also being taken.

The CRESTED MALIMBE, *Malimbus malimbicus,* of which there are several races extending from Guinea, through northern Nigeria, Cameroon and across to Uganda, is about 7 inches (18 cm) in length and the sexes are alike in colouring but the female lacks the elongated crest. Forehead, round and behind the eye and chin, black; crown, ear-coverts, sides of face and throat to chest glossy crimson-red; remainder of plumage black; wings and tail duller; bill black. The crimson feathers of the crown of the male are elongated to form a distinct crest, prolonged over the nape. With the female these feathers are short and end in an abrupt line across the back of the head. The subspecies we had, *M. m. crassirostris,* from western Uganda, were

. . . took very little fruit . . .

very insectivorous, took very little fruit but plenty of ground raw beef and the soft-food mixture. They had very little song, mostly resorting to a harsh chipping.

REICHENOW'S WEAVER, *Othyphantes reichenowi,* from southern Ethiopia to Kenya and northern Tanzania, has similar feeding habits to those of the White-headed Buffalo Weaver mentioned earlier. The sexes are much alike in colouring, the forehead, fore-crown, behind ear-coverts and remainder of upperparts black; wings edged golden-yellow; lower rump and upper tail-coverts mixed black and yellow; tail olive-green. The difference in the sexes is that with the female the forehead, fore-crown and behind ear-coverts are black, not yellow. Very little song, mostly a sharp chirping, but, in our experience, a sociable species.

The BROWN-CAPPED WEAVER, *Ploceus insignis,* with a general distribution from Cameroon to the Sudan and down into Kenya and Tanzania, is very attractive with its chestnut, black and yellow colouring. From forehead to nape the adult male is chestnut; sides of face, chin, throat, shoulders, wings and tail black; remainder of plumage golden-yellow; bill black. The female resembles the male except that from the forehead to nape is black. This species is highly insectivorous and it was our experience that, without an ample supply, they deteriorate rapidly. Peaceful, very tit-like in their movements through the trees and bushes, and even up on the roof wiring of the aviary in search of insects. They make excellent aviary inmates although their song is almost non-existent, just an occasional rasping note.

Family Sturnidae

This is the family of starlings and they belong, in the natural course, to the Old World, and there are over 100 different species. The common STARLING, *Sturnus vulgaris*, that ranges across Europe far into Asia, was introduced into the United States and is now well established there. Similarly, the INDIAN MYNAH, *Acridotheres tristis*, was introduced into Hawaii where it is now considered a pest. They range from 7 to 17 inches (18 to 43 cm) in length, and the majority are chunky birds with strong legs and bills. Since they are omnivorous, they present no problem to cater for in captivity. When breeding, the live-food supply has to be boosted for, in the early days, this is about the only diet they feed to their young. With the majority of species, the colouring of the male and female is alike.

The natural range of the CRESTED MYNAH, *Acridotheres grandis*, is southern China, but the singleton bird we had in the Boehm aviaries had been bred in Canada, exported to England, given to my wife and we brought it to the United States and gave it to Mr. Boehm. It had been a pet bird and greeted everyone with "Hello Blackie", indulging in a bobbing up and down all the time it was talking. Nevertheless, despite its tameness, it thoroughly enjoyed aviary life, was most sociable, and never interfered with any other birds in the aviary. About 8 inches (20 cm) in length, the head is glossy black with a slight bronzy-green sheen, and with a thick tuft of feathers rising like a crest from the forehead and forecrown. The remainder of the upperparts dull black, tinged with brown; base of the primaries and tips of the primary-coverts are white; tail feathers tipped white except for the central pair; underparts black, with dull white tipping to the under tail-coverts, bill pale yellow; legs

"Hello Blackie"

247

and feet dark yellow; irises orange. The white in the wings is not very noticeable when the bird is in repose but very conspicuous when in flight. This particular specimen must have been at least 15 years old when it fell victim to a weasel that got into the aviary, leaving a toll of 28 dead birds before it was caught.

The AMETHYST STARLING, *Cinnyricinclus leucogaster,* is from Africa. There are at least three races, one more or less confined to the Sudan, Ethiopia and Arabia; another from Senegal to Ethiopia and down to Uganda; the third *C. l. verreaux,* the species we had, from Kenya, Tanzania, Mozambique, southern Congo, Angola and southward to the northern parts of South Africa. The areas mentioned above are the breeding areas for the respective races for, in the nonbreeding season, the Senegal race migrates to Kenya and Tanzania, and the Kenya race goes northward to the Sudan, Ethiopia, Congo and Angola. About 8 inches (20 cm) in length, this is one of the few species of starlings where the sexes differ in colouring. The general colour of the adult male is metallic violet-plum with bronzy and greenish reflections giving it a scaly appearance; chest to under tail-coverts white; white outer webs to the outer tail feathers. The female is mottled above with black and tawny with a slight iridescent blue-black wash on the wing-coverts and inner secondaries; underparts buffish-white streaked and spotted with black. These birds have a strong flight and were often seen hawking insects on the wing. Very little song, just an interrupted whistle, but they make good aviary birds as they are sociable. Although we had a pair for many years in one aviary in which plenty of other breedings took place, the starlings made no attempt whatever to go to nest.

The ROYAL STARLING, *Cosmopsarus regius,* an African species from Ethiopia, Somalia, Kenya and parts of Tanzania, is one of the most colourful of the starling family. Head and neck all round metallic green; ear-coverts, mantle, rump and wings metallic dark blue with a purple wash; long and steeply graduated tail metallic dull gold with some blue and violet; patch on chest of metallic violet; remainder of underparts rich metallic golden-yellow. Their entire appearance is of a long, slim bird, this being accentuated by the long, slender tail. The sexes are alike and they both have a whistling, chirping call.

Mr. Boehm brought four of them back with him from Kenya but it was not until our stock had been reduced to one that any breeding took place. Full details of this have been included in the section dealing with the Spreo Starling, page 252, since, as the Spreos did all the rearing, that seemed the most appropriate place to recount it.

The BLUE-EARED GLOSSY STARLING, *Lamprotornis chalybaeus,* also from Africa with races in West Africa, the Sudan, Eritrea, Somalia and down through Uganda and Kenya to Rhodesia and eastern Transvaal, is about 9½ inches (24 cm) in total length. The species we had, *L. c. sycobius,* was from Kenya and their general colour is metallic golden-green. The entire head and neck golden-green; ear-coverts blue; wing shoulders blue and violet; black spots on tips of wing-coverts and inner secondaries; rump metallic blue; tail and throat washed with blue; upper belly metallic blue; lower belly and under wing-coverts violet. The sexes are alike and, in addition to their typical chattering, they do have a musical whistle, rather high pitched.

MEVE'S LONG-TAILED GLOSSY STARLING, *Lamprotornis mevesii,* from an area south of the Zambesi River from southern Angola across to southern Mozambique and down as far as Botswana, is mainly dull metallic dark blue and violet with a rump of metallic coppery-gold. The tail is graduated, the central feathers being elongated. We never found them to be good aviary birds since they were too timid and caused a general upset whenever anyone entered the aviary. Although at times they did give a loud, rather unmusical whistle, one mainly heard their harsh alarm call. We did not persevere with them as they were too upsetting for the nesting species.

. . . they were too timid . . .

The PURPLE GLOSSY STARLING, *Lamprotornis purpureus,* to be found from Senegal to Sudan and down into Uganda and Kenya, is a striking bird when seen in the sunlight. The forehead and sides of head metallic violet; nape metallic blue; mantle and wings metallic green; wing shoulder, rump and tail metallic blue; wing-coverts tipped velvety black; underparts wholly metallic violet and blue. They are good aviary inmates, with various calls and a curious whistling-chattering when feeding.

The ROTHSCHILD'S MYNAH, *Leucopsar rothschildi,* is to be found only in Bali, an Indonesian island located just east of Java. It is pure white in colour, with the tail and wings tipped black; bare soft blue cheeks and a large white crest. This bird is strictly protected by Indonesia and special permits have to be obtained before any may be exported. There are quite a number in captivity both in the United States, Europe and other parts of the world and every effort is being made to propagate the species as it is feared they might become extinct. We had two in the Boehm aviaries but, although they took over a nest box and made a nest of grasses, reeds and feathers, no eggs were ever laid so we could only surmise that they were two males. Even when busy carrying nesting materials they never interfered with any of the other birds nesting at the same time, and they cannot but be considered an ideal aviary bird.

Indonesian Rothschild's Mynah

The GOLDEN-CRESTED MYNAH, *Mino coronatus,* is fairly common in northern Thailand, and is also a resident of the Tenasserim district of Burma, and may be found in smaller numbers through to Malaysia. About 8½ inches (24 cm) in length, the adult male has clear yellow feathers on the crown, face, chin and throat, and there is yellow in the broad wing patch. Further, there is a bare patch of yellow skin around the eye; bill yellow at the tip shading to slaty-blue at the base; legs and feet yellow; remainder of plumage glossy black. The female is very similar except that the crest is not as long, and the yellow of the underparts is confined to the chin, the throat being black. In addition, the group of yellow, bristly feathers at the base of the upper mandible is not as distinct as in the male. A pair of them, received direct from Thailand, were housed in an aviary that they shared with Striped Kingfishers, Southern Black Tits and Blue-shouldered Robins. It was in late Spring that the female was seen carrying twigs and grasses into a closed box-type nest box made with a 2 inch (5 cm) entrance hole in the front and a hinged lid. Three eggs were laid and although they were all clear they did provide the following data. Averaging 32 by 19 mm., they were pale blue with, on two of them, a few fine brown markings, mainly at the thicker end, the third egg being clear blue. A month later the female laid a further three eggs, one clear blue as before. Although the incubation which lasted for 14 days, appeared to be carried out by the female only, I cannot be emphatic about this as the sitting bird left the nest box as soon as footsteps were heard approaching the aviary. Only one egg hatched, the other two being discarded from the nest-box and it was found that they contained fully developed chicks. The nestling was completely devoid of all body covering, had bright pink skin and a yellow gape margined in orange-yellow. Both parents tended to the rearing, live-food being the order of the day for the first seven days or so. Although the nestling's eyes were open at 6 days, only dark markings could be seen under the skin and it was not until the eleventh day that quill feathers were visible. At 18 days yellow feathers were visible on its brow and, vacating the nest at 23 days old, it had distinct yellow eye-brow markings, a yellow chin patch and pale yellow barrings on the wings. Independent at five weeks, all three birds were kept together for a further six months by which time it was apparent that the young bird was a male. It was then removed from the aviary as the adult male had begun to harass it at the feeding tray. The following year they went to nest again and, from three rounds, seven young were reared to maturity. In each instance there were three eggs, one being clear blue, the others marked as indicated above. It was noted that they can be sexed in the nest, the males having far more yellow on the brow than the females. Actually I selected a male direct out of the nest, took it home, hand reared it and it has been a household pet for the past eight years. It is as fine a coloured male as its parent was, is very tame and has picked up some of our regular sayings. The only food it has had over the entire period is soaked golden raisins, Gainesburger, a proprietory dog-food similar to ground beef in consistency, and five meal-worms daily. We always found them very peaceful birds in a mixed collection, the males only taking objection to a male of the same species.

. . . household pet for the past eight years.

SHARPE'S STARLING, *Pholia sharpei,* an African species with a distribution from eastern Congo to Ethiopia and down to Kenya and northern Tanzania, is about 9 inches (23 cm) in length and, like most of the starlings, the sexes are alike. The upperparts, including head, sides of face and sides of chest, metallic blue-black with a violet sheen; underparts pale tawny, darker on the abdomen and under tail-coverts. They were very quiet birds, the only sound we ever heard being a subdued, sweet whistle. They were timid as regards the other inmates of the aviary but not at all shy of humans.

The SPREO STARLING, *Spreo superbus,* comes from the eastern parts of Africa, where it ranges from the Sudan, through to central Ethiopia, Somalia, and down into Uganda, Kenya and the northern parts of Tanzania. It is common in these regions, going about in small parties, feeding on the ground. Fearless of man, it may be seen in populated areas, just as the common Starling is in the United States and Europe. About 9 inches (23 cm) in length, the sexes are very similar. Head and sides of face black with a fine golden sheen; neck, mantle and tail, deep metallic blue; wings metallic green above with velvety black spots at the ends of the wing-coverts. From chin to breast, deep metallic blue; abdomen and thighs chestnut, a narrow white band separating the metallic blue of the breast from the chestnut of the lower parts, under tail-coverts and axillaries white. The bill is dark and the iris is bright yellow. Their call is a cheerful chattering, quite a pleasant varied whistling, warbling song, often interspersed with the mimiced calls of *. . . singing* other birds. Their alarm note is a loud, shrill whistle. Like many *at night.* of the thrushes, they were often heard singing at night. Although gregarious in the wild, this trait in captivity appeared to be present only during the nonbreeding season for, of four birds housed in an aviary of 60 by 30 feet (18 x 9 metres), two were found killed in the later Spring. From the courting display, merely jumping around on the ground with wings drooped and necks outstretched, it became apparent that a true pair remained. By close scrutiny it could be seen that one had a shorter bill than the other but the difference was so slight that it would be extremely difficult to sex an individual bird just by this alone. The female selected a closed nest-box with a three inch (7.5 cm) circular opening at the front, making a nest of fine grasses and feathers with a cup-like depression at the rear of the box. Their first round was four eggs, clear blue green, and averaging 26 by 19 mm. Incubation, which was shared, began with the laying of the second egg, two hatching 11 days later with a further one on each of the next two succeeding days. The nestlings were covered with a dark fuzz and had gapes of red, margined in

*African
Royal Spreo
Starling Hybrid*

yellow. The rearing was shared, the diet consisting primarily
of live-food in the form of mealworms and gentles, supplied
hourly throughout the day, supplemented by whatever they
foraged for themselves. At eight days their eyes were open and
quill feathers had begun to form in the wings. Vacating the
nest at 20 to 21 days old, although their heads, necks and from
the chin to the breast lacked the sheen of the adult birds, the
underparts were chestnut but there was no white band on the
breast and the yellow iris was lacking. Independent about ten
days later, it was not until they were some seven weeks old that
the white breast band began to show and the dull black portions
took on the metallic sheen of the adult birds. Full mature colouring was attained at ten months old, but they were well over a
year in age before the yellow iris was of the same intensity as
the adult birds'. In all, over a period of five years this same pair
had some nine rounds with two to four chicks from each. Occupying the same aviary were the Royal Starlings mentioned on
page 248 and, although we had started with four, our stock was
now reduced to two. One morning one of these was found dead
on the ground and two days later it was seen that the Spreos
had gone to nest again. This time there was only two eggs.
Except for ensuring there was always an adequate supply of
live-food, not much attention was paid to the two chicks that
hatched for we considered we had gathered all the useful data

possible on the breeding of Spreo Starlings. However, when the two young birds left the nest it could be seen there was something different about them. They were longer and slimmer than the previous young starlings and their colouring was slightly different. When caught up for ringing it was apparent that they were Royal/Spreo hybirds. At no time during the nesting period was the solitary Royal Starling seen to go near to the nest box, the entire task of incubating and rearing being undertaken by the pair of Spreos. At one year old, the colouring of the head followed more to the pattern of the Spreo, although the underparts were a dull golden-yellow and the white breast band was completely lacking. See illustration on page 253.

The ROSY PASTOR, *Sturnus roseus*, breeds through south-eastern Europe and in Asia from Turkey to Turkestan, wintering in India and Pakistan. It is about 8½ inches (22 cm) in length and the sexes are alike except that the female is duller and has a shorter crest. Except for the back, shoulders, breast and belly which are rose-pink, it is a uniform metallic black, the feathers of the head, long bushy crest, throat, upper breast, wings and tail lightly tipped with buff; thighs, patches on the flanks and under tail-feathers, black tipped white. In winter dress the rose-pink feathers have a greyish appearance, this being due to the tips of the new feathers showing through, these wearing off in time so that, by the breeding season, the bird is back in its pink and black colouring. We had a pair of these birds in a large aviary containing some 20 other species. Amongst them was two pairs of PAGODA MYNAHS, *Temenuchus pagodarum*, one pair of which went to nest, see page 255. It was early in the summer when we observed the male Rosy Pastor carrying twigs to a Pagoda Mynah that was busy constructing a nest on a branch of a dogwood tree. Three clear blue eggs were laid, and incubation was shared by the Rosy Pastor and the Mynah. Two chicks hatched out about 12 days later, the third egg disappearing from the nest. The nestlings were dark skinned, devoid of any body covering, and were larger than the Pagoda Mynah nestlings that had hatched out the day before at the other end of the aviary. The rearing was shared for the first 7 days, live-food being the sole diet, after which the Rosy Pastor deserted them and returned to his true mate. The female Pagoda Mynah then added ground raw beef and blueberries to their diet and carried on rearing them. Vacating the nest at 15 days, their general colouring was greyish-brown with a darker shade on the crown.

. . . the third egg disappearing . . .

Even at that age they were about the same size as their mother and, in body shape, resembled the Rosy Pastor but the resemblance ended there, for no clear relationship to either parent so far as body colour was concerned could be defined. Owing to their size and steady growth, the Pagoda Mynah found the task of feeding them extremely difficult for she had to stretch herself up to her fullest extent to be able to get food into their ever-open gapes. They were independent 12 days after leaving the nest and, at four months of age, just before a weasel got them, they still retained their greyish-brown plumage and dark heads, and there was no sign of a crest forming.

The PAGODA MYNAH, *Temenuchus pagodarum,* is a familiar bird throughout Ceylon, India and Pakistan. About 8 inches (20 cm) in length, the sexes are very similar, the only differences being in the size of the crest, the female's being smaller, and the slimness of the female's head. Top of head, including the long, erectile, bushy crest, black; sides of head, neck and underparts rich buff except for the thighs and under tail-coverts which are white. The feathers of the neck, throat and breast are elongated, giving the appearance of hackles as they are fluffed out. Remainder of upperparts grey, with the exception of the outer flight feathers which are black; rounded tail brown, all feathers except the central pair broadly tipped white; legs and feet bright yellow; bill yellow at the tip, greenish at the middle and blue at the base, all the colours blending into one another. A pair of these birds nested in an open-fronted nest box, laying three bright blue eggs. Incubation, which was shared, began with the laying of the last egg and, 12 days later, two chicks hatched, the third egg disappearing. The nestlings were pale skinned and completely devoid of any body covering. At five days their eyes were open and wing and body feathering was beginning to show. By 10 days it could be seen that the wing feathers were bluish-grey, the flanks chestnut. Vacating the nest at 17 days old, they were pale editions of their parents except that they had brown caps instead of the black crest of the adults. At four months of age they could not be told apart from their parents if it had not been for the brown caps which they still retained. I fear I have no further data on their development for, as with the Rosy Pastor hybrids, they also fell victim to a weasel.

The RED-WINGED STARLING, *Onychognathus morio,* is also an African species of which there are some five races ranging over most of Africa from Nigeria and the Sudan down

. . . three bright blue eggs.

into South Africa. The pair we had, *O. m. morio,* was received from Lesotho. About 11 inches (28 cm) in length, the sexes are dissimilar. The adult male is glossy violet-black above with greenish ear-coverts; primaries chestnut-red with black tips; underparts glossy blue-black; bill, legs and feet, black. The head and neck of the adult female are grey, with violet and blue-black streaks; upper chest grey with broader streaks of blue-black; remainder of plumage as with the male. This pair was housed in a large, unheated aviary with numerous other species and, since the aviary was also uncovered, a pane of glass was removed from the window of a bird-room abutting on to the aviary so that the birds could come inside in inclement weather. Trays of food were kept in this room throughout the year and this was a great asset when we wished to catch any up for transference to other quarters for the winter. They had been living in this aviary some three years when the female was seen trying to construct a nest on top of one of the tree stumps in the bird-room. Since this was totally inadequate, a covered nest-box, 9 inches (23 cm) square and with an open front, was fixed there. With the male assisting in gathering materials, the female starling soon completed a nest in it consisting of twigs, bound together with mud, and lined with soft grasses. It completely filled the box with an entrance in the front. One egg, bluish-green with rufous spots and blotches was laid but it disappeared two days later. Three weeks later again one egg was produced and the female began to incubate it right away. Hatching at 14 days, the behaviour of both the male and female Red-winged Starlings underwent a complete change. Up to now they had been sociable birds, freely mixing with the others, but now, the male became most possessive of the room, not only

. . . swooping down on any humans . . .

keeping all other birds away but even swooping down on any humans who approached too near for his liking. It became an order of the day to wear protective headgear when replenishing the food in the room or making the hourly issue of live-food. About a week later the nestling was found dead on the floor, just below the nest-box. It was fairly large with a good amount of feathering on the wings and back although the head was completely bare. The following year they nested again in the same location and this time three eggs were laid, incubation beginning with the laying of the first, July 2nd., and they hatched out on the 16th, 17th and 18th. The nestlings were pink-skinned, sparsely covered with a black fuzz and had gapes of bright pink. Now that they had become more accustomed to us it was possible to watch their development. At 7 days their eyes were open and quill feathers were showing in their wings. Although one was found dead in the nest at 11 days, the other two finally vacated the nest at 22 and 25 days respectively. They were sooty black with a slight sheen, one showing this more clearly than the other, and they both possessed the chestnut-red primaries of their parents. Full independence was attained at 34 days and they were then separated from the adults who had commenced cleaning up the nest-box. Eventually they again reared two from three eggs. When the first brood was five months old, grey feathers began to show on the head and upper chest of the duller coloured one. This indicated that the degree of sheen might well be a sex indicator as soon as they left the nest. Seven further breedings of this species proved to us that such was the case.

WALLER'S CHESTNUT-WINGED STARLING, *Onychognathus walleri,* is another African species with a rather limited distribution in Kenya, Tanzania and the northern parts of Rhodesia. The sexes differ, the head and neck of the adult male glossy green, crown with a bluish wash; rest of plumage deep glossy violet; primaries dark chestnut with black ends; secondaries and tail blue-black, latter with greenish edges. The head and neck all round of the female is streaked grey and glossy green; the remainder of the plumage similar to that of the male. They did not make good aviary birds for they were far too quarrelsome and were soon disposed of to a zoo.

. . . far too quarrelsome . . .

As mentioned earlier, being omnivorous, the starlings and mynahs were relatively simple to cater for and no special food outside our regular feeding pattern was required. They were, however, gluttons for live-food and, whenever there were birds with young to rear in the same aviary as any of the starlings, special feeding platforms, trays, etc., were set up just for those birds with nestlings.

Family Oriolidae

This family is comprised of the Old World orioles, a group of some 20 species that, except for one that ranges across the southern Palaearctic Region and even into India, is typically tropical, extending from Africa, across Asia to New Guinea and Australia. All the species are exclusively arboreal, feeding on insects and fruits, and are mostly to be found in evergreen forests. With the exception of one, the Maroon Oriole, yellow is predominant in their colouring. They nearly all possess a peculiarly sweet and liquid song, together with a growling or bleating alarm note.

The AFRICAN GOLDEN ORIOLE, *Oriolus auratus,* has a general distribution across Africa from Angola to Tanzania and down into Rhodesia. About 10 inches (25 cm) in length, the sexes differ. The adult male is mainly a rich golden-yellow above and below with a black band through the eye covering the lores and ear-coverts; wings black, broadly edged with yellow on secondaries and coverts, except for the primary coverts which just have small yellow tips; tail black, broadly edged yellow. The female has upperparts of olivaceous-yellow, and the blackish stripe through the eye is less extensive; underparts less rich yellow than the male's and more or less streaked with olive.

The BLACK-NAPED ORIOLE, *O. chinensis,* is an Asiatic species, breeding in north-eastern China and Manchuria, wintering southward as far as Malaysia and Burma. About $10\frac{1}{2}$ inches (27 cm) in length, the male is golden-yellow with a black eye-stripe from the base of the pinkish bill right round the back of the neck; wings yellow edged black; central tail feathers black, remainder black edged and tipped golden-yellow. The female is tinged with green on the mantle, and the black of the wings and tail is less intense. This oriole was a regular visitor in our garden in Singapore, their early morning song being as regular in timing as any alarm clock.

. . . as regular in timing as any alarm clock.

The BLACK-HEADED ORIOLE, *O. larvatus,* is an African species where it ranges from Angola in the west up to the Sudan, across to Ethiopia and Somalia, and then down through Kenya, Mozambique, Botswana, Rhodesia and to the eastern parts of South Africa. There are at least three races that often intermingle on the boundaries of their respective areas. *O. l. larvatus* is from the southern regions; *O. l angolensis* from Angola through Tanzania to Kenya; and *O. l. rolleti* from Sudan, Ethiopia, Somalia and Mozambique. They are all very similar in appearance, the main differences being in size and intensity of colour. The species we had, *O. l. rolleti,* we received from Mozambique. About 10 inches (25 cm) in length, the sexes are much alike and, unless they are fully mature adults, it is extremely difficult to sex an individual specimen. In the mature adult male the head and neck are black; remainder of upperparts olivaceous golden-yellow; wings black, edges of flight feathers whitish, outer edges of inner secondaries olivaceous-yellow, inner edges black; coverts of inner primaries edged olivaceous-yellow; tail, variable pattern of yellow-green, decreasing in intensity of colour towards the outer feathers; with the exception of the central pair, all the tail feathers have broad yellow tips. Underparts golden-yellow, richest at the throat, gradually paling towards the vent; bill, pinkish-brown; legs and feet blue-grey. The main difference in the sexes is in the intensity of the black of the head and neck, that of the female being more dusky, and the depth of colour of the underparts. Further, both sexes have a small yellow patch in the centre of the flight feathers, this being visible when the birds are at rest, and that of the male is slightly larger than the female's.

A pair of these birds selected an open-topped nest box as their nesting site, and the female built a rather untidy, open-cup nest of coarse grasses and rootlets, with a sparse lining of Spanish moss. One egg, greyish-white with brown and grey spots was laid but, the following day the female was on the ground in obvious distress. Immediately she was caught up and transferred to the hospital room and given heat treatment as it was felt it might just be a case of egg-binding. Advantage was taken of her absence to measure the egg which was 29 by 20 mm. Looking perfectly fit the next day, but with no other egg laid, she was returned to the aviary where she promptly went back to the nest and began incubating the one egg which hatched 18 days later. The nestling was covered with snow-white down, and had a pink gape with two purple spots in the roof of the upper mandible. Although the incubation was by the female only, the male assisted with the rearing of the chick, live-food being the order of the day. At 6 days the chick's eyes were open and yellow was showing in the wing-butts, and black feathering on the back and in the flights was visible two days later. At 11 days, ground raw beef and fruit was being fed to the nestling and, at 17 days, its body and wings were feathered up but, except for some fluff, the head was bare. Vacating the nest at 19 days old, it was seen that the flight feathers were black, edged white; tail feathers yellow; yellow showing on the shoulders; underparts a dirty white, flecked yellow; fluff only on the head. The following day the chick was found suspended in an azalea bush with a broken thigh from which it did not recover. The parent birds went to nest twice more that year with two chicks from each round, but failed to rear any of them beyond fourteen days. However, the following year there was complete success, two rounds of two chicks each, being reared to maturity. Except that this time the incubation was shared, everything followed

. . . found suspended on an azalea bush . . .

the same pattern as that described above. The head started feathering up in shades of blackish-green at 20 days, and the underparts gradually turned whitish-yellow, heavily flecked with dark brown. Independence was not attained until six weeks old and, two weeks later, the fleckings on the underparts had almost disappeared. At 12 months of age the young birds' heads and necks were still not the solid colour of either parent, being faintly flecked with yellow, and the black neck-line was not clearly defined, the golden-yellow of the throat being interspersed with it giving a striated effect. It was not until their moult in their second year that they could be sexed definitely, there being one male and three females.

The BLACK-WINGED ORIOLE, *O nigripennis*, also from Africa, is more or less confined to an area from Sierra Leone to the Sudan, and down into northern Angola. Very similar in appearance to the Black-headed Oriole, but the edges of the secondaries are yellow-green, not whitish. Further, the tips of the primary coverts are wholly black, or with only a trace of white, and the central tail feathers also are wholly black. About 10 inches (25 cm) in total length, the sexes are alike.

The GOLDEN ORIOLE, *O. oriolus*, has a general distribution through Central and southern Europe, Iran, Morocco and Algeria, wintering in Africa, India and Ceylon. About $9\frac{1}{2}$ inches (24 cm) in length, the sexes are dissimilar. The adult male is golden-yellow above and below; lores, wings and tail, black; broad yellow ends to the primary coverts and to the tail feathers except for the central pair which are wholly black. The female is golden-green above; rump and upper tail-coverts golden; wings blackish-brown; tail blackish with golden-yellow tips; from the chin to the abdomen, whitish streaked with black; flanks and under tail-coverts yellow.

. . . a most vicious attack . . .

We never experienced any difficulties in keeping orioles for they readily took to our food mixtures, the fruit and the ground raw beef, the only trouble we had being when we introduced a pair of Green Cardinals into an aviary containing orioles. If we had not been very quick about it, the cardinals would have killed the orioles for they made a most vicious attack on them as soon as they sighted them. We never did keep more than one species of oriole in any one aviary so we have no knowledge as to how the different species would agree or not when housed together. We do know that the complete family of the Black-headed got along very well together.

Family Artamidae

This family is centered on Australia and the south-west Pacific, there being some 17 species in all, of which 14 are confined to the Australasian region, the others being found in Asia. They are very insectivorous and we found they did well on our soft food mixture, ground raw beef and live food, although occasionally they did partake of the diced fruit and blueberries. They are gregarious, but can be very pugnacious and require careful watching if housed with any other insectivorous birds.

The MASKED WOOD-SWALLOW, *Artamus personatus*, is about 8 inches (20 cm) in total length and the sexes are dissimilar. The adult male is slate-grey above with a jet-black face mask and throat patch, the latter edged with white. The underparts are silver-grey, the tail is forked the feathers being tipped with white. The undersides of the wings are pale silver-grey, almost white. They have short, black legs and a sturdy, powerful bill, also black. The female lacks the black mask and throat patch, these being replaced with similar markings in dark grey. The remainder of the plumage is duller than that of the male, the underparts a smoky grey.

Although in their native habitats they normally select low bushes or trees for the location of their open, cup-shaped nests, in the planted aviary a pair shared with honeyeaters and waxwings, despite many desirable nesting places, they chose a most

Australian Masked/White-browed Wood-swallow Hybrid Family

conspicuous position in one of the feeding stands. It was a trough, about nine inches (23 cm) in length, by three (7.5 cm) wide and two (5 cm) deep that was designed to hold three feeding cups. Only two cups were in use at the time and the Woodswallows took over the remaining three inch (7.5 cm) square. In order to provide more room, and to avoid interference by the other birds at feeding times, the cups were removed. A nest of fine twigs and rootlets was completed within three days, the female doing most of the constructing whilst the male collected the materials. The first egg was laid on March 13 with a second the following day. Incubation, which was shared, lasted for a period of 12 days, having begun with the laying of the first egg. The eggs were light greyish-green, clouded and splotched with shades of brown and underlying spots of grey. They measured 21 by 15 mm. The newly hatched chicks were very dark skinned, covered with grey down, streaked with sooty black. Their gapes were pale yellow with a minimum marginal colouring. As the nest was so shallow and there was a danger of the chicks falling out, a wire guard was fitted round it raising the overall height to 3½ inches (9 cm). The parent birds resented these intrusions in a physical manner, swooping down and striking at us continually while the frame was being positioned. However, they went straight back to their young immediately we finished and vacated the aviary. As with the incubation, the rearing was shared, live food being the sole diet employed. A wide variety of this was supplied in the form of mealworms, crickets and gentles, together with moths and insects captured in the night-traps.

Quill feathers were showing and the eyes were open at six days old. Leaving the nest at 14 days, they were strong on the wing and immediately portrayed a characteristic of the adults at feeding time by switching their tails from side to side as they begged for food. It was now that the parent birds began to vary the diet by introducing the fledglings to ground raw beef and diced fruit, as a supplement to the live food that was still taken in great quantity. The colouring of the young was basically grey, heavily flecked with sooty black, except for the flight and tail feathers which were plain slate-grey. One of them showed much darker face markings than the other and it turned out that this was a male. Actually it had been noticed when they were still in the nest, at 11 days, and all subsequent breedings confirmed this point that they can be sexed at this very early age. They were independent at 30 days and adult plumage was acquired at six

. . . resented these intrusions . . .

and a half months of age. In all, the pair had four rounds that year, rearing seven young, four male and three female. In each instance the young birds had to be removed as soon as they were independent as the adult male began to harass them.

The WHITE-BROWED WOOD-SWALLOW, *A. super-ciliosis,* is the same size as the former species and again the sexes differ. The adult male has a black cap which extends from the base of the upper mandible to the nape of the neck. The lower portions of the face, the throat and the upper chest also are black. A bold, white eye-stripe runs from the base of the bill, over the eye, to the back of the head. The wings and mantle are slate-grey, as is the tail, and the underparts are a deep vinous brown. The female is a duller edition, the portions black in the male being a sooty grey. Further, the underparts are a light mauvish-brown, and the eye-stripe is narrower. This Wood-swallow is to be found in most parts of Australia, except the northwestern areas, and usually in flocks with Masked Wood-swallows. With the knowledge that they congregate, two pairs had been accommodated in the same aviary for over twelve months with no problems at all. However, it was soon proved that, no matter how peaceful they may be at other times, when it comes to breeding they are very territorially minded. Early in April one male was observed feeding a female and the following day the other male was found dead on the ground, killed. To avoid any further trouble, the odd female was removed, the remaining pair immediately beginning to build a nest of coarse grasses, lined with finer grass, in a black haw tree about three feet (1 metre) above ground level. The nest measured 42 mm across the top, overall depth was 59 mm, of which 25 was taken up by the shallow cup. The first egg was laid on April 17, with a second the following day. They were grey-green with pale amber splashes, mainly at the thicker end, and measured 21 by 15 mm. Both birds incubated, taking over from each other without any delay, the eggs being uncovered for the minimal length of time. The first hatched at twelve days, the second the day after. The young birds were light skinned, covered with a greyish-black down, and their gapes were bright yellow. The rearing was shared, live food being the order of the day. The eyes open at five days and quill feathers showing at this time. By twelve days they were fully feathered in grey, heavily streaked with black and flecked with white. They left the nest at 14 days and, like the Masked Wood-swallow chicks, were flicking their tails within a matter of hours. Independent at the end of a further two

. . . are very territorially minded.

weeks, the female began tidying up her nest so the young were removed. It had been noticed with the second round that one chick had much darker feathering than its nest mate, or either of the first round chicks. Unfortunately we were not able to prove beyond doubt that this was a sex indicator for the darker chick was killed the day following its independence. However, since the other three did all turn out to be females, we did feel that, as with the Masked, they could be sexed in the nest.

. . . to try
to cross
the species.

Over the passage of time some of the White-browed and Masked youngsters had been presented to various zoos. Unfortunately the remaining two White-browed males were killed by owls at night, whilst hanging on the outer wiring of the aviary. This left us with two female White-browed and a surfeit of Masked males. It was decided to try to cross the species. The result of this experiment was that, from the first pair five first-crosses, two male and three female were reared. From the second pair we got exactly the reverse, three males and two females. It was intended to carry on with this cross-breeding by careful selection and endeavouring to produce as near as like possible to a true Masked male. However, events precluded this and all the birds were passed over to zoos.

Family Ptilonorhynchidae

This is the family of bowerbirds and catbirds, widespread in Australia and New Guinea and confined to those areas. Arboreal, they are mainly fruit-eaters, but also consume insects and molluscs.

Subfamily Ailuroedinae

This subfamily consists of the catbirds and in the Boehm aviaries we had a pair of BLACK-EARED CATBIRDS, *Ailuroedus melanotus*. This species is to be found in the Aru Islands, south of central New Guinea, and also in the extreme northern parts of Australia. About 10½ inches (27 cm) in length, the sexes are alike. The crown and nape dull brown, mottled with yellow and green; lores and ear-coverts black; back green spotted with black, larger spots on the upper back; wings and tail greenish with a bluish tinge, wings spotted at the tips of the secondaries, all tail feathers tipped white. Throat fawnish-white with black tips to the feathers; inner wing lining black; bill bluish-white. They certainly consumed great quantities of fruit and also played havoc with the shrubs and trees by nipping off the new buds. We never attempted to house them other than on their own for their stocky build and heavy bills put us off from trying the experiment. Their peculiar cat-like cry obviously is the reason for their common name.

Subfamily Chlamyderinae

This subfamily covers the bowerbirds which fall into three groups comprised of platform builders, maypole builders and avenue builders. It was of the final group that we had a pair of FAWN-BREASTED BOWERBIRDS, *Chlamydera cerviniventris*, from both northern Australia and New Guinea. About 11½ inches (29 cm) in length, the sexes are very much alike, the only differences we could detect being that the female's head seemed flatter, and the bill slightly finer. Top of the head brownish-grey with pale brown medial streaks; back, rump and upper tail-coverts a darker shade of brownish-grey, feathers with whitish shaft streaks and a slight white tipping; wing-coverts similar colour with fawnish tips; primaries and secondaries brown, the latter with paler edgings; tail brown with faint ashy tips; throat grey with brownish edges; upper breast fawn, shading to brown at the sides; lower breast, abdomen and under tail-coverts pale yellowish-buff; under wing-coverts buffish-yellow; thighs dark brownish-grey; bill black with a hooked tip.

Like the catbirds, this pair was given an aviary to themselves and each year the male built an avenue bower. Although located in different parts of the aviary each year, it always ran in the direction of north and south. One of our Australian visitors made the remark that several species of avenue bower builders construct them in a north-south direction. The bower was made of twigs, interlaced and forming an inverted tunnel with internal measurements of about nine inches (22 cm) across at the base, the sides rising some thirteen inches (33 cm), the entire affair being about two feet (60 cm) long. It was completely devoid of any decoration despite the fact of there being brightly coloured blooms in the aviary, and we had added pieces of coloured glass, foil, beads, ribbon and wool. Beyond seeing the male passing to and fro through the avenue we never witnessed any actual display, nor saw the female anywhere near to the bower. Like the Black-eared Catbirds they also were great fruit-eaters but also took a small amount of ground raw beef and their daily supply of live-food. They did not appear to have any set song but, when everything was quiet and nobody about,

. . . an aviary to themselves . . .

we would hear a number of soft, melodious notes uttered in slow succession, but were never able to see which one was making the sounds for they were always concealed in the dense shrubberies.

Family Paradisaeidae

This is the family embracing the birds of paradise, restricted to a single region of the world, the Papuan—New Guinea and neighbouring islands—with the exception of three species found in the north and down the east coast of Australia. There are some 40 species in all and they appear to be relatives of the crows and jays with their resemblance in size, robustness, stout bills, strong perching feet, their raucous calls, and their nesting and rearing habits. They are truly arboreal birds and may be found from the lowlands up into the mountains, some at considerable altitudes. They are frugivorous, insectivorous and carnivorous, and are by no means gregarious. A few species are all black with little distinguishing features beyond gloss in the feathers. In contrast, most of the males of the other species are colourful, with iridescent plumage and bizarre, decorative plumes and tail feathers. The females on the other hand are mostly plain coloured. Largely polygamous, many hybrids have been classified as definite species. Never common in private collections on account of the strict regulations prohibiting their trapping and export, Mr. Boehm obtained several pairs as a gift from the late Sir Edward Hallstrom, direct from his aviaries at Nondugl, West Highlands, New Guinea. In addition, a pair of Paradise Rifle Birds were obtained direct from Australia. One thing we did learn by keeping these birds in captivity is that, to have success in breeding, it is best to keep the sexes separate until the proper mating season comes around. This can be gauged by the manner in which the males display and give vent to their strident calls, invariably replied to by their respective females who, by that time are busy gathering nesting material. Introducing the male just prior to completion of the nest normally results in mating without delay. Further, to avoid any undue disturbance of the female whilst sitting, we made a habit of removing the male after copulation had been witnessed, or an egg had been checked and found fertile.

Never common in private collections . . .

The RIBBON TAIL BIRD OF PARADISE, *Astrapia mayeri,* from the Mt. Hagen region of New Guinea, is notable from the fact that the elongated central tail feathers in the adult male are over three times the length of the head and body combined, a proportion unknown in any other bird in the wild. The upper body plumage of the male is black with a slight bronzy sheen; lower back dull black; wing feathers deep brown; crown of head glittering golden-green extending to the nape; the bill is more or less concealed by a tuft of feathers. It has large ear-puffs, commencing green, followed by deep purple, then puffing in velvety black with a faint purple sheen. A large throat patch of bright green, followed by a band of velvety black with a bronzy tinge, succeeded by a narrow edging of bright copper; under tail-coverts black; remainder of underparts blackish-brown and only measure some 4¾ inches (12 cm), whereas the central pair of white feathers can measure anything up to 35 inches (89 cm), the last 9 inches (23 cm) or so being brownish, the feathers terminating in a sharply pointed tip. The frontal tuft of the female is not so pronounced; crown of head glittering oily green; cheeks green with a slight tinge of purple at the back; nape to middle back black with a purple sheen; lower back, rump and upper tail-coverts brownish-black; wings dark brown; tail brown, the outer feathers about 6¾ inches (17 cm) long with the central pair extending to some 12 inches (30 cm) and having broad white markings both sides of the shaft to near the end, which is brown. Chin deep oily greenish; throat and breast black with a deep purple sheen; abdomen dull black with a few pale bands on the lower flank feathers.

We had a pair go to nest in a clump of bamboos, a nest of reeds, bamboo leaves and feathers being constructed by the female only. Mating was never witnessed and the single egg, medium brown streaked with darker brown heaviest at the thicker end, was clear. It measured 37 by 26 mm., rather elongated in shape. In all the female laid on three separate occasions that season with the same result. The following year she laid again, a single egg as before, but this time, although mating had not been observed, it was felt that the egg might well be fertile for she was far more conscientious with her sitting and kept the male bird well away from the nest. To avoid any trouble, the male was removed to another aviary. Hatching at 21 days it was not possible to follow the development of the chick due partly to the location of the nest, but mostly due to the belligerency of the female whenever anyone approached near to that clump of bamboos. Vacating the nest at 24 days the young bird resembled the female but lacked the metallic sheen to the feathers. It was sexable at about six months of age by the central tail feathers

. . . in a clump of bamboos . . .

beginning to show as white with brown tips.

The PRINCESS STEPHANIE'S BIRD OF PARADISE, *Astrapia stephaniae,* named in honour of the then Crown Princess Stephanie of Austria, is from the central regions of eastern New Guinea and is another of the long tailed species. The main colouring of the adult male is black, the iridescent head feathers bluish-green merging into purplish at the nape; in front of the eye is a golden-green patch, changing to green behind the eye, and becoming purple on the ear-coverts. Upper back tinged bronze; lower back blackish-brown; wings and tail blackish-brown, except for the central tail feathers which have basal shafts narrow and white, the remainder of the feathers glossed purplish. Chin, throat and upper breast shining black with a green sheen succeeded by a broad velvety black band edged reddish-copper; remainder of underparts, brown with a bronzy sheen. The central pair of tail feathers are extremely elongated so that, of the average total length of 33 inches (83 cm) for the male, 25 inches (63 cm) are accounted for by the tail. The female is smaller, averaging 20 inches (51 cm) of which only 13 inches (33 cm) is tail, and differs in colouring being blackish-brown, tinged rufous above, except on the head, wings and tail. The head, face, ear-coverts and chin are almost black, the throat and upper-breast blackish-brown; remainder of underparts barred blackish-brown on a buffy-yellow background. Their flight is very direct, the wing beats of the male making a rustling sound like heavy silk brocade being swished to and fro. This was a great aid when trying to locate them in the heavily planted aviary, for they do tend to lurk in the heavier foliage.

. . . being swished to and fro.

This species also was bred but not before several fatalities during the pre-copulation ceremonies. Mr. Boehm made some very interesting observations during the time we were trying to breed this species and I consider it very fitting to quote his actual words. "The pre-copulation ceremonies of the Stephanie are quite vigorous and brutal; they grasp one another with their talons, usually in the thighs, or in whatever manner chance may present. At times, it actually becomes a 'mortal combat', and I say this factually, because I have had hens kill glorious males. I do not wish to conjecture on how often death occurs, but we have lost two beautiful males in this manner and I have been an observer of this combat on eight occasions. I have also seen a pair, in the throes of battle, fall into a pool of water. The birds would have drowned had not they been rescued. In all cases, their grasps on one another were so intent that they fall to the ground, and attack one another with their beaks. When the female is overpowered and becomes submissive, they will then fly to a convenient branch where he will crest his hood and shield in a display of colour that is breathtaking! At the culmination of this display, copulation ensues."

As with the Ribbon Tail Bird of Paradise, only one egg was laid which closely resembled the Ribbon Tail's except that the streaks of brown were more like paintbrush fleckings. Incubation time was 22 days and the chick left the nest at 26 days old. Incubation and rearing was by the female only since the male had been removed, live-food, ground raw beef and fruit all being used. Unfortunately the young bird was found drowned in one of the pools at six weeks of age.

. . . was found drowned . . .

The MAGNIFICENT BIRD OF PARADISE, *Diphyllodes magnificus,* another of the smaller birds of paradise, is found over a wide range in New Guinea, there being at least six races. The subspecies we had, from the eastern parts of the island, was *D. m. hunsteini,* about 9 inches (23 cm) in total length, and the sexes differ. The crown of the adult male is covered with short velvety brown feathers, edged with longer feathers of golden-brown; bare triangular patch behind the eye; a frill of longish pale yellow feathers on nape, scalloped in outline and erectile. Upper back reddish-black; lower back and upper tail-coverts reddish-brown; tail, short, broad and brown, except for the central pair of feathers which are shining green, alternating into two long wires, curved outwards at the tips, and with very narrow external webs. Primaries brown with golden edges; secondaries broader, edged golden-brown except for the tips, forming a distinct wing patch. Under the chin a small tuft of blackish-brown feathers; throat blackish-brown, followed by a narrow band of metallic blue, succeeded by a breastplate of bright green, edged shining green. Through the centre of the breastplate is a band, three or four feathers in width (it varies) of blue-tipped feathers; abdomen, almost concealed by the breastplate, is sooty-brown; under tail-coverts black. Both adornments, nape-frill and breastplate, are erected during the bird's display, mostly done on the ground. The female is pale brown above with darker tips to the feathers of the head; wings and tail dark brown with pale rufous marginings; tail slightly longer than male's but lacking the elongated central feathers; underparts dirty white, closely barred dark brown.

A pair of these birds shared an aviary for almost a year when it was noticed that the female was gathering twigs and trying to assemble them on a wide beam just above the entrance door of the aviary. An open-topped box, 8″ (20 cm) square with 3″ (7 cm) sides, was fixed there and immediately she began to construct her nest. It was an open-cup of twigs and rootlets, built entirely by the female. Whilst this was going on the male was busy stripping leaves off many of the trees and shrubs, displaying on the ground, and giving vent to his raucous call. No mud or similar bonding material was employed, the twigs and rootlets just being intertwined, very similar to nests of magpies and crows. Except for a few wisps of Spanish moss, there was no lining. Two eggs were laid, both clear, but they did provide the following data. Averaging 32 by 23 mm., they were pale brown with paint-brush like sepia markings radiating from the thicker end for about half the length of the egg. Four months later the female cleaned up the old nest and one egg only was laid this time. This she began to incubate immediately, but, twelve days later it was seen that it had been damaged for part of a dead chick was protruding through the inner membrane. The following day it had disappeared. After a lapse of three weeks, during which time the male was continually displaying but had let up on his destruction of the foliage, she laid again, an egg on each of two consecutive days. In case the male had been responsible for the previous spoiling of the egg, he was removed to an adjoining aviary. Also, in case the damage had been done by a mouse, of which there were plenty about, a metal shield was fixed over and around the nest. This was erected in stages for the female had begun to sit and it was only when she was off the nest that we added pieces of metal bit by bit so that she would get accustomed to the new look of her nest. These operations did not upset her for both eggs hatched after 17 to 18 days. The nestlings, devoid of all body covering, had bright pink skins and yellow gapes with negligible marginings, similar to baby magpies. Their development also followed that of young magpies, the body darkening on the second day until, by the fifth day, they were bluish-slate, and quill feathers were forming under the skin of the wings. Eyes open at six days, quill feathers were showing down the centre of the back. By the eleventh day the head, back and wings were feathered and, for the first time, they were seen rearing their heads for food. Despite quite lengthy vigils being maintained at various times throughout the day, the female was never witnessed actually feeding the nestlings but, judging by the feed-pans, it was assumed that the rearing was mainly carried out on ground raw beef, mealworms and

. . . done by a mouse . . .

crickets, this live-food being renewed every hour throughout the daylight hours. Vacating the nest at 16 days old, the fledglings were strong on the wing, resembled the female in basic colouring, and they attained independence at 38 days old. They were then removed from the aviary to a room in the bird-house, and the adult male was reunited to his mate. At about three months of age there did appear to be slight differences between the two young birds, one having a darker stripe running from above the eye to the back of the head, and with slightly darker underparts. I understand that they were in fact one of each sex, the yellow nape feathers beginning to show on the male at about seven months of age.

The GREATER SICKLE-BILLED BIRD OF PARADISE, *Epimachus fastuosus*, from the central region of New Guinea, is a majestic bird, the adult male about 45 inches (1 metre 13 cm) in total length, 33 (84 cm) of this being accounted for by the magnificent tail. The long sickle-like bill is black with a basal tuft; head feathers velvety black with shining metallic tips of blue-green merging into purple on the nape; face and cheeks iridescent purplish-green; down the centre of the back is a row of feathers of deep bluish-green, the remainder of the back feathers velvety black with a purple sheen on the shoulder, rump and upper tail-coverts. Primaries blackish edged purple; inner secondaries have a purple sheen. The pectoral and flank fans are difficult to describe as the feathers are so peculiarly shaped and lie in series varying in shape to make a complete fan when extended. The largest uppermost feathers of velvety black have the shafts curved downward, the lower web decreasing in width down the length of the feather until it disappears at the tip, whereas the upper web increases in width, terminating in a straight line; the second series of feathers are similar in form but shorter, and have a broad purplish-blue terminal band; the third series is of the same form but even shorter and have a broad terminal band of green with a slight purplish tinge. These feathers comprise the pectoral fans, erectile over the head. The flank fans are even more bizarre as they also are arranged in three series, succeeded by a fourth of disintegrated long narrow plumes. The first series of feathers are short tipped and hatchet shaped, and the second and third develop from this form until the longest are broad and sickle-shaped. The final series are disintegrated feathers, the largest reaching far below the flank fans. All the feathers are glossed green, blue and purple, varying in each feather, with a beautiful final effect. The tail is wedge-

. . . even more bizarre . . .

shaped, comprised of broad, sharp-pointed feathers, the edges upcurved so that the feather is broadly V-shaped; the proportions of the feathers vary but all are blackish, glossed with purple, less noticeable on the outer feathers. The female is smaller, body length about 10 inches (25 cm), and much more subdued in colouring. The crown of the head reddish-brown with darker flecks; back olive reddish-brown, paler on the rump; upper tail-coverts pale olive; wings olive-brown margined reddish; throat blackish-brown; remainder of underparts whitish-brown with barring of black right through to the under tail-coverts where it becomes more rufous. The tail is very graduated, about 13 inches (32 cm) in length, and reddish-brown.

The SUPERB BIRD OF PARADISE, *Lophorina superba,* from the western parts of New Guinea, is one of the smaller species, about 9 inches (23 cm) in length, and the sexes differ. The general colouring of the adult male is black with a brownish tinge; the back feathers slightly disintegrating at the tips; wings dark brown; tail blackish-brown with the central pair of feathers velvety black. Crown and nape are metallic bluish-green and, from the base of the nape there is a band of long feathers, velvety black with a slight bronzy sheen. These feathers disintegrate at

the tips and are erectile into a huge nape fan. Chin bronzy-black, succeeded by a breast shield of metallic scaly bluish-green feathers, small below the chin, becoming larger as they proceed downwards on the breast and lengthening rapidly at the sides, and capable of great display which usually occurs when the nape fan is erected. Remainder of underparts black, the feathers on the flanks lengthened and disintegrating. The female has the top of head, nape and cheeks black with a slight purplish tinge, and a patch of white tipped feathers behind the eye. Back, dark olive-brown with a reddish tinge; wings and tail brown, with reddish-brown edges to the feathers; throat blackish with white tips; remainder of underparts fawnish with regular blackish cross-barrings.

The LESSER BIRD OF PARADISE, *Paradisaea minor*, is from the Papuan Isles and western New Guinea. The sexes are dissimilar, the male about 15 inches (38 cm) in total length, the female slightly smaller. The male in nuptial plumage is most attractive, the long side plumes bright yellow; head and upper back yellow; remainder of upperparts, including wings and tail, reddish-brown with a small yellow wing-bar; forehead and chin blackish; throat metallic green, a narrow black line dividing it

From left to right: Movements in the dance of the Lesser Bird of Paradise of New Guinea

from the remainder of the underparts which are reddish-brown. There are two, long, barbless central tail feathers, or 'wires', about 12 inches (30 cm) in length. Their mating display is spectacular, some poses being shown in the illustrations on pages 272-273. The top of the head, the face and throat of the female are black; nape yellowish; back, wings, upper tail-coverts and tail deep chestnut-red; underparts, including under the wings white.

The RED-PLUMED BIRD OF PARADISE, *Paradisaea raggiana*, about the same size as the preceding species, is from the southern central regions of New Guinea. The male in nuptial plumage has side plumes like the Lesser Bird of Paradise but they are a bright crimson-red. Top of head through to nape yellow; back dark reddish-brown; bright yellow wing-bar; wings and tail reddish-brown; chin metallic green with a narrow throat band of yellow; breast dark brown; remainder of underparts dark vinaceous. It also has a similar pair of long, central tail 'wires' as with the Lesser Bird of Paradise. The female's top of head, face and throat are blackish-brown; back of head, nape and narrow throat band dull yellowish; back, wings and tail deep chestnut-brown; upper breast dark chestnut-brown merging into dull vinaceous through remainder of underparts. Their display is very similar to that of the Lesser Bird of Paradise and, like that species, they give vent to their strident calls incessantly whilst displaying.

The BLUE BIRD OF PARADISE, *Paradisaea rudolphi,* named after the then Prince Rudolph of Austria, is from northeastern New Guinea and is about 12 inches (30 cm) in length. The adult male has a white bill; head, neck, chin, throat and mantle velvety black, the mantle forming a cape; above and below the eye is a thick arc of white feathers, unjoined and not forming a circle around the eye; back and rump feathers black with broad bluish tips; tail blue with paler margins and, except for the central pair of feathers, which are very long, the tail feathers are narrow and have small racquet-like tips of pale blue. Wing feathers blue margined paler blue, brighter on the coverts; lower breast and abdomen are blackish with maroon, almost crimson, tips and elongated into two sets reaching across the body. Further plumes, dark blue at the base followed by paler blue, the undersides half reddish-white, extend from the sides of the body well beyond the end of the tail. When displaying, this species has a habit of swinging from a branch upside down, all the plumes flanking its body like a huge fan. The

. . . from a branch upside down . . .

female is like the male but lacks the plumes, and the underparts are different. Breast dull brownish-black; abdomen dull reddish barred brown; flank feathers lengthened and blackish.

The PARADISE RIFLE BIRD, *Ptiloris paradiseus*, is from the mainland of Australia, with a distribution from central Queensland to central New South Wales. The adult male is mainly a velvety black with a slight bronzy tinge, except on the back of the head and the wings which are purplish. Crown of head and throat metallic blue-green, the same colour as the central pair of tail feathers and the lower abdomen. At the base of the bill is a tuft of black feathers. Thickly built birds, they are about 11½ inches (29 cm) in total length, the bill accounting for about 2 inches (5 cm) and the tail for four (10 cm). The female is feathered in various shades of brown, forming a distinct pattern. Cheeks and crown of head dark brown flecked with pale buff, fleckings terminating at the nape; light fawn eyestripe from the base of the bill, over the eye, to back of head; mantle a lighter brown with a greenish shade; flight and tail feathers reddish-brown; upper tail-coverts sepia. From the chin to the under tail-coverts pale fawn which, from the upper chest downwards, is lined with V-shaped markings, light brown and small at the outset and gradually thickening and darkening as they spread down the body; under tail-coverts reddish-brown. We had a young pair, they take four to five years to come into colour, but their youth did not prevent the male displaying. They were about the friendliest of the family we ever had, and the most mischievious for many a time they probed through the wire netting and altered the setting of the thermostat controlling the heat in the aviaries. I fear that more than once some of the men working in the aviaries were told rather severely not to meddle with it when one day we saw the male Rifle Bird really enjoying himself as he grasped the knob and turned it round. They enjoyed a game of catching mealworms tossed to them in the air. If one fell a bit short they would swing right round on a branch and try to grab it before it reached the ground. The display of the male was quite a ritual, he assuming postures like a ballet dancer at times. Some of the positions can be seen in the illustrations on pages 276 and 277. It must be truly spectacular when the male is in full colour and the light catches the sheen and iridescence of the feathers.

The TWELVE-WIRED BIRD OF PARADISE, *Seleucidis melanoleucus*, from the lowlands of western New Guinea, is about 16 inches (41 cm) in length. The adult male has a very

. . . altered the setting of the thermostat . . .

275

ONE—The male "Rifle Bird" casually stretches his wings, first right, then left.

TWO—Stretching himself to his full height he peals out with a loud raucous call of "yaas, yaas."

Dance of the Rifle Bird c

FIVE—She now increases her speed of flight, flying faster and faster, coming ever closer with fewer intervals of rest. The tempo of his dance picks up. His pirouetting increases. Whirling and wheeling he extends his wings to the fullest in an umbrellic arc.

SIX—Now tension has reached its peak. He begins to snap his head from side to side with mandibles open to their fullest, showing the bright apple green of their interior to her.

THREE—Then suddenly he seems to click into position and becomes an animated toy, as it were. It is here that one feels his tension.

FOUR—He now becomes as one drugged by the passion of his feelings, completely unconscious of everything but his love-to-be. The female Rifle Bird begins to fly back and forth in the area of his vision apparently oblivious to his presence. He begins to bow and scrape turning always to face her line of flight.

Australia

EIGHT—The climax is reached when she, no longer able to resist the rapture, flies to the edge of the stage where he enfolds her within his wings.

SEVEN—The snapping of his head at this point becomes so malevolent that the "cracking" of the bones of the neck is audible, as is the impact of the head itself against the bow of the wings—and all the while he calls loudly, clearly, "yaas, yaas, yaas."

broad breast fan of soft velvety black feathers, the outer feathers extending outwards with broad, bright green metallic tips; a bill, long and black; head flatish and black with a slight gloss and a bare patch behind the eye; back, black with a bronzy tinge; wings and tail, black with a slight purplish tinge at the edges of the feathers; chin and throat black; profuse flank feathers of bright yellow, disintegrated and showing twelve elongated wiry black shafts, strongly curved backwards. The female has the same long bill but lacks the breast fan and the flank plumes. Top of head through to the shoulders black with a purple sheen and a bare patch behind the eye; remainder of upperparts reddish-brown; underparts from chin to under tail-coverts pale buffish-white closely barred with brown, the barrings small and indistinct on the throat and entirely missing from the under tail-coverts.

. . . should be seen in the sunlight . . .

To really appreciate the beauty of birds of paradise they should be seen in the sunlight when the iridescence and sheen of the feathers can be viewed to the best advantage. Further, the males should be observed when displaying for then every adornment is made full use of as they compete for the attention of the females. Provided they were kept at reasonable temperatures, not too hot and not too cold, 45 degrees Fahrenheit (7 degrees Centigrade) and 80 maximum (27 degrees Centigrade), we experienced no difficulty in housing them for they partook readily of the fruit-mix, soft-food mixture and ground raw beef. Mealworms and crickets were given morning and night, every hour when rearing young, and every other day they had a dead white mouse, size depending on the species being fed. As mentioned earlier, they do require careful supervision during the breeding season, particularly when both sexes are housed in the same enclosure.

Family Corvidae

This family embraces the crows, jays and magpies and is almost cosmopolitan, being abundant in the temperate regions of the Northern Hemisphere, but unrepresented in New Zealand and most island groups in the Pacific. The typical crows have a distribution almost as wide as the entire family but are completely absent from South America. Jays are to be found in the Nearctic, Palaearctic, Oriental and the northern parts of the Neo-tropical regions, and magpies in the same areas except for the intrusion into South America.

They are all large birds, by the general standards of Passeriformes, and they include the largest forms of that order. Stout, fairly long and powerful bills; legs and feet sturdy, the legs strongly scaled in front and booted behind, and being very strong on the wing are the general characteristics of the family. The sexes are alike in colouring and the majority have predatory tendencies. They are mainly carnivorous, although many of the smaller species take insects, fruit and such items as acorns and seeds from pine-cones. Mainly gregarious, even at breeding time, they will vigorously protect their nesting area against all comers and, when approaching such sites, it is always advisable to wear protective headgear.

. . . advisable to wear protective headgear.

The MAGPIE JAY, *Calocitta formosa*, from Central America is a large bird, adult males in full colour being some 24 inches (61 cm) in length, 15 inches (38 cm) of which may be accounted for by the tail. The general colour is blue above, white below, with boldly white-tipped outer tail feathers; a black crest, sometimes white-tipped. The amount of black in the head varies, some birds being white on the face and throat with a narrow black chest-band; others black throughout most of the face and throat. The variation is geographical, the species ranging from Mexico to Costa Rica.

The Asiatic Hunting Cissa

The HUNTING CISSA or GREEN MAGPIE, *Cissa chinensis*, is an Asiatic species being found in the forest lands along the Himalayan foothills from India through to Burma. It is about 15 inches (48 cm) in length and the sexes are alike, mainly a brilliant green. Two black bands encircle the eye and end in points on the nape; wings red-brown, spotted black and white; long green tail feathers tipped black and white; bill, legs and feet coral-red. They have a harsh, raucous call, usually ending on a high note, and a very shrill whistle. The plumage of these birds does have a tendency to fade to a delightful shade of pale blue in captivity, due apparently to lack of certain ingredients in their diet. We had one pair that arrived from India green but, after two years housed in the bird-house, they turned blue. By then we had an aviary they could have to themselves and they were released into it early one April. The aviary was unheated, but roofed and planted and, except for covering the sides with plastic during the winter months, the birds were given no artificial heat. By the spring of the third year in there they had regained most of their green colouring. Their diet over these years had been ground raw beef, the soft-food mixture and blueberries, supplemented with mealworms and two white mice for each of them every day. It was about this time that we received a

young bird direct from India that was blue on arrival and turned green two years later. This opened a question to us, are they blue as nestlings? We were not fortunate enough to breed them so, as far as we were concerned, the question remains unanswered.

This opened question . . .

The YUCATAN JAY, *Cissilopha yucatanica,* is from Central America, being found in the Yucatan Peninsula, British Honduras and eastern Guatemala, one of three species of this genus, their basic colouring being black heads and underparts, with light blue on the upperparts. One of the distinguishing features is that they have yellow feet and legs, a slight frontal crest, and the upperparts are cerulean blue. They are about 13 inches (33 cm) in length.

The SAN BLAS JAY, *C. san-blasiana,* the second species of the genus from the same area, and even intruding into the southern parts of Arizona in North America, is about 12 inches (30 cm) in length. This has an inconspicuous frontal crest, is rich blue on the back, rump, wings and tail; solid black otherwise. We only had these birds for a short period as we had no spare proper accommodation for them. The third species, Beechey's Jay, *C. beecheyi,* about 14 inches (35 cm) in length, was never in our possession.

The PIED CROW, *Corvus albus,* is an African bird with a wide range from Senegal in the west, clear across Africa and down to South Africa, also in Malagasy but absent in Namibia. They are a large bird, some 15 inches (38 cm) in length, and the general colour is black and white. There is a broad white collar across the base of the hind-neck; chest to upper belly white; rest of the plumage glossy blue-black and the sexes are alike. We received one specimen from Mazambique but, as with the two species of jays referred to above, lack of suitable accommodation led to it being sent to a zoo.

The AZURE-WINGED MAGPIE, *Cyanopica cyanus,* is from south-western Europe and eastern Asia, there being sub-species in Asia and one, *C. c. cooki,* in Spain and Portugal. It was the latter race that we had a pair of. Some 13 to 14 inches (33 to 36 cm) in total length, of which nearly half is accounted for by a long, graduated tail, the sexes are alike. The upperparts are greyish-brown; underparts being a paler hue, and the flanks a distinct grey-brown. The wings are azure-blue, the black inner edges of the primaries only visible in flight or when the birds are preening themselves. A glossy black cap covers the entire upper portion of the head, running through to the nape and down over the ears; buffish-white throat; legs, feet and bill slate-grey.

Two of them occupied a planted aviary of some 20 by 16 feet (6 by 5 metres) and, in May of one year, they built a rugged nest of twigs and alfalfa stalks in the "V" joint of the upper framework supporting the aviary roof. Both birds appeared to be equally industrious and they completed it in about six days. Six eggs were laid in all, one each day, and, since all literature available to us quoted that the normal clutch was three or four, we feared we had two females. We were never able to tell which one was incubating for, although they had been colour-banded originally, they had torn their bands off. It was noticed, however, that at one time of the day the sitting bird would be facing up the aviary, away from the house, and at other times it would face in the opposite direction. This behavourial pattern was constant and we never found out whether they were just following the sun, or if one was more interested in watching what was going on when it was on the nest. All doubts regarding the eggs were dispelled twenty days after the laying of the first egg for a chick hatched out. The next three days saw another on each day until there were four, ugly, flat-headed, completely bare young birds in the nest. One died at two days old and, since no more came along, the remaining two eggs were removed and found to be clear. The eggs were buff coloured with umber splashes, heaviest at the thicker end, and they measured 26 by 20 mm. Both parents took part in the rearing which was mainly carried out on meal-worms, dead baby mice and ground raw beef. The nestlings thrived on this diet and their eyes were open and quill feathers showing in their wings at five days old. The next five days, or when the eldest was ten days old, showed that they had fairly well levelled up in development, and it was hard to pick out major, minor or minimus. All three left the nest on the same day, when the eldest was eighteen days old, and when they were caught up for banding, it was seen that the body colour was buffish-brown, the flights being blue. The little stubby tails were blue also and the cap was grey with black streaks. They were some eight weeks old before the light chin and throat really showed, and the cap became the glossy black of the adult birds. At four months they could not be told apart except for the coloured leg-bands they wore. At no time, despite careful watching, was it possible to be definite as to which was the male and which the female of the parent birds.

. . . torn their bands off . . .

We now come to the genus *Cyanocorax,* of which there are 10 species, all inhabitants of America. We had but three of them.

The PILEATED JAY, *C. chrysops,* from southern Brazil, Uruguay and Argentina, is very dark blue above, pale yellow below; head black marked with blue and silver-grey and, on the crown of the head there is a thick, short black top-knot. They are about 14 inches (35 cm) in length, and a most handsome bird.

The AZURE-NAPED JAY, *C. affinis,* about 15 inches (38 cm) in length, has a range from Costa Rica to western Venezuela. The crown, sides of head, throat and breast are black; ring around the eye and a moustachial streak cobalt-blue; nape pale violet-black; back violet-brown; wings and tail dark blue; underparts and tips of tail feathers white. Again, suitable accommodation precluded us from retaining these birds.

The GREEN JAY, *C. yncas,* is only about 11 inches (28 cm) in length and has a longish tail. They are to be found from southern Texas, through Mexico to Honduras, Venezuela, Ecuador, Peru and Bolivia. The frontal feathers are stiff, directed forward, lengthened and are cobalt-blue, the same colour as the cheeks and a line above the eye. Crown and nape white, tinged blue; sides of head and breast black; back, wings and central tail feathers bright green; underparts and remainder of tail feathers bright yellow. A pair of these birds, after having been studied as living models for one of Mr. Boehm's porcelain creations, was released into an aviary containing turacos, flycatchers and sunbirds. Within the month they built themselves a rough nest of twigs in the upper branches of a crab-apple tree. Four eggs, greyish spotted brown and lavender, mainly around the thicker end, were laid and, after about 14 days of incubation, they hatched. It is not known if the incubation was shared or not for the adult birds were so alike that they could not be told apart and no changing over on the nest was ever observed. It was not possible either to study the development of the chicks for the nest was inaccessible. The eggs had been seen when an electrician was fixing some insect night-lights up in the roof of the aviary. Once the chicks hatched the parent birds adopted a typical jay attitude, diving at us whenever we approached the nesting area and keeping all other birds well away from the nestlings. It is estimated that the young birds were some 18 days old before they vacated the nest, closely resembling their parents, even to diminutive nasal tufts. It was about 6 months before they attained full adult colouring. The main diet for rearing was livefood and ground raw beef, although they did take a little fruit as well.

. . . diving at us . . .

The OCCIPITAL BLUE PIE or RED-BILLED MAGPIE, *Urocissa erythrorhyncha,* is an Asiatic species found throughout the Himalayan foothills, through Burma and up into China. The subspecies we had, *U. e. magnirostris,* was from western Burma, the Arakan district. The sexes are alike normally but, with this subspecies, there is a difference in the colour of the iris, that of the adult male being golden-brown, the female's golden-yellow. Young birds have eyes the same colour as the adult female, the change in respect of the males occurring at about nine months of age. With some of the other races there is no difference in the eye colour. The adult male is some 26 inches (66 cm) in total length, about 18 inches (46 cm) being accounted for by the long, graduated tail. The basic colourings are black, blue and white, against which background the red bill, legs and feet make a conspicuous contrast. The head, neck and breast are black with white feathering running from the crown of the head to the nape; upperparts purplish-blue, much brighter on the wings, rump and tail; flight feathers have white tips and outer edges; long, graduated tail blue, tipped white, except for the extremely elongated central pair which has a black bar above the white tips. Underparts white with a pale lavender tinge. The female is identical except that the thighs are greyer and, normally, is slightly smaller than the male.

This pair built a nest of twigs in a crab-apple tree and six eggs were laid. They permitted me to examine the eggs each day and they were creamy pink covered with reddish streaks and blotches, heavier towards the thicker end. I subsequently measured one and it was 27 by 20 mm. All the incubation appeared to be carried out by the female who could be readily identified by a bare patch on her throat where the male had consistently plucked her. Incubation began with the laying of the first egg and covered a period of some 19 days in all. Five chicks hatched out all told, one on each successive day, the sixth egg being clear and I was able to obtain the above measurements. They were very large chicks, completely bare of all body covering, but they grew rapidly and quill feathers were visible in the wings at five days old. It was now that the parent birds became very belligerent towards us and extreme caution had to be observed when taking their feed in. I still bear a scar on my forehead where the male bird struck me with his bill when I went to put some live-food in a tray close to the nest.

. . . a scar on my forehead

Three left the nest at 26 days, joined by the other two the following day. Their diet consisted of live-food in the form of crickets and mealworms, plus white mice and ground raw beef. Two mice were given each day to the parents normally but, when the chicks arrived, this was increased to six and finally to ten a day. The young birds closely resembled their parents except that the bill, legs and feet were slate-grey and did not begin to acquire the red shade until they were some ten weeks old, by which time the central tail feathers were almost fully grown. The entire family was left in the one aviary and there was never any bother with them. They did not breed again due to the fact that they were disposed of, some to Jean Delacour's aviaries in Clères, France, and others to zoos in the United States.

*Mr. Boehm
at work in
his aviaries*

Bibliography

David A. Bannerman; The Birds of West & Equatorial Africa

A. G. Glenister: The Birds of the Malay Peninsula, Singapore
   & Penang

Francois Haverschmidt: Birds of Surinam

Tom Iredale: Birds of Paradise & Bower Birds

J. A. Leach: An Australian Handbook

Praed & Grant: Birds of Eastern & Northeastern Africa

A. A. Prestwich: I Name This Parrot

Roberts Birds of South Africa as Revised by McLachlan &
   Liversidge

R. Meyer de Schauensee; The Birds of Colombia

Walter Scheithauer; Hummingbirds

Bertram E. Smythies: The Birds of Borneo & The Birds of
   Burma

George Miksh Sutton: Mexican Birds

Thomson, A. Landsborough (Ed.): A New Dictionary of Birds

Joel Carl Welty: The Life of Birds

Above:
Mrs. Boehm with
Jackson's Whydah
in the aviaries

Index of Scientific Names

Index of Common English Names

297

Notes . . .

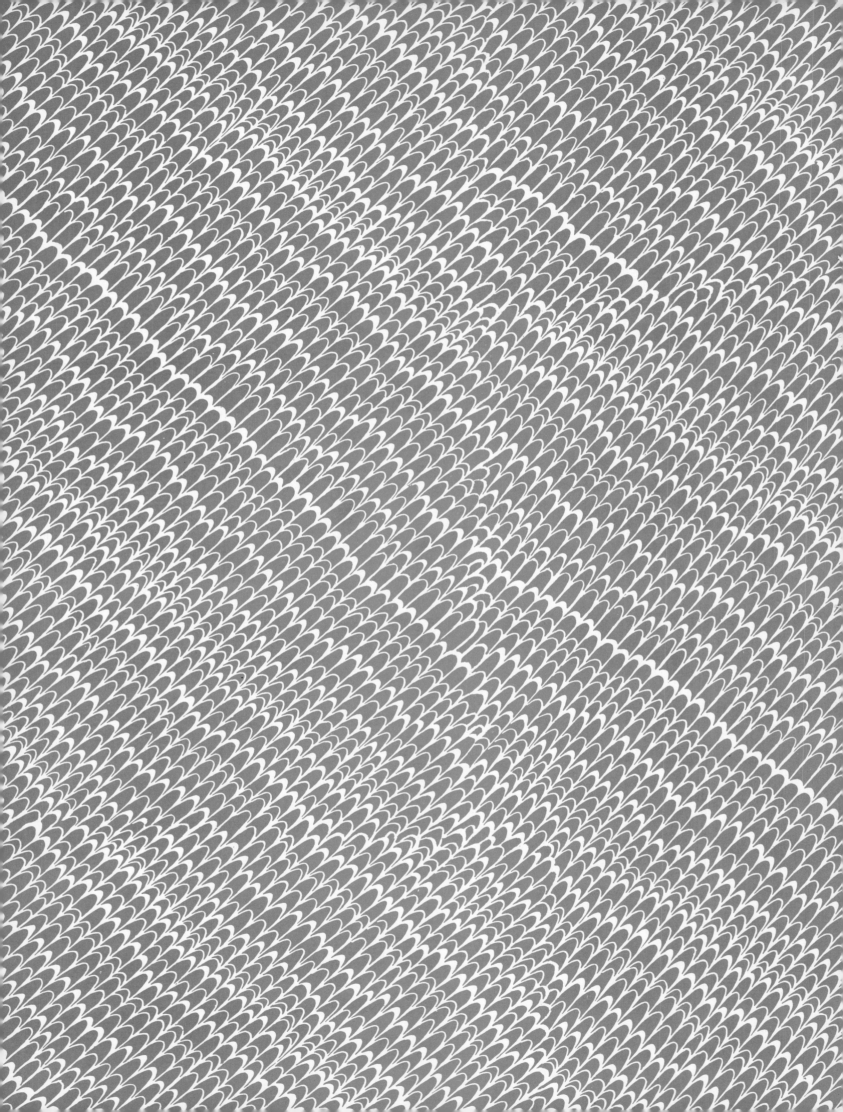